42225

Developing Mathematical Thinking

CRPYK

Developing Mathematical Thinking

A reader edited by Ann Floyd
of the Open University

 ADDISON-WESLEY PUBLISHERS LIMITED

in association with the OPEN UNIVERSITY PRESS

Addison-Wesley Publishing Company
Wokingham, England · Reading, Massachusetts ·
Menlo Park, California · New York · Don Mills, Ontario ·
Amsterdam · Bonn · Sydney · Singapore · Tokyo ·
Madrid · San Juan

Published in 1981 for the Open University by
Addison-Wesley Publishers Limited

Selection of the material and previously unpublished
material © 1981 The Open University

Set by the Castlefield Press of Northampton
Printed in Great Britain at The Bath Press, Avon.

First printed in 1981
Reprinted 1985, 1988 and 1990

ISBN 201 10237 4

The EM235 Course Team

<<<<<<<<<<<<<<<<<<<<<<<<<<<<<<<<<<<<<<<<<<<<<<<<<<

Chairman   Ann Floyd

Leone Burton
Nick James
Roger Lowry
John Mason
Jean Nunn
Tim O'Shea
Michael Peet
Glenna White

Designer   Roger Laishley

Secretary   Chris Golding

Many other people have also made contributions to the course.

Contents

Acknowledgements

The publishers are grateful to the following for their kind permission to reprint material in this book: Chapters 1 and 18: Alistair McIntosh; Chapters 3, 4 and 5: The Controller of Her Majesty's Stationary Office; Chapter 6: Fontana Paperbacks; Chapter 7: Penguin Books Ltd (Copyright © Richard Skemp, 1971); Chapter 8: Macmillan Education; Chapter 9: Princeton University Press (How to solve it: Copyright © G. Polya, 1957); John Wiley and Son Inc (Mathematical Discovery); Chapter 12: Scott, Foresman and Co (Psycholinguistics: Copyright © Scott, Foresman and Co 1971); Chapter 14: Kathey Hebbeler; Chapter 15: H. Ginsburg and Van Nostran Reinhold Co Ltd; Chapter 16: The Mathematical Association; Chapter 17: University of Chicago Press; Chapter 19: Daphne M. Kerslake; Chapter 21: David Fielker; Chapter 22: Marie Kuper and Marion Walter; Chapter 23: C.L. Taylor; Chapter 24: Professor A.C. Bajpai.

OVERVIEW

What is mathematical thinking? A simple answer is that it is what mathematicians do. But what *do* they do? Certainly they do not spend their days doing beautifully laid out calculations with never a single mistake, nor in constructing elegant proofs with never a faltering step. Their time is much more likely to be spent investigating problems of various kinds, in the course of which they will go up many a blind alley, following up hunches: it is most unlikely that they will proceed unerringly to any sort of solution without a single digression. Of course, mathematicians are more adept investigators than their colleagues with other specialisms for two main reasons. To begin with, thanks to their extensive experience of such problems, they are likely to have developed a set of useful tools in the form of standard procedures which they can use whenever they see the need. They can readily solve many kinds of equation and perform calculations. Their second advantage lies in the fact that they have probably learned a great deal about useful ways of attacking mathematical problems which make them likely to proceed more quickly.

But the need to investigate and solve mathematical problems is not restricted to the professional mathematician. The layman needs to solve problems too, though they may be less mathematically esoteric. He, too, will benefit from having a set of tools, even if it is a relatively limited set, and from having a general idea about how to tackle an unfamiliar problem.

Thus in the school years the needs of the future mathematician and his friends with other interests are much the same: both of them need to develop mathematical thinking in the sense described above. This book and the Open University course of which it is a part are concerned with how this might be achieved.

This view of mathematical thinking as the thinking that is needed to solve unfamiliar mathematical problems is far from new. Polya put this well, many years ago:

> 'Mathematical know-how is the ability to solve problems — not merely routine problems but problems requiring some degree of independence, judgment, originality, creativity.' (*see* chapter 6, p. 71)

Yet such mathematical thinking is sadly lacking in many classrooms today. The 1979 report on secondary education includes the statement:

> 'There was little feeling that one can puzzle out an approach to fresh problems without having to be given detailed instructions,' (*see* chapter 4, p.38)

while the first report from the Assessment of Performance Unit (APU) based on a 1978 survey, concludes

'Most eleven year olds can do maths involving the more fundamental concepts and skills and do simple applications. There is a fairly sharp decline as understanding is probed more deeply into more complex settings and unfamiliar contexts.' (*see* chapter 5, p. 54)

The situation does not seem to have changed much over the years. The following comment was made by an HMI in 1895:

'The accuracy of the work is all that can be desired, and in many cases marvellous: at the same time the oral test shows that the children are working in the dark . . . [This] shows itself in the inability . . . to solve very simple problems.' (*see* chapter 1, p. 6)

Difficulty in problem-solving seems to have been with us for some while. This is attributable to at least two factors. One of these is that the standards by which the results of mathematics education are judged too often concern only the children's facility with tools — multiplication, adding fractions and so on. The pressure on teachers is predominantly in terms of these. Far less external concern is expressed about children's problem-solving. The 1979 report on secondary education, referred to above, puts this clearly:

'Many schools are not finding it easy to strike an appropriate balance between the varied demands which are being made on them at the moment. . . . The dilemma . . . is accentuated by current demands for "greater numeracy" because the notion of numeracy is so often ill-defined. In a great many cases the schools are responding by concentrating narrowly on computational skills, devoid of context or application, in a way which easily becomes counter productive. The notion of numeracy should certainly include more than accurate computation — it should include . . . the ability to apply knowledge in fresh circumstances.'

The second factor contributing to the difficulties children have with problem-solving is an uncertainty as to how such mathematical thinking can be developed.

Now in fact a great deal of general advice about teaching mathematics has been given over the years, and *implicit* in much of it is the view of mathematical thinking already described, as well as the means of developing it. Alistair McIntosh summarises such advice well:

'Use materials and start from practical activities. Give children problems and freedom initially to find their own methods of solution. . . Emphasise and encourage discussion by children.' (*see* chapter 1, p. 6)

This book and its associated course wish to make strategies for developing mathematical thinking much more *explicit*. The vision is of children working away with enthusiasm in a great variety of meaningful contexts. Sometimes there will be open-ended investigations, perhaps of patterns with numbers or shapes. On other occasions the focus of interest might be one of the four basic operations of adding, subtracting, multiplying and dividing; children might be trying to find quicker ways of adding two digit numbers than simply counting on one at a time, for example. Yet again the activity might be playing mathematical games with each other, or trying to programme a computer. Whatever the activity, children will expect there to be comprehensible reasons for what they do, or for what happens in any set of circumstances. They will question each other, their teachers, and themselves. Whenever it is helpful they will make a record of their actions and the reasons governing them, as well as any conclusions they draw.

The essence of this approach is captured in the phrase 'do, talk and record', first used by Nick James, now a member of the course team, but then an advisory teacher. Children *do* all manner of activities, *talk* about them with each other and their teachers, and *record* some of what happens.

The sceptic might be forgiven for remarking that such an approach might work very well with a small group of well-motivated children, but with a class of thirty or more it is a recipe for deafening chaos in which little productive work ever gets done. The same sceptic might well comment that this approach to developing mathematical thinking might be a good idea now and then, but that a great deal of other time would have to be spent in developing mathematical tools, which would, he was sure, require a completely different approach. He might be persuaded that the tools could be developed as a natural spin-off by the following anecdote from one of those case studies.

Two practising teachers, Deryn Harvey and Carole Senior, describe in chapter 26 how a group of children were working together on sharing counters equally between a group of people. The idea of dealing them out one by one, like a pack of cards, came naturally enough, and the process was soon speeded up when someone suggested that it would be quicker to deal the counters out three at a time. The other children could see the sense of this, and the group continued to do this for a while until one of them, Stephen, claimed to have a much quicker method for the current problem involving 72 counters and 6 people. This was to give each person 10, leaving 12 over, so that there would be 2 more for each person. Stephen had to convince the group that this really worked, and when they all adopted the same method, this led naturally, without any mystifying sleight of hand, to the conventional method of doing division. Through exploring ways of sharing out counters 'fairly' these children had acquired one of the standard tools in the school curriculum. But this was not all they gained from the experience, for it had also involved them in exploring problems for themselves. Furthermore, the arithmetic made sense – they understood it.

One enormous advantage of teaching mathematics in this way is that children do actually enjoy tackling problems, as long as they present attainable challenges: they will engage in such activity for its own intrinsic satisfaction, as Margaret Donaldson suggests in chapter 6. Furthermore they engage in mathematical problems quite spontaneously and often find solutions quite independently. Kathy Hebbeler, in chapter 14, describes the ease with which many pre-school children can solve addition problems, given a practical context. Herbert Ginsburg, in chapter 15 describes his analysis of the difficulties two nine year olds and two eleven year olds were having with formal arithmetic. He found that they all had evolved quite viable methods of their own which were quite adequate in most circumstances. The trouble was that their informal methods

3

bore little relation to the conventional formal methods they were expected to be using. In chapter 10, Bob Samples describes the enthusiasm with which children explored a set of pendulums, and Christine Billinge describes in chapter 23 how her pupils were absorbed in investigating a variety of geometric patterns, often finding their own original ways of expressing these.

This book then puts forward the view that mathematical thinking will be developed most effectively by involving learners in a wide range of manageable challenges; in some cases the creativity will lie in the means of solution, as in individual methods of doing calculations, and in other cases the creativity will lie in both means and ends, as in more open-ended investigations of patterns. Its five sections consider this from different perspectives.

Section 1 sets the historical scene: its two chapters draw heavily upon quotations from a wide range of past documents, concerning both what it was felt mathematics education should be and what it in fact was.

Section 2 amplifies this by drawing a much fuller contemporary picture, including extracts from two recent reports from the Inspectorate, and the first report from the Assessment of Performance Unit.

Section 3 explores the nature of mathematical thinking described above in more detail and depth. Some of its chapters are a psychological background for doing, talking and recording. Others explore aspects of the approach more fully. One key theme is the use of language in the mathematics classroom: if children and teachers are to discuss mathematical ideas with each other, some thought needs to be given to what is involved in communicating such ideas.

Section 4 is a collection of writings about particular mathematical topics such as addition, tables, algebra, geometry, and word problems.

Section 5 is four accounts, by practising teachers, of what is involved in developing mathematical thinking in this investigating, problem-solving and discussing manner when there are thirty or more children to be considered. They all feel it can be done, though they do not minimize the initial difficulties.

SECTION 1   The historical context

Introduction

When faced with a contemporary challenge, it would be wise to find out whether past experience might not provide some useful insights. Certainly it has been said more than once that mathematical education was more satisfactory in the past than it currently is. If that is indeed true, then perhaps we should find out why and thus discover a means of improving the present situation.

The two articles in this section follow this line of enquiry. Between them they span a wide range of reports from the Inspectorate, specially appointed commissions, and a few other sources; they look back over the last hundred years or more, thus including the entire period of universal elementary education. Both articles are primarily collections of quotations with commentaries.

In chapter 1, Alistair McIntosh concludes that the general state of affairs has changed remarkably little; he can find no conclusive evidence that there was ever a period when the situation was markedly better. Furthermore he maintains that there have been few, if any, new insights into more effective ways of developing mathematical thinking.

In his view the real problem is not deciding on the best advice to give, but in ensuring 'its translation into accepted and practical terms'. However, as the nature of the advice is to use practical activities, allow children to discuss and argue, and to find methods for themselves, the demands on teachers are considerable. Chapter 2, by Sister Mary Timothy Pinner, is much concerned with this. She maintains that from the *teacher's* point of view, things have in fact changed considerably over the last fifty years, and that much more time and space is needed to enable teachers to cope with the challenge posed by the need to develop a rationale for their actions when faced with an explosion of curriculum materials of all kinds. She would like to see a situation in which groups of teachers investigate these challenges together. If it is a good thing to allow and encourage children to tackle problems collectively, then teachers should be enabled to do the same.

1 When will they ever learn?

Alistair McIntosh

Source: Forum, vol. 19, no. 3, summer 1977

There are a great many things I want to say about primary mathematics: but some may not be true, in which case they will confuse the issue, and others may indeed be true, which will only confuse the issue even more.

However I can start from certain assumptions.

1 Most people are aware that there is a great debate going on.
2 Most people are not aware that it has been going on for over a hundred years.
3 At least as much sense (and nonsense) was being talked then as now.
4 It may help to give some glimpses of the historical perspective.

What follows then is largely a collection of quotations from the past 150 years of debate about mathematical education at primary level. The bases for selection were that I had read them (though much is excluded), had found them stimulating, and believe them relevant. I admit to a certain malicious glee at the sure knowledge that some will misconstrue my personal attitude to certain of the extracts. They will read approval where there is none, and disapproval where I registered agreement.

So my preface will end with another assumption.

5 It is more important that people should think than that they should think what I think.

> '*Standards of instruction to allow a school to be certified as efficient* (1876/7)
> 50 per cent of those above 7 years will be individually examined (in reading, writing and arithmetic). One half of the children examined ought to pass in two subjects. One half of the children so passing ought to pass in arithmetic.

> 7–8 years: Form on blackboard or slate from dictation, figures up to 20. Name at sight figures up to 20. Add and subtract figures up to 10: orally from examples on the blackboard.
> 8–10 years: Simple addition and subtraction of numbers of not more than 4 figures: multiplication tables to 6 X 12.

10+ years: The four simple rules to short division (inclusive).'
(*Report of the Committee of Council on Education,* 1876/7)

The new code of 1877 set standards for payment by results in elementary schools.

Standard I was intended for 7 year olds.

'Addition and subtraction of numbers of not more than 4 figures. Multiplication tables 6 X 12.'

In 1875, 11 per cent of children aged 10 and over were still in Standard 1. In that year only 60 per cent of Standard 1 children examined in the East Midlands passed.

'We set four sums for each standard and a child earns the grant, as a rule, when two are right.'

How well did they retain this knowledge, drilled into them in Standard I, when, four or so years later, they were in Standard V?

'In a class of 58 children in Standard V, only 11 could encounter with success the difficulties of a sum in simple addition. (1879)
62 per cent of Standard V children took 1 from 10 000 correctly. (c. 1910)'

Comments by HMIs of the time:

'I must confess to some surprise at the extremely poor result in arithmetic. (Kent and Sussex 1875)
If children fail in other subjects they fail more often here (in arithmetic). It is a subject which seems beyond the comprehension of the rural mind.
In arithmetic, I regret to say worse results than ever before have been obtained — this is partly attributable, no doubt, to my having so framed my sums as to require rather more intelligence than before: the failures are almost invariably traceable to radically imperfect teaching. (Stafford and Derby, 1876)
The failures in arithmetic are mainly due to the scarcity of good teachers of it. (Devon 1876)
Ask a pupil—teacher how he can tell by simple inspection that 1980 contains the numbers (i.e., is divisible by) 2, 3, 4, 5, 6, 9, 10 and 11; the pupil—teacher gasps for breath, and the head-master hides in the classroom. (1896)
The accuracy of the work in Standards I and II is all that can be desired, and in many cases marvellous: at the same time the oral test shows that the children are working in the dark. In these standards, at least, far too much time is given to the mechanical part of the subject. The result of this unintelligent teaching shows itself in the inability of the upper standards to solve very simple problems. (1895)
There is a prevailing opinion that the London elementary school children of today are slower and less accurate in computation than they were ten years ago. I have searched for evidence in support of this contention, but have failed to find it. I am, therefore, inclined to relegate the belief to that group of opinions which have reference to the annual deterioration of Academy pictures, the increasing degeneracy of each new generation of

men, and other palpable fictions. But even if there has been a slight loss of accuracy, there has been a great gain in intelligence; and intelligence is an equipment incomparably more valuable than facility in calculation.'
(Board of Education, *Special Reports on Educational Subjects*, vol. 26, p. 16, 1912.)

'It is the experience of many good teachers that . . . it is found to be unnecessary before the sixth year is passed . . . to do any formal Arithmetic on slates.'

(Reports, 1895/6)

'The conscious teaching then of number, as of other definite lines of thought, is to be begun in the classroom with a pupil whose age is not less than six years.'

(Board of Education, *op. cit.* p. 61, 1912)

'Instruction in many primary schools continues to bewilder children because it outruns their experience. Even in infant schools, where innovation has gone furthest, time is sometimes wasted in teaching written "sums" before children are able to understand what they are doing. The NCDS Survey shows that 17 per cent of children start doing sums in infant schools before the age of $5\frac{1}{2}$.'

(Plowden, *Children and their Primary Schools*, p. 196, 1966.)

'There was no evidence that the amount of formal number knowledge attempted in the infants department bore any relation to attainment later on in the junior school.'
(Biggs, *Mathematics and the Conditions of Learning*, NFER, p. 267, 1967.)

'Recent statistical research (carried out by the Committee of Seven of the Northern Illinois Conference on Supervision) points to the probability that in our traditional curricula we teach the rules of arithmetic much too early and that great waste of time and effort on the part of both pupil and teacher could be avoided by deferring for some years instruction in such rules as long division. (Among the many striking results of the Committee's inquiries is the discovery that the optimum mental age for beginning to learn long division is 12 years 7 months).'

(E.M. Renwick, *The Case Against Arithmetic*, 1935)

'In general we feel that the results show that teachers of first year secondary school children should not, except in the case of very bright children, take their understanding of multiplication and division for granted.'
(Margaret Brown, in *Mathematics in School*, vol. 6 no. 1, p. 10, January 1977.)

'If a child be requested to divide a number of apples among a certain number of persons, he will contrive a way to do it, and will tell how many each must have. The method which children take to do these things, though always correct, is not always the most expeditious. . . To succeed it is necessary rather to furnish occasions for them to exercise their own skill in performing examples rather than to give them rules. They should be allowed to pursue their own method first, and then should be made to observe and explain it; and if it were not the best, some improvement should be suggested.
Examples of any kind upon practical numbers are of very little use, until the learner has discovered the principle from practical examples.

When the pupil learns by means of abstract examples, it very seldom happens that he understands a practical example the better for it; because he does not discover the connexion until he has performed several practical examples, and begins to generalise them.'

(*Intellectual Arithmetic,* by a teacher of youth, pIV, 1840)

'One general point we noticed throughout the interviewing (with 10–12 year olds) was that almost all children could produce successful strategies for solving problems, even when they did not recognise the operations involved.'

(Margaret Brown, in *Mathematics in School*, vol. 5 no. 5, p. 16, November 1976.)

'A footnote to Schedule I requires you (i.e., HMI) to satisfy yourself that the reasons of arithmetical processes have been properly explained and understood. This is a department of school work which has been much overlooked. . . It is therefore desirable that you should very frequently ask the teacher of the class to give a demonstration lesson on the subject; and he should so work out an example on the blackboard as to make the reason for every step of the process *intelligible and interesting* to the scholars. You should point out that no instruction in the rules of arithmetic can be really valuable unless the process has been made visible to the scholars by numerous concrete examples, by actual weighing and measuring, by transactions with real coins. . . When children obtain answers to sums and problems by mere mechanical routine, without knowing why they use the rule . . . they cannot be said to have been well versed in arithmetic.'

(*Reports*, 1895)

The Hadow Report on *The Primary School* (1931) is a document of unresolved conflict. Its brilliant vision of the primary school in general terms clashes sharply with the sometimes reactionary observations on arithmetic.

'The criterion (of the Junior School) must above all be the requirements of its pupils during the years when they are in its charge, not the exigencies of examinations or the demands of the schools and occupations which they will eventually enter. It will best serve their future by a single-minded devotion to their needs in the present, and the question which most concerns it is not what children should be . . . but what, in actual fact, children are. (p. xiv)

It must remain important to emphasize the principle that no good can come from teaching children things that have no immediate use for them, however highly their potential or prospective value may be estimated. (p. 73)

The curriculum is to be thought of in terms of activity and experience rather than of knowledge to be acquired and facts to be stored. (p. 75)

We believe that arithmetic in the primary school should mainly be concerned with the fundamental processes or "rules". (p. 140)

It is common knowledge that abstract numbers present no difficulties to children. (p. 140)

It is not reasonable to expect a child in the primary school to justify the process he employs, say, in subtraction.' (p. 141)

Curriculum Bulletin No. 1: *Mathematics in Primary Schools* (1965) and The Plowden Report (1966) can be considered together. The one strongly influenced the other. Both make assertions which are impressive, but not quite convincing. Curriculum Bulletin No. 1 is a much stronger document for mathematics: but Plowden contains some toughness which is often overlooked.

> '(There is) unchallengeable evidence that sound and lasting learning can be achieved only through active participation.   (Curr. Bull. p. xi)
> Although discovery methods take longer in the initial stages (between the ages of 5 and 8 or 9) far less practice is required to obtain and maintain efficiency in computation when children have been enabled to make their own discoveries.   (Curr. Bull. p. xi)
> When children explore for themselves they make discoveries which they want to communicate to their teacher and to other children and this results in frequent discussion. It is this changed relationship which is the most important development of all.   (Curr. Bull. p. 1)
> Instead of being presented with ready made problems in a textbook the children find their own problems or are given them in a "new form".
>   (Plowden, p. 237)
> There is ample evidence that many of the claims for the new approach (to mathematics) are well founded.'   (Plowden, p. 238)

The Report makes five suggestions for evaluating children's progress:

> '1 Objective testing within schools.
> 2 Primary schools should hear regularly from secondary schools how their children compare over a period with children from other schools.
> 3 HMI should help teachers to know what to expect from children in the circumstances of their neighbourhood.
> 4 Surveys of the quality of primary schools by HMI at regular intervals.
> 5 Recurring national surveys of attainment.   (from pp. 201–2)

> The new approach . . . has not removed the necessity for a very carefully thought out scheme of work in junior schools, for careful individual records of progress, for practice in computation and for accuracy.'
>   (Plowden, pp. 237–238)

Bennett's *Teaching Styles and Pupil Progress* is critically examined by Gray and Satterly in *Educational Research*, vol. 19, no. 1. They conclude that, at best, no valid conclusions can be reached on the basis of the published evidence. He has failed adequately to control for external factors such as the eleven-plus, the research design has serious flaws, and the statistical and educational significance he attaches to his results is both exaggerated and one-sided. Two relatively minor instances are given here:

> 'A possibly inconvenient result showing that high-achieving boys in informal classes do very well indeed in mathematics is, apparently, "difficult to interpret since this group contains only four boys and is thus unlikely to be reliable". (p. 92). This is a perfectly proper caution. It comes as a considerable surprise, therefore, to find in the very next sentence that Bennett's interpretation requires our acceptance as reliable of a result based on only three girls in formal classrooms.   (Gray, p. 50)
> It could of course be argued that the sample studied is not representative

of primary teachers as a whole. This may be true, but the HMI study of teaching practices, contained in the Plowden Report, found little regional variation   (Bennett, p. 54)
   The various categories were *far from being evenly spread* over the areas of different authorities.'   (Plowden, p. 102)

The fact is that Bennett makes a number of sensible and useful comments and is worth reading *provided* that one accepts only those assertions and opinions for which intelligible and corroberative statistics are given.

   'It is surely time to ignore the rhetoric which would have us believe that informal methods are pernicious and permissive.   (Bennett, p. 163)
   The central factor emerging from this study is that a degree of teacher direction is necessary.'   (Bennett, p. 162)

Postscript

Sixty to one hundred years ago, steps for the improvement of primary mathematics were being advocated. They included, as we have seen:

1   Don't start formal work too early.
2   Use materials and start from practical activities.
3   Give children problems and freedom initially to find their own methods of solution.
4   Children must have particular examples from which to generalise.
5   Go for relevance and the involvement of the child.
6   Go for reasons and understanding of processes. Never give mechanical rules.
7   Emphasize and encourage discussion by children.
8   Follow understanding with practice and applications.

It is doubtful if one child in a million has received a mathematical education consistently following these principles at every stage. Recent reports, and recent research, have done little more than expand on these rather aged methods, currently called 'progressive'.

   Like Ballard in 1912, I can find no *evidence* that standards are falling. What should concern us far more is why the lessons of sixty years ago, consistently advocated and upheld since then, have not yet extensively been put into practice. The aims are almost universally agreed in principle: their translation into accepted and practical terms for the majority of primary teachers has not yet come about. The current outcry is against a revolution which has not yet happened. If we take, not a timid and unnecessary step back, but this belated and modest step forward, I am prepared to believe that standards would rise.

2 Mathematics: its challenge to primary school teachers from 1930 to 1980

Sr Mary Timothy Pinner

Source: specially written for this volume

≪≪≪

Introduction

'It is more important that people should think than that they should think
what I think.'   (McIntosh, see chapter 1, p. 6)

There have been so many challenges placed before primary school teachers in the
last few decades that it would not be surprising if they had given up thinking.
These challenges may be viewed in the context of general educational trends in
which three broad stages may be identified (Taylor, 1978):

Before the 1960s Although some reorganisation of school structures is apparent
and there is evidence of the introduction of some progressive ideas into primary
school, there was really little change in the technology of teaching.

During the 1960s These were years of unparalleled expansion at all levels. There
was express interest in innovation both in content and in method and numerical
growth provided expanding resources which resulted in new projects, programmes,
journals and numerous conferences and meetings. Developing sociology and
psychology provided background theory. However, many of these influences
came from outside the school.

During the 1970s This was a time of steady state after expansion and before
contraction. The emphasis began to centre on the teacher as the organiser of
teaching resources and as a school-based curriculum designer.

In addition, teaching had become a much less private activity both within a
school, namely, team teaching and more open classrooms, and outside the school,
namely cooperation with social workers and the demands for accountability and
standards.

Since it is useful to consider changes in mathematical education in the context
of changes in primary education, and since, for various historical reasons, it
seems appropriate to consider the first stage mentioned above in two parts,

pre- and post-1950, the following plan has been adopted for analysing the challenges facing teachers:

1 1930–1950: providing some educational and mathematical background to the later years of major change.
2 Primary education 1950–1980: exploring some developments and publications and their relationship to the three broad stages in educational trends.
3 Mathematics 1950–1980: exploring developments and publications in mathematical education and their relationship to the three stages and to general primary education changes.

1930–1950

The deliberations of these two decades, although inevitably interrupted by the war years, prepared the way for the developments and publications of the later years both in relation to primary education and mathematics. It is also important to remember that the implementation of the 1944 Education Act provided the environment in which the primary school curriculum could be developed. However, before that the Consultative Committee on the Primary School, chaired by Sir William Hadow, had challenged some of the traditional curriculum patterns in its report presented in 1931:

> 'The traditional view, still widely held, that memory is especially strong in young children and that the primary stage is pre-eminently the time for a great deal of routine work, requires large qualification. Reliance should be placed at this stage not only on mechanical memory, but also on that aspect of memory which is assisted by reasoning and understanding . . . the power of reasoning in children between the ages of 7 and 11 appears to be more highly developed than is generally supposed.
>
> We are of the opinion that the curriculum of the primary school is to be thought of in terms of activity and experience rather than knowledge to be acquired and facts to be stored.
>
> The traditional practice of dividing the matter of primary instruction into separate "subjects" should be reconsidered. The treatment of a series of central topics . . . may be a useful alternative . . . it is however essential that adequate drill be provided in . . . arithmetic.'
>
> (Recommendations 19–34)

These recommendations required the teacher to relate the organisation of teaching situations to the learning needs of the pupils; individual work and group activity were to be combined with traditional class teaching. However, although the heavy responsibility imposed on the teacher to be imaginative, adaptable and creative was recognised, the support needed by the teacher was not yet fully appreciated, since the main suggestions for help related to material facilities (buildings, class size, etc.) and initial training (three years rather than two being suggested). The importance of in-service support became apparent later as the implications of the new ideas emerged.

References to mathematics in the report were very brief, only half a paragraph in conjunction with science (which is mentioned first) being included in the main sections. The emphasis was consistently on content, even in the appendix, 'Suggestions for teaching the various branches of the curriculum'. Some extracts are revealing since they indicated that a synthesis between the child centred/ experience theme of the general curriculum and the content of the arithmetic syllabus had still to be more fully explored:

> 'Arithmetic should mainly be concerned with the fundamental processes or "rules". The chief problem for the teacher is how to secure a thorough mastery of these basic operations without devoting too much time to them . . . the fundamental operations belong to the abstract side of mathematics and are most simply and effectively dealt with in the abstract . . . any discussion as to the way processes should be taught may be left to the numerous text books on method . . . but the knowledge (of how a process works) is no substitute for rote knowledge (of the facts) . . . however . . . increasing attention should be paid to the application of arithmetic to matters in the children's environment . . . money, shape, size, weight.'   (pp. 175—182)

Computational accuracy and practical exploration were both advocated but the reader is left with a sense of unresolved tension between these aims. Perhaps this is one of the reasons why the Mathematical Association took so long to produce its first Primary report (1955), which, by its own admission, was the outcome of many deliberations. Three separate committees were established (1938, 1946, 1950), although some continuity was maintained since two people served on all three and the unpublished scripts of earlier deliberations were always available for consultation. The reasons for the delay in publication are instructive. The war interfered with meetings of the first committee, though it had already embarked on its task of considering the teaching of mathematics to children under eleven when war was declared. It had concentrated its attention on the content of a Junior school syllabus, enquiring into current practice and preparing a detailed arithmetic programme for discussion. The second committee, appointed for four years, ran out of time. This is not surprising since it listened with great sensitivity to the challenge of its time:

> '. . . it did not share the belief of its predecessor that a curriculum should be drawn up prescribing the mathematics to be taught at each stage of the primary years. Instead, the members discussed children's approach to number through play and the use of apparatus; much time was spent grading the steps of a new process and considering the apparatus through which it should be learnt. This led to deeper inquiries into the nature of the processes themselves and further questioning of the nature of children's mathematical development.'   (Preamble p. v)

In the light of this accumulated wisdom and experience, the third committee presented their own formulation of a small body of principles for teaching mathematics at primary level. These principles will be more fully discussed in a later section.

The Hadow report had recommended a child-centred curriculum; subsequent decades presented a developing theory of psychology and more mathematical content for integration into this curriculum. The accident of war and the courage of a group prepared to 'hasten slowly' provided time for growth. Time and space

14

are essential for growth and maturation for children and educators. But, by 1950, the input of theory and content had only just begun; the challenge of change and the need for time and space to reflect and make decisions were to be key themes in the next three decades.

Primary education 1950—1980

The three stages mentioned in the introduction are reflected in both the timing and the content of three primary school reports published in these decades:

1 *Primary Education*, Ministry of Education, 1959.
2 *Children and their Primary Schools*, Plowden Report, 1967.
3 *Primary Education in England*, DES, 1978.

The first of these took up themes explored previously:

> 'The report (Primary school 1931) emphasises that . . . the curriculum is to be thought of in terms of activity and experience rather than knowledge to be acquired and facts to be stored.' (p. 7)

It then asked teachers to give more critical consideration to the quality and substance of what children are asked to learn. The structure of the primary school and the fields of learning it presents were considered in detail, but one theme about the teachers' role begins to emerge: their responsibility for informed choice.

> 'The arrangement of the room (for infants) and the uses to which the equipment is put are the teacher's responsibility . . . equipment and materials will fail in their purpose unless through them the children learn effectively and learn what is of value. Whether or not they do this depends largely on the teacher's power to think ahead and organise. It is a pity there has been so much misunderstanding about what is called "activity" . . . the teacher's responsibility for what is offered to the children . . . for the maintenance of good standards of performance is in no way diminished. . . .
> . . . the different parts of education are closely interwoven . . . but not all haphazard and without plan . . . the whole kept steady by records of general and individual achievement.
> School schemes . . . provide a framework within which the individual teacher can make adjustments and adaptations . . . they have to be constantly under review and checked against the teachers' experience and their records of what has been profitable and valuable to do.'
> (pp. 45, 52, 61, 97)

This role of responsibility was outlined in general and then elaborated in relation to particular subjects. Some of the mathematical references are cited here because they indicate trends which will recur in later documents.

> 'All apparatus used should have a purpose which the teacher clearly understands even if the children do not.
> Teachers must carefully consider mathematical ideas and relations or they cannot see the structure of the knowledge they wish children to have or diagnose a child's difficulties.

15

> Cooperation between teachers . . . to preserve continuity of teaching of mathematics; discussion of how children have learned, their achievement of ideas and processes, what they have not done . . . meetings are [essential to communicate] the knowledge and judgement of the previous teacher (which is more reliable than testing).'　　　　　　　　(pp. 191, 196, 201)

Activity with a purpose can only be achieved by the teacher's planning, coordinating and cooperating, so that the child's individual progress is assured. The import of the teacher's role in the child's development was even more clearly spelt out in the Plowden report (1967) where, after discussing the structure of primary education and the children in the school, a section on the adults in the school began with the statement:

> 'In every section of our report we have been forced back to the teacher's role and its importance,'　　　　　　　　(§873)

and immediately this role was set in the context of the child:

> 'Our study of child development has emphasised the importance of maturation in learning. The corollary is not to make the teacher's role passive but to underline the importance of diagnosing children's needs and potentialities.　　　　　　　　(§874)
> Similarly, as we have surveyed the ways children learn, the demands made on teachers are frighteningly high. . . . the teacher who used to give a set lesson could manage on a little knowledge and use it over and over again. Far more knowledge about subject matter and how children learn is called for in teachers who continually have to exercise judgement, to think on their feet . . . they have to select an environment which will lead to useful discovery . . . to lead from behind.'　　　　　　　　(§875)

But the report continued by elaborating on the varying forms of on-going support for teachers, presenting in-service education as a challenge and a responsibility:

> 'The unique freedom of English schools is defensible only if teachers prove themselves equipped to meet its demands. Initial training is no more than a basis. In-service training a necessary superstructure.'　　　　　　　　(§1013)

Noting the place and purpose of school-based support:

> 'There is an important place for both *informal consultation* and more *formal discussion* among staff as a whole . . . staff meetings should be held regularly and there should be a central theme for discussion of which advance notice has been given.
> Now that the primary curriculum is being widened it is increasingly difficult for them [heads] to keep up to date with all developments and it is sensible that they should invite the help of assistant *teachers* in preparing schemes, in *giving advice to their colleagues* and in selecting books, materials and equipment.
> (But) support from within is not enough. . .
> We have been impressed by the work of *advisory teachers* . . . who concentrate on help for teachers . . . much of their time being spent teaching in a classroom.'　　　　　　　　(§§933, 934, 946)

Noting also the available external structures:

'*One term courses* provide a flexible means of meeting changing needs, giving teachers time to become familiar with new content and methods and to try out experiments free from day to day teaching responsibility. *National courses* can make new findings known . . . those who attend them can help local courses . . . in their home area.

Local courses ought to start from a knowledge of what local teachers are doing; they can provide opportunities for teachers to meet others . . . the work done on courses can be followed up in *teachers' groups* or in schools. The diffident can be encouraged to break new ground but not so hastily that disheartenment is the outcome.

Residential courses have a value of their own . . . in local centres equipment and materials can be tried out and discussed and ideas gained at residential courses can be appraised after being tested in schools . . . In rural areas the *follow up* is best provided by meetings in different schools . . . with advisory teachers.' (§1017–1020)

The challenges of change were not merely listed but the means for their dynamic implementation were outlined:

'. . . the future will depend on the extent to which we can produce teachers with the necessary knowledge and understanding to use and improve the material made available to them. . . .

This slow building up of teachers . . . is perhaps the most difficult and rewarding aspect of in-service education.' (§1019)

The third report (1978), surveying primary education, evaluated the education of a representative sample of children at certain stages in the primary school.

The main issues centred round the curriculum, its effectiveness for children and its implementation by teachers. The survey presented teachers with facts about children's observed achievement in varying organisation situations and noted both persistent difficulties and methods being used to solve them, difficulties relating to learning and teaching. Some of the mathematical references contained more detailed comment on trends already noted in the earlier reports:

'Even when the curriculum is clearly defined and priorities are agreed upon, the range of work and the range of pupils presents a formidable challenge to the knowledge and skill of an individual teacher.' (§840)

How could this challenge be met?

'Some schools already adopt forms of cooperative or team teaching which allows teachers to work from their strengths.

If a teacher is only a little unsure, guidance from a specialist may be enough. . . in some cases a specialist may have to take full responsibility for a class . . . but the class teacher is best placed to coordinate their whole programme'. (§842–844)

But:

'The great majority of teachers with posts of special responsibility have little influence on the work of other teachers . . . they need time to perform their duties, (§845)

which include having:

'. . . to draw up schemes of work, give guidance and support to other staff.
. . . be responsible for procurement of resources, develop means of assessing
the effectiveness of the guidance and resources they provide, visit other
classes . . . and keep up to date.'   (§846)

And finally the survey elaborated not merely the need for in-service education or
its possible patterns, but its specific aims, pointing to two major functions:

'1 Positive staff development based on the strengths of the individual,
 2 Raising the expectations which teachers have of children and so achiev-
    ing a clearer definition of the curriculum.'   (§865)

Or, in even more detail:

'Courses should enable teachers to understand the nature of these skills
(mathematical and others) and how to teach them in a context which relates
to the rest of the school work and the real world in which children live.
      . . . helping teachers to assess children's capabilities . . . by observing
their work and by diagnostic tests . . .
      . . . becoming familiar with a range of teaching techniques, to under-
stand the advantages and disadvantages of each, and choose what is immediately best . . . a choice taking account of the teacher's strengths . . .
[for] a technique beyond a teacher's operational skill will be inefficient.'
                                                                                       (§856–861)

These reports, then, present a series of educational challenges to teachers:

'How to *organise learning activities/experiences* for children.
How to organise learning activities for *individual* children.
How to organise *progressive* learning activities for individual children.
How *best personally* to organise progressive learning activities for individual
children.
How to *collaborate with colleagues* in organising.'

Mathematics 1950–1980

The three stages mentioned in the introduction are again reflected in the publications relating to mathematics:

Before 1960s:	*Teaching of Mathematics in Primary Schools,* Mathemati- cal Association, 1955.
During 1960s:	*Mathematics in Primary Schools,* Schools Council and HMSO, 1965.
—	*Primary Mathematics – a Further Report,* Mathematical Association, 1970.
During 1970s:	*Mathematics 5 – 11,* HMI discussion series, 1978.

However, two dimensions of change and their inter-relationship must be considered in this section. They are both mentioned in the Mathematical Association
report (1955) cited above: curriculum content and the learning processes. The
report considered both aspects, stating that:

'The aim of primary teaching is the laying of a foundation of mathematical
thinking about the numerical and spatial aspects of the objects and activities
which children of this age encounter'   (p. v)

But the emphasis of the report was on children and their learning:

* 'Children developing at their own individual rates learn through their active response to the experiences which come to them; through constructive play, experiment and discussion children become aware of relationships and develop mental structures which are mathematical in form and are the only sound basis for mathematical techniques.' (p. v)

Two aspects of understanding were considered important:

* 'the teacher's understanding of how children learn, the child's understanding of concepts'

and both of these present challenges to the teacher not merely at an organisational level but also in terms of justifying the approaches employed. The report's three-fold analysis of ideas about mathematics in primary schools highlighted the levels of understanding required by the teacher:

'1 the interaction between a child's mind and the concrete situations of his environment, i.e. the substance of his experience,
2 the growth of mind and mental powers as they are exhibited in the child's growth towards mathematical thinking,
3 the mathematical ideas themselves and their development and inter-relation.' (§1.0)

Activity and experience, as advocated by the primary reports, is now related to mathematics and this clearly places additional demands on teachers to understand both mathematics and mathematical thinking. The report attempted to give some ideas about teaching approaches discussing children at different stages; it also notes some pitfalls and challenges for the teacher:

'Chronological age is not of itself a test for readiness for a new process.
(§1.11)
Sprinkling apparatus about the classroom and leaving the rest to the children . . . does not of itself provide rich experience.
A child's experience is total, mathematics is part of it and can only be isolated in the mind of the teacher. (§2.11)
In topic projects . . . teachers need to foresee the enquiries children will make and offer materials to evoke further experiment . . . much of the help the teacher will have to give will be individual and will make demands . . . never met in class teaching. (§2.93, 2.95)
In group work it is assumed that the teacher can ascertain the child's rate of progress. . . . in testing it is necessary to go behind and beneath the superficial response . . . to investigate the underlying mental activity. . . . a true test of mastery of a mathematical principle or process is an ability to apply it to a new situation. . . . testing is a continuous process bound up naturally with the process of learning. . . . it is a daunting task relating to each individual. (§5.2, 5.22)
There is a quantity of apparatus on the market and teachers need to examine it critically before adopting it. . . the criterion is whether children in fact learn from it and this can only be decided by the teacher after observation.' (§6.61)

These comments match almost exactly the list of concerns noted in *Primary*

Education (1959) both generally and mathematically. Some guidance was given to teachers about 'activity' teaching for specific topics but the summary of research on mathematics teaching was mainly related to arithmetic and showed that teachers too lacked experience and activity of their own on which to reflect. However, *Mathematics in Schools* (1966) showed that thinking and activity were taking place. It provided an illustrated account of both children and teachers exploring mathematics, indicating in considerable detail the type of activity which was being undertaken in classrooms, schools and teachers' centres at this time. This experience was the background to the second Mathematical Association report in which there was much more conscious awareness of the changes teachers were having to face:

1 mathematical education rather than arithmetic techniques,
2 understanding and developing a child's mathematical learning,
3 new ideas in mathematical content requiring both personal understanding and the development of appropriate teaching methods.

This report was keenly aware of the changes not merely in relation to the child but also in relation to the teacher and so (as in the Plowden report) the emphasis was shifted from the child's activity to the teachers' professional development. Changes in the classroom were continually related to developing understanding, to organisation, and to subject content:

> 'The things a child says and does . . . are to the discerning teacher sightings by which to assess progress along the path of understanding. Much of the research into stages of developing understanding is based on observation . . . (so, too) the teachers' opportunity to recognise understanding arises from discussion (between teacher and children) . . . (also) children derive insight and understanding from active experience; opportunities to describe, discuss or depict what they have been doing provide the means by which this can be brought about. Teachers have a dual role to play . . . by under-standing children's capabilities and ways of thinking (i.e. being a good listener, following and developing the *child's* line of thought) . . . and by grasping the essentials of mathematical thinking (exploring the growth and development of mathematics *at their own level* so as to be able to communicate these insights to children).
>
> There is no ready-made prescription with a guarantee of success to answer the problems of class organisation . . . teachers need the opportunities to discuss together the work which they largely do in professional isolation . . . the habit of working together for teachers and children is a first pre-requisite for successful class organisation. Many teachers are faced with the problem of change in their approach to the learning of mathematics . . . their greatest help is to meet others and discuss ideas and problems . . . a sense of oneness with others will ensure growing confidence for those who are hesitant.'   (chapter 1)

This report then recognised both the aspects of change confronting the teacher of primary mathematics and the difficulties inherent in the situation. The suggested solution was the active involvement of teachers in their own development and the practical model which received the most attention was the teachers' centre.

'In seeking to promote understanding in pupils, the teacher's starting point is to endeavour to realise personally the nature of understanding as an essential element in mathematics itself and in the learning and teaching of the subject.

Teachers themselves are the ones to decide in experiment how changes can be planned to the children's best advantage but there is an obstacle at present. Because of the rapidity with which change has come about not many teachers in the primary school have been able to acquire the necessary knowledge to appraise and assess the opportunities with which they are now faced. They do not always know, for example, where the particular mathematical items they teach lead nor how the work is to be followed up in subsequent years. An overall integrated view of the subject to serve as a kind of map to guide the teacher is lacking, as are the tools to produce such a map. . . The roots of the problem lie deep . . . mathematics began for most of us in the traditional study of arithmetic. We did not at the time reach the stage of reflecting on the subject as a mode of thought and of considering its origins, conceptual basis content, scope and structure; in short asking what the subject is all about.'   (Appendix)

This, then, is the challenge with which the report concludes:

'The difficulty is to keep abreast of current knowledge. Change has become the outstanding feature of the educational scene and constant re-education and re-adjustment are demanded of all concerned. The teacher's job has taken on an entirely new look.'   (Appendix)

From now on the interrelation between the two dimensions of curriculum content and the learning processes becomes a new challenge to the teacher; already confronted by the expansion and development of content and alternative approaches to organising learning experiences in the primary school, these must be combined in the compilation of guidelines and schemes. Curriculum development and its evaluation are underlying themes to the primary survey; not only what is being taught and how, but also how effectively and the means of remedying identified deficiencies. The HMI handbook of suggestions *Mathematics 5 – 11* aimed to give teachers some guidance in these areas, and since it was published after the primary survey, its suggestions may be examined in this context.

The primary survey reported that 88% of the schools sampled had a scheme of work or guidelines for mathematics, the handbook of suggestions sought to ensure that help is given to

'that large number of teachers who experience difficulty in translating the the scheme into an effective mathematics programme'   (p. 7)

The task was not minimised in any way:

'the primary teacher today is faced with a considerable task brought about by the changes which have taken place in mathematics. These have involved new content, new terms, new concepts and what may be regarded as a new approach to the teaching of the subject . . . the primary teacher confronted with the task of providing wide experience for children can be bewildered by the wealth of apparatus, material and equipment available. Informed choice must be made bearing in mind the needs of individuals in the class, in the school.'   (p. 7)

21

And again, working through 'integrated studies'

> 'requires understanding of the mathematical potential of a wide variety of situations and this in turn demands more mathematical knowledge than many teachers possess.' (p. 7)

Since the task is formidable for the individual, it is clear that planning is vital and cannot be achieved by teachers in isolation. Teachers are encouraged to make 'continuing attempts to develop their professional judgement' and *Mathematics 5 – 11* indicates areas in which this judgement may be required and some means by which this development may be achieved. This developmental approach for teachers is clearly illustrated in the section on mathematical aims:

'Aid to help plan programme	Listed below are some of the aims within the primary school from which objectives will later be derived. It is not an exhaustive list and the order is to some extent arbitrary.
Area for professional judgement	It will however allow the teacher to consider their relative importance
Means of developing judgement	and encourage discussion with colleagues who share in the planning of work throughout the school.'

(p. 5)

Areas in which professional judgement may be required are illustrated:

> '*Assessment* might be regarded as a procedure which challenges the teacher to define aims and objectives more clearly and subsequently leads to more effective teaching and learning. . . the results may or may not reflect what the teacher believes she has taught. . . these procedures require great courage and professionalism. (p. 10)
> . . . a careful scrutiny of *materials, schemes* of work, of text *books*, workcards, equipment and *apparatus* to see if they are providing what is required. (p. 11)
> The teacher has to use judgement, continually making decisions about the need to repeat *experiences,* to extend them, to consolidate vocabulary, to question, to answer. . . (p. 14)
> Teachers need to *choose words* with care; they also need to see that children use words with care; they also need to help children see the common factors there are in what appear to be different experiences. (p. 18)
> Establishing a proper *balance between* investigation, *experiment, memorisation* and routine *practice* is a problem for every school and every teacher. (p. 42)
> The *pacing of work* calls for careful professional judgement based on knowledge of both children and subject. (p. 75)
> The *use of* this material (structured *apparatus*) is a skilful matter and primary teachers need to recognise the range of experience to which children can be introduced in the different aspects of the work.' (p. 82)

Means of developing this judgement were often linked to the area of exercise. However, some more general approaches were also indicated:

> 'This judgement (relating to evaluation and diagnosis) can often be sharpened by *collaborative work* within the school or the teachers' centres. (p. 11)

Teachers need to keep *careful records* of each child's progress and knowledge . . . find out its extent by observing and questioning; . . . this should take place regularly.

This booklet has been issued in the hope that it will provoke *discussion*.

Teachers should be familiar with some of the extensive *literature* which is available and engage in discussion of the material with other teachers in the school. (p. 82)

In-service education must be directed above all to the development of the teacher's capacity to make judgements . . . (p. 11)

with *courses* not only offering opportunities to stimulate development and helping teachers achieve realistic goals but also enabling them to improve on their own understanding of mathematics and the way children learn.' (p. 12)

Collaboration and *discussion* were keynotes of the handbook as expressed in the final exhortation:

'it is hoped that this book will contribute to the continuing discussion of what ought to be taught and what might be taught and that further clarification of these two matters will also help those concerned to decide on the methods and forms of organisation best suited to their purposes.'

(p. 76)

The primary survey provided evidence that some teachers with a post of special responsibility for mathematics gave vitally important support to other members of staff. The handbook endorsed this role linking it with the theme of discussion and collaboration:

'[They can] concern themselves with far more than the organisation of mathematical books and apparatus . . . [they should] instigate in-service training within the school and work alongside teachers in their classrooms to further the process. . . through support at this level other teachers gain knowledge and confidence . . . and there develops a coherent and systematic policy for mathematics throughout the school.' (pp. 11, 75)

These reports, then, basically repeat the series of educational challenges already offered to teachers with the addition of a substantial new element, so that the culminating challenge of the series becomes:

'How to collaborate with colleagues in organising progressive *mathematical* learning activities/experiences for individual children.'

Conclusion

Alistair McIntosh, in Chapter 1, reflects mainly on some of the problems of teaching arithmetic and the advice given to teachers in this context. The advice has changed little through the years and yet, regrettably, it has not been 'extensively put into practice'. However, as the documentation in this article shows, these problems and this advice need to be considered in a wider context.

What are the problems of teaching children other mathematical concepts?
How are the problems and advice related to considerations of how children think and learn mathematics?

23

What is the relationship of the advice to the various dimensions of curriculum structuring?

How can teachers be helped to organise and reflect on their teaching of mathematics?

A teacher's confidence may be weakened through lack of knowledge in two areas:

1 Personal mathematics. Did they as children
    (a) start formal work too early?
    (b) use materials and practical activities?
    (c) find their own methods of solution?
    (d) have opportunities for discussion?
    (e) see the relevance of mathematical ideas?
    (f) Was most of their own early mathematical work computation?

2 Classroom procedures. Do they *understand*
    (a) the value of a variety of teaching approaches?
    (b) the learning situations created by specific experiences and apparatus?
    (c) Have they *retained* not just the content but also the insight gained in initial/inservice education or has the enthusiasm generated by some experiences dispersed with time?
    (d) Are they able to *apply* ideas for teaching mathematics to their own classroom?
    (e) Are they able to *create* the appropriate experience for an individual child to learn or clarify a specific idea (such as, use or devise suitable apparatus)?

In summary, the contemporary challenge of mathematics in the primary school raises certain questions for teachers:

1 Do I understand the main idea of *this* (specific) topic?
2 Do I know something of its relationship to other aspects of this topic, to other mathematical topics and to topics outside mathematics?
3 Can I myself recognise when to use this idea?
4 What do I know about how children learn this idea? What other ideas does it depend upon knowing (essentially), where will children have difficulties initially and later?
5 Which experiences/apparatus may help them learn the idea and overcome difficulties? Am I conversant with a *variety* of experiences/apparatus relating to this idea?
6 How should I introduce *this* idea to *these* children?
7 How can I recognise children's lack of understanding?
8 How can I create opportunities for discussion with children about this idea?
9 How can this idea be related to other (non-mathematical) classroom activities?

This list of questions is not intended to be exhaustive, but simply to raise some of the issues continually facing a teacher in relation to a succession of mathematical topics. However there are two more important questions:

10 Can I find someone to talk to *now* if I have any difficulties?
11 Do I share approaches and learning situations with others through displays and/or discussions?

An affirmative answer to each of these two questions changes the whole context of the earlier set from 'I' to 'we' so providing the supportive atmosphere for thinking constructively, for developing professional judgement and for meeting the contemporary challenge of mathematics.

References

Report of the Consultative Committee on the Primary School, Board of Education, HMSO, 1931.
Research and Reform in Teacher Education, William Taylor, NFER, 1978.
Primary Education, HMI, HMSO, 1959.
Children and their Primary Schools, DES, HMSO, 1967.
Primary Education in England, DES, HMSO, 1978.
The Teaching of Mathematics in Primary Schools, Mathematical Association, Bell, 1955.
Mathematics in Primary Schools, Curriculum Bulletin No. 1, HMSO, 1966.
Primary Mathematics – a Further Report, Mathematical Association, Bell, 1970.
Mathematics 5 – 11, HMI, HMSO, 1979.

SECTION 2 The contemporary context

<<<<<<<<<<<<<<<<<<<<<<<<<<<<<<<<<<<<<<<<<<<<<<<<<<<<<<

Introduction

This section consists of extracts from three recent reports, two concerned with primary and one with secondary education. Each of them is based on large-scale surveys, though they were not all carried out in the same way, partly because they were done for different purposes. The primary and secondary reports from the inspectorate (chapters 3 and 4) are distillations from observations in a large number of classrooms: they present a picture of contemporary classroom practice in all its variety, and comment favourably or unfavourably as the case may be. In the primary case their comments also draw upon the results of a written test, but this plays a relatively minor role. The survey of the mathematical performance of 11 year olds, carried out by the Assessment of Performance Unit (chapter 5) is of a very different kind: its brief particularly excluded any comment on individual schools, however anonymously, for its purpose was to provide a national picture of the mathematics that children could or could not do. Its report is therefore based on the results of tests. These were predominantly written ones, sent to the schools with pupils involved in the survey for their teachers to administer. However, a small proportion of the tests were of a practical kind, and these were given to the pupils concerned by a team of peripatetic testers.

3 Mathematics in primary education in England

HM Inspectors of Schools

Source: Primary Education in England, a survey by
HM Inspectors of Schools, HMSO, London, 1978. Chapter 5,
sections 6.28–6.31; chapter 8, sections 8.21–8.22, Appendix I (vi).

≪≪

[This chapter contains virtually all the material pertaining to mathematics in the primary survey. It falls into four parts. The first part contains some general observations, while the second describes in more detail the mathematics being taught in primary classrooms, together with some comments on teaching approaches. The third part deals with the written mathematics test, coded E2, with some comments on the results. Finally the last part consists of some brief overall conclusions.]

General observations

The findings of this survey do not support the view which is sometimes expressed that primary schools neglect the practice of the basic skills in arithmetic. In the classes inspected considerable attention was paid to computation, measurement and calculations involving sums of money, though the results of these efforts were disappointing in some respects.

In describing what their schools set off to achieve in mathematics, heads' comments indicated clearly that they attached considerable importance to children achieving competence in the basic skills of arithmetic and understanding mathematical processes. There was almost universal reference to the rules of addition, subtraction, multiplication and division, to computation and to concepts such as weight and number. This common view was reflected in the statement of one head who said his intentions were: 'To teach the children their tables. To teach the four rules of number in relation to money, decimals, fractions, time and measurement, along with some basic geometry. To show why and how these processes work so that children can understand them and use them accurately.' Many heads also referred to the importance of children gaining confidence, enjoyment and satisfaction from their work in mathematics.

Children were given individual assignments of work in mathematics in over four-fifths of all classes. In half of the 9 and 11 year old classes and in two-thirds of the 7 year old classes the allocation of individual assignments was a usual method adopted for organising the work in mathematics. The presentation of assignments was usually by means of commercially published work cards, work cards devised by the teacher or, to a lesser extent, the use of textbooks.

In most classes where textbooks were used, they were employed appropriately to introduce a new aspect of mathematics or to provide suitable practice in a particular process. Commercial work cards were used to present work in almost all 9 and 11 year old classes and in nearly three-quarters of the 7 year old classes. Work cards devised by the teacher were less frequently used in the older classes but extensively used in 7 year old classes.

Children were grouped by ability for their work in mathematics more commonly than in any other subject. There was a tendency in a number of classes to use individual work-card assignments when it would have been more appropriate to draw the group together to work from the blackboard or from a textbook. Direct teaching and discussion have an important part to play in the teaching of mathematics and in some classes this was inhibited by too great a reliance on the use of individual assignment cards. Television programmes were used in the teaching of mathematics in about a fifth of the 9 and 11 year old classes.

Content

In the majority of classes arithmetic was given appropriate attention and in no class was this aspect of the work in mathematics being ignored or neglected. In all the classes attention was given to calculations involving whole numbers and the processes of addition, subtraction, multiplication and division, although this kind of work was not sufficiently emphasised in about a fifth of the 7 year old classes. In about a third of classes, at all ages, children were spending too much time undertaking somewhat repetitive practice of processes which they had already mastered. In these circumstances there was often a failure to make increasing demands on the children's speed or accuracy, or to introduce new and more demanding work. This and other issues concerning the teaching of mathematics are discussed in [. . . the later section on the mathematics test E2, taken by 11 year olds involved in this survey.]

In almost all the classes some work was undertaken which was designed to help children to understand place value. Work was also given to help them to recognise simple number patterns. For the younger children this included activities such as counting by adding in 2s, 3s, 5s and 10s, doubling numbers or identifying odd and even numbers. For older children the work included the full range of multiplication tables and finding multiples and divisors beyond the limits of the tables. In nearly nine out of ten of the 11 year old classes this work involved drawing children's attention to some of the broader implications, such as understanding that the order of numbers can be changed without affecting the result in addition or multiplication but that this is not so in subtraction or division. This kind of work was taking place in less than half of the 7 year old classes.

Activities involving counting and estimating took place in most classes although there was room for more of this kind of work in about half of the classes. Practical activities designed to promote the understanding of quantitative description and the ideas of addition, subtraction, multiplication and division were introduced in well over four-fifths of the 9 and 11 year old classes and nearly all the 7 year old classes. However, in over half of these classes the practical activities undertaken were insufficiently demanding, for example, they were often confined to repetitive activities involving measuring and weighing and the children's attention was not drawn to the mathematical implications of what they were doing.

The notion of a fractional part was introduced when discussing everyday things in over half the 7 year old classes, four-fifths of 9 year old and nearly all 11 year old classes, although in many classes this was only touched on and the work was not fully developed. For the younger children the work was mainly concerned with practical activities involving halves, quarters or thirds, while the older children progressed to the idea of equivalence and the techniques employed in the calculation of fractions. In a few 7 year old classes children were introduced to the notion of decimals, usually associated with the recording of amounts of money or metric measures. It was more common for such teaching to be introduced at a later stage, within the programme of about three-quarters of 9 year old classes and almost all 11 year old classes. Nine out of ten 11 year old classes were taught to carry out calculations involving the four rules of number to two decimal places or more.

The importance of learning to handle money in everyday transactions and acquiring a sense of its value in relation to simple purchases was recognised in almost all the classes. Work involving the measurement of length, weight, area and time took place at some time in nine out of ten classes at all ages, the work progressing as the children grew older. For example, while 7 year olds were frequently taught to tell the time or measure each other's height, 11 year olds were often introduced to the twenty-four hour clock, carrying out assignments based on rail or flight schedules, or to activities such as calculating the area of the playground or the height of the school building. Occasionally such work was linked to ideas in elementary physics as, for example, when the children in an 11 year old class made simple pendulums, recorded the number and rate of oscillations and determined their relationship to the length of string and the weight of the pendulum bob. In another 11 year old class the study of a river in science involved the estimation and calculation of speeds and the amount of water flowing; the children measured the width and depth of the river and the slope and angles of the bank.

When children are asked to 'find the answer' to a problem in arithmetic, they are usually being asked to complete an unfinished statement; for example, 'six and nine more make . . .', or '$81 - 16 = . . .$', or again '$(4 \times 320) - (2 \times 55) = . . .$' If, however, the missing part lies in the middle of the statement it may be represented by a symbol; for example $6 + \square = 15$, or again $1280 - \square = 1170$. The use of symbols gives precision in the recording of mathematical statements; some symbols are essential to any progress in mathematics and were taught in all classes. In about half of the classes children were introduced to additional symbols such as 'box' diagrams or arrows. Where children understood the meaning of these symbols and could use them appropriately to express a mathematical relationship, this provided a useful dimension to their work in mathematics. For some children, however, a proliferation of symbols tended to create confusion rather than clarification. In some cases, particularly in the older classes, more attention could usefully have been given to more precise and unambiguous use of ordinary language to describe the properties of number, size, shape or position.

Children used various forms of visual presentation for their work in mathematics in about four-fifths of all the classes. This ranged from making simple table squares with multiples picked out in colour, to the drawing or construction of block or line graphs, pie-charts or three-dimensional shapes. In about a fifth of the classes there was evidence of mathematics being linked to work in other areas of the curriculum, and this sometimes provided opportunities for visual presentation of mathematical data. For example in an 11 year old class children visited a church as part of a local study and were able to watch the bellringers at work. They observed the different order of the changes rung and, on their return to school, considered the possible presentations. Subsequently the children devised a diagram to illustrate the possible sequences.

Mention has already been made of the link between mathematics and physical science. This connection could be more fully exploited in the work children do both in mathematics and science as in a 9 year old class where children were constructing a model following a visit to a windmill; discussion of the gears provided the teacher with the opportunity to introduce the notion of ratio and to follow this up in the children's work in mathematics. Again, in a 7 year old class the children were working on 'ourselves' as a mathematical topic. They recorded and constructed graphs of their bodily measurements and, using a stopwatch, recorded each other's variations of pulse rate following the performance of a number of different physical activities.

Many ideas encountered by children, for example weight, volume, density, speed or velocity are common to mathematics and physical science but the connection was rarely made explicit. Similarly, precise measurement is essential to both disciplines but techniques of measurement acquired in mathematics were seldom applied to the children's work in experimental science or vice versa. Geography is another subject where ideas common to both subjects, for example, scale, coordinates, direction finding, angles, or longitude and latitude, were seldom linked in the work which children did in either subject; much more could be done in this way, especially with older children.

Mathematics test (E2)

[This test was given to 11 year olds in the survey, and yielded further information on the children's abilities.]

Most of the items used in this test are to be included in future surveys and so cannot be made public. Those reproduced [here] have been chosen to indicate the range of items. They include some on which children scored well and others that many found too difficult. The percentage of children getting each item right is shown to the right of the test. The children were generally allowed 45 minutes to complete the test, but longer if they were still making progress through it.

		Correct responses (%)
A	 Ann Bob Carol David Eric Fred Each time somebody buys a savings stamp for 10p they stick a square on the chart. (a) Who has saved most? _____ (b) How much money have the children saved altogether? _____	94 84
B	How much change would you expect from a £1 note if you spent 43p? _____	83
C	 This 4 centimetre square has been cut into 5 pieces A, B, C, D and E The shape of D is a square. Which two pieces can be fitted together to make a square? _____ and _____	92
D	 1p 2p 5p 10p 50p I have these coins in my purse. Put a ring around the sums below which I can pay exactly. 8p 2p 54p 66p 69p	59

31

	Correct responses (%)

E

Paddington	06 15	07 50	09 45	10 45	11 45	12 45
Reading	06 55	08 24	10 19		12 19	
Swindon	07 38	09 08	10 54	11 19	13 04	13 19
Bath	08 14	09 44	11 29	12 18	13 42	14 22
Bristol	08 30	10 00	11 45	12 35	14 00	14 40

This is part of the railway timetable, showing the times of trains leaving Paddington and the times they leave stations on the way to Bristol.

Use the information from the timetable to answer this question:

Which is the latest train which I could take from Reading to be in Bath by 2 o'clock in the afternoon?

_____

47

F

The cost of a week's shopping

	Mrs Jones	Mrs Smith	Mrs Brown	Mrs Green
Groceries	£10.00	£7.50	£5.50	£8.20
Bread	£ 1.50	£0.72	£0.85	£1.20
Meat	£ 3.53	£2.75	£2.65	£3.25

How much does Mrs Brown spend altogether on a week's shopping?

_____

64

G

$$16 \times 35 = 560$$
$$\text{so } 17 \times 35 = 560 + \square$$

Underline the number for which $\square$ stands

A 560

B 35

C 17

D 16

37

H $\cdots$ is a 3 figure number

Tick the true statements

A $\cdots$ must be bigger than 99
B $\cdots$ must be bigger than 100
C $\cdots$ must be smaller than 999
D $\cdots$ must be smaller than 1000
E $\cdots$ must be bigger than 199

20

	Correct responses (%)

I   Which of these has the smallest answer
 	
   A   5673 x 8
   B   5673 ÷ 8
   C   5673 − 8
   D   5673 + 8
 	
   _____
	
	61

J 7 hundreds, 5 tens and 12 units total _____	 69

K   Which fraction is smallest?
    Put a ring around the smallest fraction.
 	
   $\frac{1}{2}$ $\frac{3}{4}$ $\frac{3}{8}$ $\frac{1}{4}$ $\frac{5}{8}$
	
	40

L   A class has between 20 and 30 children.
   When they have teams of 6 there are no children left over.
   When they have teams of 5 one team is short.
 	
   How many children are there in the class?   _____
	
	49

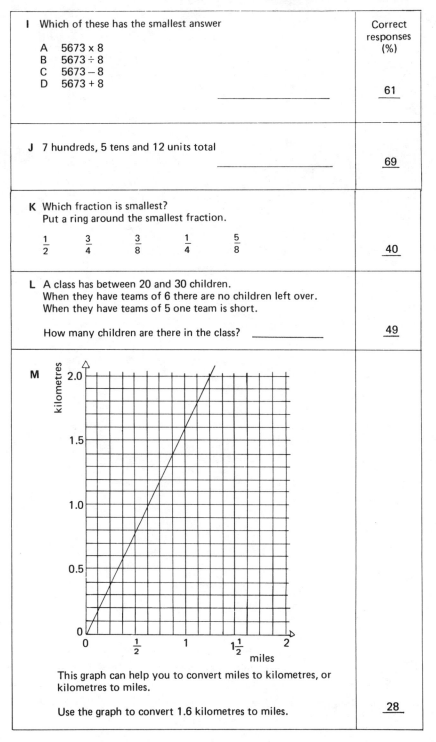

M

This graph can help you to convert miles to kilometres, or kilometres to miles.

Use the graph to convert 1.6 kilometres to miles.   28

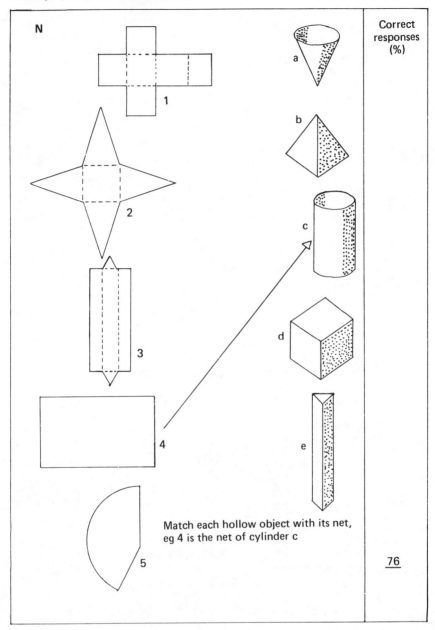

N

Correct responses (%)

Match each hollow object with its net,
eg 4 is the net of cylinder c

76

The 4991 11 year olds who sat the mathematics test, E2, were drawn from 346 of the sample schools, i.e. all sample schools with 11 year olds. The test contains fifty items. Of these, ten were concerned with the properties of whole numbers, ten with handling everyday situations and ten with geometry; twelve dealt with graphical representation and the remaining eight were a miscellaneous group.

The detailed statistical analysis of the results is shown in tables 1 and 2. A mean total raw score was obtained of 27.97 out of 50 as compared with the anticipated score of about 25 [. . .]; 10 per cent of the children scored more than 41, and 9.6 per cent scored 14 or less. There was no statistically significant difference in the total scores achieved by boys as compared with girls, though the boys did significantly better on the items concerned with graphical presentation.

Educational judgement, as well as statistical analysis, is required in interpreting the results of the test. It is hoped that the test items [included here] will help teachers and others to form a view of how well the children performed. Subjective examination by HM Inspectors of responses to the full test leads to the view that the results are disappointing in some respects when account is taken of the amount of time that is given to mathematics in primary schools.

There is a variety of reasons why children may fail to give a correct answer. Some children probably read questions incorrectly and a small number [. . .] could not read them at all. Even so, the test results may well indicate that between 10 and 15 per cent of children have difficulty in counting and adding accurately when using groups of tens and units. Some 60 to 70 per cent of children managed sums involving somewhat more complicated numbers, though some of these children may have been perplexed where they were required to produce two or more correct answers (see examples D and H); the percentage of correct responses falls noticeably where an unusual symbol is included (50 per cent of the schools appear not to introduce the □ of question G), or where there was need for a clear understanding of place value (particularly question H).

The responses to the two graphical items [included here] may show that teaching too seldom goes beyond this to the point where children become

Table 1   E2 mathematics test, Total raw score. Percentile distribution for boys, girls and all pupils, age corrected to 11 years 2.5 months

Possible range of scores 0—50

Percentile	Boys' score	Girls' score	Boys' score minus girls' score	All pupils
90	41.8	40.2	(+1.6)	41.0
80	37.8	36.5	(+1.3)	37.1
70	34.4	33.3	(+1.1)	33.9
60	31.5	30.5	(+1.0)	31.0
50	28.4	27.9	(+0.5)	28.2
40	25.6	25.1	(+0.5)	25.4
30	22.9	22.4	(+0.5)	22.7
20	19.4	19.3	(+0.1)	19.3
10	14.6	14.8	(−0.2)	14.7

It can be seen that as the level of scoring increases, the slight superiority of boys over girls also increases. There was no statistically significant difference in the total scores achieved by boys and girls.

familiar with other forms of graphical presentation, e.g. linear graphs. On the other hand, the geometrical items shown were dealt with successfully by three-quarters or more of the children; others involving transformational symmetry or requiring an appreciation of changes of compass bearing were, not surprisingly, found more difficult.

Taking the test as a whole, it is clear that more children would have scored better if they had appreciated the general rules that can be seen operating in the large number of separate examples they work during mathematics lessons in schools, so that, for example, the answers to questions G and I could have been obtained by inspection.

The children spend a considerable amount of time on mathematics and the work in this subject is better matched to their abilities than is the work in most other subjects — though the more able children often work at too low a level. In the light of these efforts, the scores achieved in the NFER mathematics test, E2, are disappointing.

It seems clear from this part of the survey that individual assignments should not be allowed to replace all group or class work in mathematics. Teachers can by working regularly with a group or the whole class, quicken the pace of mental response and encourage accuracy. They may also, in these circumstances, more readily draw children's attention to general rules in the work they do and so help to create a better understanding of the ways in which numbers behave. Children need to practise mental and written calculations in the four rules of number, including whole numbers and, when they are ready, decimals and fractions. They also need to use numbers in connection with practical activities. The forms of questions and the forms of answers required ought to be varied so that children are not put off by an unusual word, or combination of words or symbols. More of the examples worked by children could usefully lead to multiple answers. The work in mathematics should not be confined to the four rules of number: children in those classes where the programme included all mathematical items taught to 80 per cent of classes for the age group did better in the mathematics test.

Comment

Mathematics is given a high degree of priority in the curriculum of the primary school. For average and less able children within the classes inspected, the work in mathematics, together with that in reading, was more consistently matched to children's capabilities than their work in any other area of the curriculum. However, for the children who showed most marked mathematical ability the work was often too easy and it is a matter for concern that these children's abilities were not fully extended in their work in this subject. The responses to the NFER mathematics test E2 show that the efforts made to teach children to calculate are not rewarded by high scores in the examples concerned with the handling of everyday situations. Learning to operate with numbers may need to be more closely linked with learning to use them in a variety of situations than is now common.

Table 2 E2 mathematics test. Percentage of children answering each item correctly

Item number	Percentage of correct answers	Item number	Percentage of correct answers
1 (Aa)	94	26 (K)	40
2 (Ab)	84	27 (F)	64
3	87	28	60
4	96	29	76
5	92	30	49
6	82	31	18
7	86	32	62
8 (C)	92	33	55
9	78	34	60
10	72	35	54
11	80	36	52
12	86	37	42
13	15	38	23
14 (B)	83	39	42
15 (D)	59	40	84
16	57	41	37
17 (E)	47	42 (G)	37
18	41	43	17
19 (J)	69	44	30
20 (N)	76	45 (M)	28
21 (L)	49	46	35
22	45	47	20
23	71	48	27
24	31	49	19
25 (1)	61	50 (H)	20

Note: The letters shown after fourteen of the item numbers correspond to the test items reproduced.

The extensive use of individual work-card assignments resulted in some children repeating known processes rather than being taken on to the next stage of their learning. In addition there is a place for more direct teaching of a whole group or class in mathematics. Most classes were grouped according to their attainments for work in mathematics and this arrangement could provide opportunities for teachers to deal with a particular topic or process with a whole group. In some cases it is more efficient to teach the whole class than to attempt to teach each new aspect of mathematics individually to each child. Challenging questions and quick recall of number facts, including multiplication tables, are essential in the learning of mathematics and often require a lively and sustained contact between a teacher and a group of children.

4 Mathematics in secondary education in England

HM Inspectors of Schools

Source: Aspects of Secondary Education in England, A survey by HM Inspectors of Schools, HMSO, London, 1979. Chapter 7, sections 4.1—4.25; sections 5.8—5.11, sections 5.20—5.28, sections 6.1—6.18, sections 10.12—10.17.

≪≪

[This chapter contains a substantial proportion of the mathematical material in the secondary survey. The extracts chosen fall into four parts. The first deals with particular content areas — arithmetic, algebra, geometry and logic. The second describes the availability and use of practical materials. The third part focuses upon the teaching approaches found, and the ways in which pupils responded to these, and the fourth part contains some general conclusions.]

Some aspects of content

The place of arithmetic and standards in it

Standards of competence in arithmetic are a matter of public concern and debate. Concern over standards in arithmetic has been expressed for a great many years, but at the present time discussion is complicated by recent changes. There have been changes in syllabuses, and changes in social needs, arising from new patterns of employment and from the availability of calculators and computers. In almost all of the schools seen in the survey very considerable time was spent on arithmetic; and the skills in which, it is said, some school leavers lack proficiency were certainly being taught. All the schools gave a prominent place to practice in the four rules of number, including work with money, decimals and fractions. They expected their pupils to know the elementary number facts of addition and multiplication on which the more advanced processes are based. Where there were weaknesses it was hardly ever through lack of attention to the problem.

In spite of this in the course of the survey some schools were found where, as in former times, the arithmetical competence of some of the pupils was unacceptably low. Not infrequently this was associated with difficulties arising from the catchment areas which the school served, and where this was so, full allowance must be made. The improvement of standards of mathematical attainment involves more than teaching method alone.

Before possible ways of improving arithmetical competence can be discussed, it is necessary to recognise the extent of the problem. The weaknesses in arithmetic were, for instance, such that there could be a poor response from a class of pupils who were asked to multiply by 10 or by 100. Some pupils had difficulty even with doubling simple numbers, and many saw no absurdity in answers to elementary calculations which were wrong by a factor of 10 or 100. There is no abrupt discontinuity in the spread of mathematical ability, and whatever provision may be made in special schools there will always be some children in ordinary schools who achieve only minimally in the subject.

The problems which affect the majority of the school population are, perhaps, indicated by the following two quotations:

> 'This group (say, the bottom ten in the year group) were able to calculate using the "four rules" and pencil and paper. Their grasp of fractions was appreciably better than that of decimals. They were unable to make rough estimates with any real confidence. In most other respects they could deal with "down-to-earth" mathematics, but were not always confident when reading the textbook on a new aspect of the subject. They made many of the classical mistakes in changing the subject of formulae.'

> 'Work with the least able 15 to 20 per cent gives cause for some concern: their grasp of basic principles and their ability to retain knowledge and draw on skills other than those immediately practised is poor. Teaching approaches need revision and greater thought needs to be given to nurturing understanding and confidence than to covering the syllabus.'

If all schools were no worse than this there might be less concern about standards than is being publicly expressed at the moment. But these paragraphs were written after visits to grammar schools which were by no means inferior schools of their type. The paragraphs are a warning against expecting too much in the matter of numeracy from schools which cater for the full range of ability.

In the descriptive accounts which were written about the schools visited, general comments that pupils were competent in basic arithmetical skills outweighed adverse comment by about two to one; although highly adverse comments were more common than high praise. However, where *understanding* of the essential ideas was concerned the balance of comment was unfavourable.

A more quantitative appraisal of the overall position was provided by HMI's answers to the question 'Is there competence in realistic arithmetic?' The word 'realistic' is important. Success in repetitive exercises on (say) technical points involving the manipulation of fractions or decimals was, in itself, not taken as sufficient evidence of competence. Competence demanded a certain ability to apply skills, and to choose a skill which was appropriate.

Pupils on GCE courses were assessed as competent in 86 per cent of the schools in the sample providing such courses; the corresponding figures were 62 per cent for CSE courses and 37 per cent for non-examination courses. (These assessments made some allowance for the different standards to be expected at these different levels.)

The effect of modern courses on arithmetical competence has received extensive public discussion. The differences between traditional and modern courses are by no means clear cut, and proper levels of arithmetical competence can be achieved in either framework. An analysis was made of the extent to which pupils on traditional, compromise and modern courses were competent in realistic arithmetic. The analysis was restricted to the 161 full-range comprehensive schools for which comparable data were available.

Modern courses received somewhat less favourable assessments in this respect, and this applied to courses at each level – GCE, CSE and non-examination. In many cases compromise courses had been developed by schools with the expressed intention of avoiding the deficiencies in arithmetic and traditional algebra to which they believed modern courses were prone. In this aim these courses had succeeded.

Problems often arise when pupils have to apply arithmetical skills, but some pupils have difficulties enough in performing standard calculations in isolation. The survey produced many cases of pupils having difficulties with fractions and decimals. These topics have presented difficulties in schools for as long as they have been studied, and there is no sound evidence which permits comparisons between generations. However, within the context of the classroom, with a teacher asking familiar questions, most pupils achieved a certain competence in these matters. The roots of this competence could, however, be distressingly shallow; and if the teacher of another subject expected a fresh application of the ideas, or if the pupils were presented with an unexpected test in unfamiliar language, failure was frequent. This has long been so; and a cure is unlikely to be found by an unrelieved diet of further practice on a succession of narrow techniques. The development of pupils' arithmetical skills as well as the development of more general mathematical abilities depends on the approach that is adopted to the subject matter. Teaching approaches are discussed [. . . later on in this chapter].

Much of the arithmetic teaching seen during the survey gave a larger place to elementary statistics and to the calculation of probabilities than was given in the past, and this trend is to be encouraged. Some schools also gave a place to the investigation of number patterns; studying, for example, sequences of numbers growing according to some law. This gave opportunities to conjecture results, to test the conjectures and to relate arithmetic and algebra. On the other hand, some traditional pieces of arithmetic, such as tests of divisibility, were little in evidence. Items such as this could be studied more, not as routine skills, but for the opportunities they offer for investigation and discussion.

Provision for algebra

Algebra had a more uncertain place in courses, and there were considerable disparities between what was attempted in different schools. The amount of algebra which it is feasible to undertake with pupils of different mathematical attainment varies greatly, but even so schools varied much in the algebra which they considered appropriate for pupils of comparable ability. Traditional courses usually made more provision for repetitive exercises on matters of technique, such as the use of brackets and the handling of formulae. However these aspects of algebra received some degree of attention whatever the type of course, and the proficiency of the pupils was not always proportional to the effort expended.

The attention given to traditional, manipulative algebra was assessed in the different courses provided, in each school visited. Where schools provided GCE courses, reasonable attention was given in 84 per cent of the cases; 67 per cent of the schools providing CSE courses gave reasonable attention to traditional algebra in these courses. In the remaining cases insufficient attention was given to this aspect of mathematics, or the evidence was unconvincing.

Traditional, compromise and modern courses in the 161 full range comprehensive schools were compared for the provision they made for traditional algebra. At GCE level the percentage of schools making reasonable provision for traditional algebra were 96, 86 and 75 per cent respectively. At CSE level the percentages were 84, 72 and 60 per cent.

Comparable assessments of non-examination courses are not given because they raise different problems. In many cases where algebra was taught in non-examination courses it was excessively preoccupied with mechanical skills and insufficiently concerned with uses which the pupils could understand. Sometimes these courses contained no algebra at all when a modest amount, within the pupils' capabilities, would have been appropriate. These issues are part of the much larger problem of designing courses for the less able.

The exercise books in a number of schools showed that although a great deal of time was spent on algebraic manipulation, at whatever level this was done, only little of this time was spent applying the techniques to problems or using the techniques to deduce further information in some other area of knowledge, such as science or craft. Algebra was rarely used to investigate popular number tricks and puzzles.

Some aspects of algebra are covered in modern (and compromise) courses which were not covered in traditional ones. Traditional algebra was concerned, almost entirely, with using symbols to denote numbers, but non-numerical entities can be described by algebraic symbols using ideas such as sets, relations, transformations, groups and matrices. Modern courses often included some matrix algebra – commonly in connection with transformations of the plane. They usually included something of the algebra of sets (although nothing of the *theory*), but this was little developed and even when it was done it was not necessarily taken even as far as the experimental derivation of the elementary laws of Boolean algebra. Vector algebra occurred quite frequently, but this was not unknown in traditional courses. Symmetry was quite extensively studied, using a small number of over-worked examples, such as folded ink-blots. But there was little analysis of more complicated symmetric patterns and very little that could properly be described as the algebra of groups. The view that modern courses are more concerned with 'abstract' algebra than traditional courses were has little foundation and the traditional algebra seen in courses of all types was taught in a predominantly abstract way.

The time has come for a careful reappraisal of the aims and content of algebra courses, and of ways of teaching the subject. In any case the teaching of traditional algebra has long presented difficulties in schools and it is a branch of mathematics which remains a mystery to many adults. The advice given in the publications of the professional associations over the years is insufficiently known; it could be more extensively practised.

Geometry and spatial ideas

The geometrical experience of almost all pupils in the earlier years of the secondary school involves practical work in two and, more rarely, three dimensions. Common objectives across the whole ability range are that pupils should learn to draw simple diagrams using geometrical instruments, and that they should know and understand the common properties of geometrical figures. Courses usually contain Pythagoras's theorem, the properties of parallel lines and of circles. In most schools considerable time is spent on numerical calculations of length, angles, area and volumes. In almost all courses leading to external examinations these calculations also involve trigonometry. However, in the mathematics lessons observed, although much time was spent on calculations with these physical quantities, the teaching was seldom concerned with whether the pupils could use the appropriate measuring instruments properly, except the ruler and protractor.

The survey confirmed the common belief that the study of geometry as a deductive system has declined. Deductive geometry involves the demonstration of properties of plane figures, which are often intuitively obvious, by means of logical proofs of Euclidean type. The reduced emphasis on proofs of this kind cannot be a matter for regret as far as the majority of pupils is concerned, because in the past logic for its own sake was appreciated by only a small minority. It must however be a matter for substantial regret that nowadays very able pupils are not receiving any effective substitute for what they have lost. Further, it seems that the logical coherence of related results, together with the logical demonstration of results which are not intuitively clear from an appreciation of the symmetry, is insufficiently stressed in the courses given to many pupils of average ability.

Newer types of course introduce ideas such as rotation, reflection, translation and magnification. This work is often related to the algebra of vectors and matrices. These ideas can be organised in a logical way, but this aspect received little emphasis in the lessons seen, even with the abler pupils. Sometimes attention was given to the ways in which transformations combine, and not infrequently the work was well illustrated by diagrams.

At all levels of ability there was much drawing of graphs of many kinds, although insufficient attention was given to the interpretation of graphs from a variety of sources.

The practice continues in schools of providing technical drawing as a separate examination option, and it is taken by pupils with widely varying abilities, although it is not commonly taken by pupils at either end of the ability range. This subject makes a substantial contribution to the geometrical knowledge of many pupils, but knowledge of this kind appears to be seldom assessed by current employers' tests. In schools technical drawing is most frequently treated as a technical skill and its wider educational potential is insufficiently realised. The best current practice needs to be more widely known.

Mathematics as a logical system

The mathematician can see his subject as a logical system, and perceive the inter-relations between the various parts. With the courses seen on the survey there could be little expectation that even the abler fifth year pupils could develop much appreciation of what this means. This was true whether the courses were described as 'traditional' or 'modern'. There was minimal opportunity to see any overall logical structure, because for so much of the time the pupils were operating within a comparatively short-range set of rules. There was little encouragement for abler pupils to develop any overall view of what mathematics was about, or to become familiar with ideas of proof as a mathematician understands them. Pupils certainly did not meet the idea of proof within a clearly defined mathematical system, to which there were parallel, equally acceptable logical systems. This is a stringent requirement, which was not met in the past either; but it was one of the aims when modern syllabuses were introduced, and more could be done to achieve it.

Excessive time was spent in some 'modern' courses on a surfeit of rather trivial exercises which were originally intended to explain the logical structure of the subject; but these exercises were not developed enough to do so. Thus, it is possible to use modular arithmetic as an example of an axiomatic system, or it can be used to illuminate logical points concerning the number system in everyday use; but it serves no purpose if it is studied only at the level of self-contained exercises.

In a similar way, the language of sets and relations was originally developed to clarify logical ideas within mathematics. But if, as in many courses, the ideas are taken no further than the initial exercises, the serious purposes are not served.
[. . .]

Provision of materials

The use of practical material

In general there was a disappointing lack of reference to the applications of mathematics throughout the teaching of the subject. The use of realistic source material such as timetables, catalogues, newspapers, magazines, plans, maps or instruction manuals was very limited. Material of this kind, and an experimental or practical approach to some of the topics in the course, were found in some 10 per cent of GCE courses, in 20 to 24 per cent of CSE courses and in some 30 to 40 per cent of non-examination courses.

Extended work based on topics or projects occurred in some 25 to 30 per cent of CSE and non-examination courses, but very little in GCE courses. Schools were found where a topic approach led to work of high quality. In one CSE Mode 3 course the staff, working as a team, had been at pains to produce unusually good source material for reference. This included actual copies of official forms, order forms, tax tables, ready reckoners and timetables. The work arising was largely arithmetical but because of the expert way it was handled it provided a useful preparation for life after school.

In another school the exchange rates used in money calculations were kept right up to date, and the pupils were using carefully selected resource material to create attractive, well-designed workcards themselves. The pupils devised questions as well as answering them, using books not on mathematics but on general topics.

The topic approach is, in itself, no guarantee of quality and it does not necessarily involve the pupils in pursuing individual lines of investigation. Some courses of outwardly the same structure as those above were open to grave objections. There were cases where pupils worked through printed handouts in a highly directed way, and appropriate resources were lacking. In one school, work was done on 'calculating devices', but no such devices were to be seen, and the pupils regurgitated material from folders produced by other pupils in previous years. Pupils working on 'surveying' or 'mechanics' did nothing of either, but copied material from obsolete textbooks. In another school the pupils had been given exercises headed 'calculating machines' but there were no machines, and they had been kept occupied by doing the addition of six figure numbers with pen and paper.

[...]

Calculators

The price of electronic calculators dropped dramatically in the course of the survey. Towards the end, it was common to find pupils using their own calculators, although teachers did not generally encourage their regular use except within statistics courses. It was probably too early to expect that the impact of very cheap electronic calculators on the teaching of computation should have been fully considered. The necessary change of emphasis from routine paper and pencil calculations to approximation, estimation and mental manipulation of relatively small numbers in order to check the operation of calculators has not yet been appreciated. The new approaches which are possible in mathematics at all levels of ability, and the wider range of problems which can be attempted, have still to be exploited. It is not the intention of the examination system to hinder the introduction of new ideas into the curriculum, and at present some examination syllabuses permit the use of calculators, although many do not. However, questions about the use of calculators in schools need to be decided on merit, and not pre-emted by the current examination syllabus.

There was a vestigial and declining use of mechanical calculators; but the use of the slide rule was common, with between 30 and 40 per cent of pupils on examination courses being introduced to them, though it was not clear whether they were used especially to help in the understanding of ratio, or more generally as calculating aids.

The availability of electronic calculators for schools is increasing rapidly and the real impact of cheap computer power has yet to be felt. Over the next few years opportunities for the use of these facilities are likely to increase, and their proper use will demand radical rethinking of some parts of the syllabus.

Computers

The computer could provide an exciting stimulus, as a report on a boys' grammar school showed:

> 'Computer studies pupils were so well motivated that they were often at school at 8 o'clock in the morning and still at school at 6.30 at night in order to use the terminal. Such momentum was generated with pupils creating and solving problems that work would have continued even without the presence of a teacher.'

On the other hand the presence of the machine did not necessarily provide the stimulus, for in some schools there were computer terminals which were not being used.

Most of the work done with computers in the fourth and fifth years took place in the context of either CSE or O-level computer studies courses within an option scheme. There were very few schools which had non-examined computer studies or where use of the computer was part of the mathematics courses.

Table 1 Schools and pupils involved in the use of computers: by type of school

	Type of school*					
	Mod	Gram	FR Comp	RR Comp	Trans	All schools
Percentage of schools involved						
Year 4	17	6	31	31	19	23
Year 5	16	6	33	29	15	23
Number of schools	94	51	163	45	26	381
Percentage of pupils involved						
Year 4	4	1	5	3	2	4
Year 5	3	1	5	3	2	4
Approx number of pupils in each year group (thousands)	11	5	36	8	5	64

*Mod: secondary modern; Gram: grammar; FR Comp: full-range comprehensive (11–18); RR Comp: restricted-range comprehensive (11–16); Trans: school in process of transition.

The lower involvement of grammar schools, and the overall involvement of only 4 per cent of the pupils may be noted.

Some further 9 per cent of schools made use of the computer in some other way, mostly by running computer clubs.

National examination statistics show a similar picture, with a steady increase in the number of schools offering courses, but with only a minority of pupils involved even in schools where computing facilities are available. These figures suggest that the impact which the computer has made on school courses is much less than is often suspected.

The advent of microprocessors will make cheap computer power available on a significantly different scale in the future. However, the take-up of computer studies courses is limited if these are available only as options, and different methods will have to be used if increased numbers of school pupils are to appreciate the capabilities of these remarkable machines. Possible strategies might include the use of computers to run simulations in science and geography, to provide data bases in history and to investigate numerically some of the ideas current in many modern mathematical syllabuses. No activities of this kind were reported in the survey.

Teaching approaches and pupils' responses

The classroom approach

The impressions which a pupil receives of mathematics at school and the memories which he carries of the subject into later life depend on the style of teaching he receives. Style is difficult to define, and difficult to assess in statistical terms, but it is a major factor in the provision which a school makes for the teaching of the subject. Over the first three years, while the predominant method was traditional class teaching, variations on this pattern were frequent; but in the fourth and fifth years the influence of examinations is stronger and the prevailing approach to mathematics teaching observed in the survey was narrow.

While teacher and pupils alike worked hard and showed commitment and considerable interest and enthusiasm for the subject, in the majority of the classrooms the teaching did not aspire to do more than prepare the pupils for examinations. By this criterion, the material for study was selected and the effectiveness of the work judged. In addition, it was evidently believed that the best preparation for examinations was direct practice of the kind of question that is eventually asked.

The work was predominantly teacher-controlled: teachers explained, illustrated, demonstrated, and perhaps gave notes on procedure and examples. The pupils were led deductively through small steps and closed questions to the principle being considered. A common pattern, particularly with lower ability pupils, was to show a few examples on the board at the start of the lesson and then set similar exercises for the pupils to work on their own. There were few questions encouraging wider speculation or independent initiative. At its best, and given pupils who were sufficiently capable, this style of teaching achieved what it set out to do. At the worst it became direct 'telling how' by the teacher, followed by incomprehension on the part of the pupils. What was lacking in this approach, even at its best, was a sense of genuine enquiry, or any stimulus to curiosity or appeal to the imagination. There was little feeling that one can puzzle out an approach to fresh problems without having to be given detailed instructions.

Oral work was too often limited to brief responses from a few pupils in answer to questions that provided no opportunity to exchange ideas or examine hypotheses. The work for the least able was sometimes designed to make the minimum linguistic demands. We quote some observations of this kind:

'What was lacking in the teaching was any real development of mathematical language, communication, discussion, group work or sustained mathematical investigation undertaken independently of the teacher. The pupils' response to this seemed to be one of quiet diligence (true of the general attitude in this school) without any commitment or enthusiasm. Their calculations were accurate, there was little participation, contribution or apparent enjoyment of the subject.'   (Mixed modern)

'The lessons seen at all ability levels were traditionally presented with little demand being made on the pupils to use mathematical language other than in simple monosyllabic responses. Even the more able pupils were reluctant to use mathematical vocabulary although it may have been known to them. For almost all pupils any discussion of mathematical problems and ideas was a novel experience.'   (Mixed comprehensive)

'Very little opportunity was given for the pupils to express themselves orally in mathematics lessons and this resulted in some very confused statements in the exercise books when anything in the nature of an explanation was demanded.'   (Mixed modern)

'The teaching depended too heavily on text books and worksheets. Seldom was there any direct teaching, or good oral work with lively responses. Too often there was a lack of pace; classes were noisy and restless and at times there was an obvious lack of sympathy between the pupils and the teacher.'
(Mixed comprehensive)

'The teachers used language only to instruct, explain and illustrate; rarely were questions asked of pupils requiring thought and alternative answers, although there was some individual discussion of pupils' difficulties. It cannot have been easy to discuss concepts and their relationships with pupils over half of whom were non-indigenous, but the attempt needed to be made from the time pupils entered school. Staff spoke of the difficulty pupils had in understanding problems and formulating them mathematically, but this activity is a part of mathematical education.'   (Mixed modern)

The potential of mathematics for developing precision and sensitivity in the use of language was underused; and this underuse was, as often as not, deliberate. The teachers evidently considered that the use of symbols and the performance of numerical calculations presented problems enough. The writing of continuous prose was hardly ever required, and there was small demand even for the pupils to present a clearly expressed logical argument, in which symbols and English words formed a grammatically connected paragraph. While this was the prevailing mode, some freer and more open use of language was certainly found; and some of the happiest exchanges were quite informal. A boy stopped his teacher on the stairs and urgently asked for confirmation of a method by which he wanted to estimate the number of seeds in a sunflower head; in a few moments of profitable conversation the boy refined and improved his idea. But, in general, insufficient value was attached to this kind of simple conversation about the mathematical aspects of everyday things.

As a closely related matter, there was perhaps insufficient practice of very simple mental arithmetic, aimed at building up confidence on examples which were well within the pupils' capacity if they were given sufficient time for reflection. In many schools the common practice of timetabling mathematics in double periods meant that brief daily practice in simple mental arithmetic (once considered desirable) was no longer possible even if the teachers had wished to provide it, and it appeared that no effective substitute for these short bouts of frequent practice had been found out.

The requirements of examinations (as they were perceived), unconsidered reaction to public criticism and, in some cases, the teachers' insufficient general knowledge of the applications of the subject combined to bring about a narrow approach to mathematics, as a whole, and to arithmetic in particular. This was often so even when the school's schemes of work professed aims which were more liberal. The extent to which this criticism applies is indicated by the overall graded assessments for mathematics provision given in section 10. The provision was considered unsatisfactory for the more able pupils in some 15 per cent of the schools, unsatisfactory for the average pupils in 26 per cent, and for the less able in 47 per cent. The most frequent cause was the narrowness of the approach, and when the provision was no more than 'acceptable' (without rising to 'creditable') the cause was often the same.

The following observations, made in two schools, describe the situation in many others:

> 'The teachers themselves said that the teaching style consisted of teaching the rules and then applying them. In many of the lessons seen, these rules were taught without any attempt to base them upon understanding and often concerned numerical ideas which were unrealistic. To give one example, pupils were taught to correct numbers such as 2.6676 to 3 decimal places although many of them had little idea what a decimal was. Expressing 10p as a decimal of a pound or the length of their pencil as the decimal of a metre proved extremely difficult. In another lesson pupils had been taught to use square root tables but found the question "Can you work out an approximate value of the square root of 10 without using your tables?" very strange. Applications referred to by teachers were invariably of the textbook exercise type; problems from everyday sources, whose point could be seen by the pupils, were seldom presented. The teaching approach was resulting in the withering away of common sense.'
>
> (Mixed modern)

> 'The main things contributing to the low assessment in mathematics are the lack of variety in the content of the courses and the dull, unimaginative approach in the teaching. The top band are prepared for the 16-plus examination but the work seen during the survey visit — and references to previous exercises — indicated an over emphasis on the four rules in arithmetic. Any work in algebra relied on certain rules like "change the side and change the sign", and for calculus notes were dictated and no attempt was made for pupils to understand what was happening.'
>
> (Mixed full range comprehensive)

Arithmetical computation and the needs of the outside world

Teachers tend to be polarised in their attitudes to arithmetical computation. A substantial number of teachers regard computational practice as an end in itself, although the majority probably recognise the need to apply computational skills to needs arising elsewhere. Sometimes the mathematics staff within a school were divided on this important matter, and quite different emphasis was given to the practice of routine skills with different classes in the one school. In other schools a consensus had been reached; but there were wide differences between schools in the extent to which calculations with fractions or decimals received regular practice, and in the extent to which they were practised with reference to a variety of realistic applications. It was very common for the schemes of work in the schools visited to refer to the need to relate the mathematics taught to the problems of everyday life, but the convincing realisation of this aim was much more rare.

While arithmetic was much practised it was comparatively rare to see the skills used to build up further knowledge. Thus practice of addition and multiplication was seldom incorporated in the investigation of any deeper questions such as the properties of prime numbers, or of the numbers which arise when objects are packed or stacked in various ways. An investigation of (say) the properties of recurring decimals was rarely used to stimulate further practice on division. Practice was nearly always regarded as a sufficient end in itself.

The following account relates to a boys' modern school, catering for the ability range 0 to 60, which is exceptional only in the degree of deprivation amongst its pupils. It exemplifies in an acute form a much more general problem:

'The objectives of the mathematics department are expressed almost entirely in terms of arithmetical skills; this is highlighted by the fact that the highest objective, even for the most able pupils, is CSE Commercial Arithmetic and Statistics. Having considered the deprived nature of the area and the quality of the intake in which, about fifty per cent have learning difficulties (linguistic or mathematical or both), the head of the department has decided that these narrow objectives are the only objectives which are realistic in the circumstances. Narrowness also characterises the teaching style; few resources are used other than textbooks; although the pupils work individually most of the time this is mainly on repetitive mechanical exercises providing only negligible opportunities for initiative.'

Often the teacher's response to weaknesses in calculation was a direct attack on the standard procedures for calculation, believing that pupils would learn simply by watching the processes performed and repeating them afterwards. On some occasions these methods appeared to work satisfactorily, at least in the short term. But such a concentration on calculation, devoid of application and motivation, was often counter productive, and the teacher's problem was to recognise when the method was failing and to know what else might be tried. This is illustrated by these extracts from accounts of two mixed modern schools.

'There is real concern about the lack of basic skills in arithmetic, but efforts to remedy this take the form of more and more sets of questions on fractions and decimals without identifying the basic number deficiencies that are at the heart of the problem. It is not surprising that mathematical activity could not be found in other areas of the curriculum and in science mathematical work was avoided where possible.'

'This was a school in which the mathematics department was almost too aware of the importance of basic computational skills and of the necessity to provide adequate opportunities for practice. Almost every group seen was doing computation of some kind. There was thus little apparent variety so far as the pupils were concerned and a resultant inability to apply computational skills in a wider context. This was illustrated in an extreme way by the case of one fifth-year boy in the bottom group who was faced with the problem of finding the cost of five shirts at £2.40 each. When offered the use of a calculator, which he rapidly understood how to use, he performed the operation as an addition sum and obtained the wrong answer because he entered the cost six times instead of five. When it was suggested that there was a simpler method he was unable to see that he could obtain the answer he required by using multiplication, even though it transpired that he was not without some knowledge of his tables.'

Where there were weaknesses in simple calculations the situation was sometimes aggravated by excessive insistence on standard routines. Cases were seen of calculations which should have been done mentally being referred to standard algorithms and rituals; $2\frac{1}{2}$ per cent of 100 was calculated at length in several steps. In another case $10 \times 2 \times 0.5$ was calculated by two fully set out multiplications, in the course of which multiplication by 0.5 required two lines of multiplication which had subsequently to be added. Time was wasted on quite inappropriate methods — for example on converting simple fractions to percentages using logarithms. There is definite value in illustrating the reliability of the standard procedures by using them to check examples which can be done in the head, but it encourages poor numeracy if the standard methods are expected, and even required, when simpler and more direct methods are better.

The least able pupils were almost always taught in comparatively small groups, often made smaller still by absence. In these groups, while appropriate time was nearly always given to the cultivation of computational skills, teachers who were anxious to bring about improvements did not always have the insight to understand the nature of the pupils' difficulties; or they had insufficient knowledge of current remedial practices to know what to do if repeated practice failed to establish the skills they were trying to cultivate. This area demands a sizeable provision of in-service training. This training could often be provided by the head of department if the overall work load and the pattern of the timetable permitted it.

The groups of pupils next above the lowest in achievement also presented problems. Many of these groups received well intentioned teaching, concentrating on a narrow range of arithmetical skills, but the results were disappointing to all concerned. The greatest progress was made where the teacher had the personal qualities to capture the interest of the pupils, to convince them that success was possible, and to produce an agreeable variety of work which provided regular opportunities to use the constantly needed skills. Teaching of this quality was not always available, but in many classrooms more could have been done to explain the methods of calculation which continued to present difficulty. In a few cases children at this level were no longer being given even the obvious straightforward explanations of how a calculation is done, in the belief that they must have been taught this already, and that further repetition would be fruitless.

Comparatively little work was seen in which a standard method of calculation was explained at greater length, perhaps with physical apparatus, with careful attention to the details of the process, and with the intention that the underlying reasons should be clearly understood. In some cases much time was spent on extensive, but still superficial, practice on calculations such as $2\frac{1}{4} - 1\frac{3}{4}$, when the time could have been better spent on calculations more closely related to everyday problems, treated in a way that developed understanding and encouraged commonsense short cuts. For example to subtract 99p from £1.42 by the usual written procedure is unnecessarily long, but some pupils need continued help if they are to see that, in this case, to add 1p to 42p is very much easier.

The concern teachers feel if their pupils achieve poorly in computational arithmetic is understandable; but if the cure involved no more than stepping up practice on a narrow range of written calculating procedures the numeracy problem would already have been solved. Practice needs to be carefully controlled, and supplemented by:

1 improved diagnosis of pupils' individual difficulties,
2 a better appreciation of the role of language and oral work,
3 more effective use of the applications of the ideas, both in the world around and in other subjects in the school.

During the period of the survey, public attention turned increasingly to the relation between the mathematics taught in schools and the mathematics required in industry, and more generally to the mathematics required in adult life. Recent discussions have had an effect on schools which cannot be assessed quantitatively from survey data, because the question did not have the same urgency when the survey was planned and comparable data were not collected from all the schools. However, sufficient individual cases were seen towards the end of the visits to suggest that there may now be a substantial problem requiring further investigation. The indications were that unsympathetic (and sometimes inadequately informed) general criticism had reinforced a number of schools in an already narrow approach to mathematics.

It is known from information collected during the survey, and from information collected elsewhere, that working parties have been set up in many areas to establish better liaison between schools, further education and industry, and that substantial benefits have resulted from the discussions that have taken place in some of these groups. But even where the teachers had participated in local groups and been involved in the construction of local test papers in arithmetic which were reasonable and well balanced, the courses which were eventually taught in preparation for the papers could still be exclusively preoccupied with the repetitive practice of low-level skills. Problems demanding the everyday use of language were receiving insufficient attention; and computation was practised with inappropriate or excessively difficult numbers, unrelated to practical questions in which it is necessary to subject the calculation to commonsense checks.
[...]

Summing up

Many schools are not finding it easy to strike an appropriate balance between the varied demands which are being made on them at the moment, and it is understandable if they sometimes find the demands contradictory. In particular, a number of schools experience difficulty in reconciling the broader range of mathematics which is contained in the newer schemes of work and examination syllabuses with the need to maintain proficiency in traditional arithmetical skills. The dilemma of these schools is accentuated by current demands for 'greater numeracy', because the notion of numeracy is so often ill-defined. In a great many cases the schools are responding by concentrating narrowly on computational skills, devoid of context or application, in ways which easily becomes counterproductive. The notion of numeracy should certainly include more than accurate computation — it should include the ability to make rough estimates, and the ability to apply knowledge in fresh circumstances, working to the appropriate degree of accuracy. The practice of the most successful schools in the survey showed that broad syllabuses are completely compatible with competence in traditional skills.

The tendency of schools to concentrate on a narrow range of skills, because they believe it to be an appropriate response to the demands which are being made on them, or because they believe it to be the most effective way to ensure success in the examination syllabus to which they are committed, increased towards the end of the survey. This was to some extent a reaction to the trend over the previous fifteen years to broaden both approaches to the subject and the range of topics examined. This trend has produced an unsatisfactory balance in the pattern of work in a number of schools where the new ideas have been adopted uncritically. Some schools seen in the survey with modern or compromise syllabuses were presenting a great variety of topics which overloaded their pupils, particularly those who were not among the more able. The possible harm in such schemes of work is not in the breadth and variety themselves, but in the failure to identify the ideas which are essential for later progress (and which have to be mastered) amongst the wider range of ideas which offer opportunities for exploratory thinking and which make the subject more interesting. The remedy for such an omission is not to swing to the opposite extreme, but to consider the various needs which the scheme of work has to meet, and keep the content of the course and the teaching methods under continuous review.

Whatever the mathematics syllabus, the ideas were, far more often than not, presented in a very narrow way. This was so even when the range of topics, as with some modern syllabuses, was large. Topics which had been introduced by textbook writers because of the opportunities they offered for discussion and exciting development were reduced to routine exercises, and the teaching aspired to do little more than cover the skills required. Illustrations or applications of the syllabus which were not examined were rarely taught. Mathematics was too little related to the world outside and to other subjects in the school, even when these subjects either needed to apply mathematical techniques directly (as in science), or when they gave broader illustrations of ideas which were explicitly on the syllabus. The lack of success in bringing out the purpose of the skills and techniques studied in mathematics is not due intrinsically to the syllabuses in use (traditional or modern); it is far more a matter of the way in which syllabuses are interpreted. It was in non-examination courses, and in some cases CSE courses, that the clearest attempts were made to base teaching on topics from the world outside; but much remains to be done to provide suitable source material and to develop the ideas in ways which capture the interest of the pupils and convince them that the ideas matter.

Some mathematical ideas might best be encountered for the first time in other classrooms of the school, with subsequent coordinated follow-up in mathematics lessons. High priority should be given to the establishment of better interdepartmental links, especially with the science and craft departments, where the effect of inadequate liaison can frequently be seen. Teachers in these other departments likewise have a responsibility to recognise their influence on pupils' mathematical development. It is important to use mathematical language which the pupils understand, and to listen sympathetically to the language which the pupils offer. The thoughtful and precise use of language, with the minimum technicality, plays a bigger part in pupils' mathematical development than is sometimes recognised.

Mathematics lessons in their turn could make a more substantial contribution to pupils' general language development. The subject offers opportunities for discussion, pupil with pupil, and pupil with teacher, which are insufficiently taken up. This does not necessarily demand any infusion of fresh mathematical topics into the classroom, as questions which are common in any course can be handled from this point of view. In a similar way, more encouragement could often be given to the orderly presentation of written solutions to problems. Some pupils may find difficulty enough in performing the calculations, but all should be urged, within their capacity, towards clear and concise expression. Mathematical signs make sense only if they occur in properly constructed sentences. The need for clear presentation is especially plain when mathematical ideas are used in other subjects. Where the need for development on these lines is accepted, schools might initiate staff discussion.

While it was not a matter for systematic study in the survey, it was evident that the development of the teaching of mathematics in a school can be handicapped if enterprising work is misunderstood by parents, local employers or further education institutions. As the scheme of work in a school is developed, it is advisable to find ways of discussing the school's aims and methods with these groups of people. Such discussions are important for other reasons as well. As the survey proceeded it became clear that locally instituted tests of numeracy were playing an increasing, although still small part in determining the curriculum of the pupils, especially the less able. The purpose of such tests, and the extent to which the purpose is being achieved, require continuing review.

5 The mathematical performance of 11 year olds in England and Wales in 1978: the first report from the Assessment of Performance Unit

D. D. Foxman, M. J. Cresswell, M. Ward, M. E. Badger, J. A. Tuson and B. A. Bloomfield

Source: Foxman, D. D. et al., Mathematical Development: Primary Survey Report No. 1, HMSO, London, 1980. Section 1.2; sections 1.4–1.6; figures 3.8, 3.12, 3.18 and 3.22; sections 4.35–4.43, sections 6.6–6.14.

⋘⋘⋘

[This chapter consists of extracts from the report of the first survey of the mathematical performance of 11 year old children in England and Wales. The survey was conducted by the National Foundation for Educational Research on behalf of the Assessment of Performance Unit (APU) of the Department of Education and Science. The extracts have been divided as follows:

1 a description of the general approach to monitoring mathematical performance;
2 examples of the written test items, and the associated results;
3 examples of the practical test items, and the associated results;
4 a summary of the overall results.]

A description of the general approach to monitoring mathematical performance

In the survey, printed tests requiring short written responses were administered to a representative national sample of about 13 000 pupils attending schools in England and Wales whose eleventh birthdays occurred in the school year of testing. A sub-sample of the main sample, consisting of over 1000 pupils, also took practical tests administered by itinerant testers in one-to-one interviews. A separate sub-sample of over 1500 pupils completed questionnaires administered by their own teachers on their attitudes to mathematics as a whole and to various topics within it. Altogether pupils from about 1000 schools participated. [. . .]

APU policy is that monitoring should reflect the diversity of the mathematical curriculum. This applies both to the range of content taught and to the variety of mathematical activity which takes place in the schools. The framework [for monitoring mathematical performance] needed to be compatible with the APU curriculum model in which mathematics is construed as a line of development and not simply as a subject.

The Steering Group on mathematics identified three requirements: the classification should reflect the structure of mathematics, take into account what is known about the learning of mathematics, and provide evidence to inform current discussions on the mathematics curriculum.

It was decided to use a two-way categorisation: by content and by learning outcome. In order to select the categories the mathematics monitoring team studied a variety of classification schemes. These generally agreed on three main categories of content, namely, geometry, measures and number, while others often mentioned included algebra, sets, functions and graphical representation.

The same main categories of content and outcome were used for both 11 year olds and 15 year olds. At the secondary level, work on sets is most evident in relation to algebraic structure. The work done in primary schools on representing data in graphs and charts is part of another major category of mathematics – statistics – which uses the concept of probability as its theoretical basis. From this it appeared that five main content categories: geometry, measures, number, algebra, and probability and statistics, would be a sufficiently extensive umbrella to cover the mathematics content known to be taught to both the 11 and 15 year old age groups.

The main content categories subdivide differently at the two age groups but the difference is mainly one of balance; sub-categories of number must constitute a greater part of the primary curriculum than of the secondary curriculum while the reverse is the case for sub-categories of algebra. Here only the primary sub-categories are considered.

There are variations between schools in the emphasis placed on new or modern mathematics and traditional mathematics; this is particularly evident in geometry and algebra. For example, in geometry the notion of transformations is a modern topic while traditional geometry includes basic Euclidean ideas. Within algebra sets represent modern work and generalised arithmetic traditional. In measures there is a convenient subdivision between unit measures (money, time, temperature, weight/mass etc.) and mensuration (length, area, volume, capacity). The number category at primary level includes work on whole numbers, fractions, decimals and percentages. The four rules have a prominent place in all schools and in most at least some 11 year olds will have been introduced to basic ideas about rate and ratio and concepts such as factors, multiples and prime numbers. The number category conveniently subdivides by the type of outcome of pupils' learning as well as by content; there is a need for information on pupils' understanding of concepts, on their skills in computation and on their performance in applying number concepts and skills in various contexts.

The main content categories were divided into 13 sub-categories as shown in table 1. The purpose of the framework is to ease the task of interpreting the data and it is not supposed that the various areas of mathematics can be confined within such clear-cut boundaries. The same structure applies with perhaps more

Table 1 The curriculum framework: main categories of content and outcome

Main content category	Type of performance or outcome	Concepts, skills, applications	Generalisation and proof	Investigations and creativity	Attitudes
Measures		Money, time, mass, temperature			
		Length, area, volume, capacity			
Geometry		Shapes, lines, angles			
		Symmetry, transformations, co-ordinates			
Number		*Concepts: whole number* *Computation: whole numbers and decimals* *Applications of numbers*			
		Concepts: decimals and fractions *Computation: fractions*			
		Ratio and rate			
Algebra		Generalised arithmetic			
		Sets and relations			
Probability and statistics		Probability and data representation			

The right-hand columns carry the spanning annotations: Liking, difficulty and utility of mathematics • Liking and difficulty of mathematical topics in the 13 sub-categories

force to the different outcomes of learning, six of which have been defined. These are:

1 concepts,
2 skills,
3 applications,
4 generalisation and proof,
5 investigations,
6 attitudes to mathematics.

Mathematical *concepts* are tested by items involving the recognition of a relationship. For example, an item testing the concept of multiplication might evoke recognition of the relationship between multiplication and addition. Some mathematical concepts (e.g. number) form a complex network of relationships; a single item could only test perhaps one aspect of one of the relationships.

Skills are learned routines which are tested in the form in which they have been practised. Apart from computation, mathematical skills include measurement of length with a ruler, drawing a circle with compasses and solving a simple algebraic equation.

The type of performance classified as *applications* is a particularly important one for the cross curriculum model. It is under this heading that test items using contexts from different subject areas would be placed, but for the first primary survey it was decided that the category should consist of items testing the ability to select and carry out the appropriate mathematical procedure in a range of everyday contexts.

Items testing pupils' performance in *generalisation and proof* and *investigations* of open situations have not been included in this first round of monitoring but are being developed for possible inclusion in subsequent surveys.

Versions of the scheme adopted for the classification of outcomes had been developed prior to the appointment of the monitoring team. However the characterisation of learning outcomes is more problematic than the classification of content, partly owing to differences in views on the nature of learning, but also because the categories are not clearly differentiated. For example, many skills or practised routines are dependent for their success on an understanding of underlying concepts. Further, a pupil's performance may not match the outcome being tested. This is illustrated by the following item which is intended to test an aspect of the concept of multiplication, the recognition of the relationship between multiplication and addition:

$12 \times 18 = 216$
$13 \times 18 = 216 + \square$
What should be the number in the box?

A pupil who understands the concept and recognises the purpose of the question is most likely to place 18 in the box provided. But the correct answer can also be obtained by finding the product of 13 and 18 and subtracting 216. This way of arriving at the answer demonstrates computational skill rather than an understanding of the relationship between multiplication and repeated addition. It is obvious that unless the way in which a pupil tackles an item is known it cannot be unequivocally classified on the outcomes dimension.

In spite of these difficulties of classifying outcomes, the dimension is invaluable as a check that sub-categories contain items testing as wide a range of mathematical activity as possible. This intention is exemplified in table 1, by showing the content dimension intersecting the outcomes categories. In practice, because of the balance of the mathematics curriculum, some sub-categories have items testing mostly one outcome (e.g. concepts in symmetry, transformations, coordinates or applications in probability and data representation), while in number the extensive coverage of all three types of outcome warranted separate sub-categories for each of them.

The difficulties of classifying performance which arise from not knowing how a question is tackled mainly occur in written tests when pupils' methods cannot be probed as they can be in the practical mode of assessment.

Three types of assessment instruments were used in the 1978 survey. Concepts, skills and applications in the sub-categories of content were assessed in written and practical modes, and attitudes were assessed partly in the practical mode but mainly by the administration of attitude questionnaires. [. . .]

A total of 647 written items were assembled into 26 tests, each consisting of a different selection of items from three of the 13 sub-categories. The combinations of three sub-categories within each test were arranged so that all tests contained items from at least one number or measures sub-category. Each test consisted of about 50 items. Pilot tests had shown that few children needed more than 50 minutes to attempt these but schools were asked to allow pupils to continue working for as long as they wished, where possible.

The practical tests were administered by 21 experienced teachers of 11 year olds who were nominated by their local authorities and trained to administer the tests by the NFER monitoring team. Each tester visited up to ten schools and tested six pupils per day from those selected by the sampling procedure. Pupils from about 150 schools took part in the practical tests.

Each practical test given to a pupil comprised three of the twelve topics which had been developed from the survey. The topics consisted of a series of questions on the same theme, chosen to give a reasonable variety of material from the range of sub-categories of the curriculum framework. Emphasis was placed on assessing pupils' understanding of mathematical ideas in practical situations.

Examples of written items, and the associated results

[This section consists of four figures (see Figures 1–4 on pages 59–62) taken from chapter 3 of the report. Each figure has the same format, and includes five items, with the percentage of children who performed each successfully (referred to as the item facility) as well as the percentage who did not, or who omitted the item altogether.]

An example from the practical tests (fractions) and the associated results

This topic was designed to look at fractions in two ways. The child was first asked to cut up a piece of string into fractional parts. Some coloured plastic squares were then shown and questions asked about fractions of the total number of squares.

The first question asked pupils to 'cut this string in half'. The response was taken as correct where pupils used a method such as folding to find the centre.

The pupils were then presented with one of the halves and asked to 'cut off $\frac{1}{4}$ of this piece'. Among the 64 per cent who were successful were those who ended up with $\frac{1}{4}, \frac{1}{4}, \frac{1}{2}$ as well as those with $\frac{1}{4}, \frac{3}{4}$. The drop of 22 per cent in the success rate here, from 86 per cent to 64 per cent was not simply because there were two cuts to make. Whereas for one fold the two ends came together,

Figure 1   Items from length, area, volume, capacity
Item cluster: area
Mean sub-category score — 54 per cent

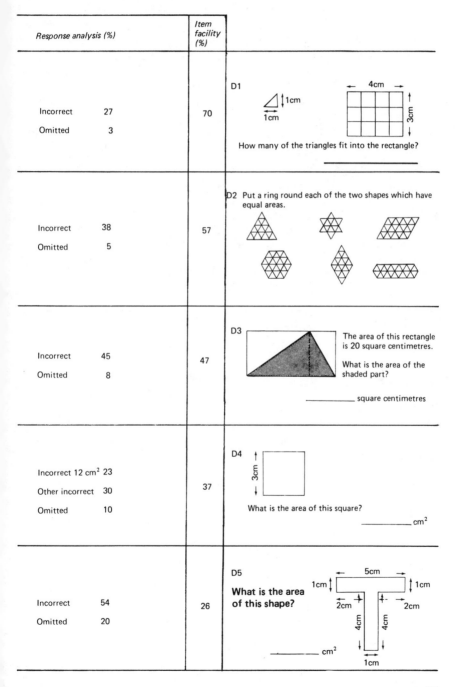

Response analysis (%)		Item facility (%)	
			D1 How many of the triangles fit into the rectangle?
Incorrect	27	70	
Omitted	3		
			D2 Put a ring round each of the two shapes which have equal areas.
Incorrect	38	57	
Omitted	5		
			D3 The area of this rectangle is 20 square centimetres. What is the area of the shaded part? _____ square centimetres
Incorrect	45	47	
Omitted	8		
			D4 What is the area of this square? _____ cm²
Incorrect 12 cm²	23	37	
Other incorrect	30		
Omitted	10		
			D5 What is the area of this shape? _____ cm²
Incorrect	54	26	
Omitted	20		

Figure 2   Items from concepts (decimals and fractions)
            Item cluster: decimals
            Mean sub-category score: 48 per cent

Response analysis (%)		*Item facility* (%)	
Incorrect	19	79	F1 Put these decimals in order of size, smallest first. 0.3 0.1 0.7 0.6
Omitted	2		
0.56 is: ☐ greater than 1.3 29 ☐ equal to 1.3 11 Other incorrect 1 Omitted 5		54	F2 Tick the line that is correct. 0.56 is less than 1.3 0.56 is greater than 1.3 0.56 is equal to 1.3
Incorrect	41	47	F3 How many times is 0.1 greater than 0.01?
Omitted	12		
Incorrect	54	34	F4 What number is 10 times 0.5?
Omitted	12		
Incorrect	76	21	F5 Put these decimals in order of size, *smallest* first. 0.07 0.23 0.1
Omitted	3		

Figure 3   Items from applications of number
Item cluster: division
Mean sub-category score: 54 per cent

Response analysis (%)		*Item facility* (%)	
Incorrect	11	83	**J1** A bar of chocolate can be broken into 18 squares. There are 6 squares in each row. How many rows are there? _____ rows
Omitted	6		
Incorrect	17	76	**J2** Spoons are sold in boxes containing half a dozen. If I want 30 spoons, how many boxes shall I buy? _____
Omitted	7		
Incorrect	25	66	**J3** 150 people are coming to see the school play. The chairs are arranged in rows of 15. How many rows of chairs will be needed? _____
Omitted	9		
Incorrect	34	53	**J4** 256 children are going to have tea at the Christmas party. 8 children can sit at a table. How many tables will be needed? _____
Omitted	13		
Incorrect	37	25	**J5** A batting average in cricket is found by dividing the number of runs scored by number of times out. Fill in the following table. Name No. times out No. runs scored Average Boycott 5 500 _____
Omitted	38		

Figure 4   Items from generalised arithmetic
            Item cluster: equations
            Mean sub-category score: 38 per cent

Response analysis (%)		Item facility (%)	
Incorrect	6	88	M1 Find which number □ stands for. $12 - \square = 8$ □ = _____
Omitted	6		
Incorrect	19	75	M2 Find which number △ stands for. $51 + \triangle = 90$ △ = _____
Omitted	6		
Incorrect	30	63	M3 n stands for a number. $n + 4 = 21$ so $n + 5 =$ _____
Omitted	7		
Incorrect	39	51	M4 B stands for a number. $B - 9 = 21$ so $B - 10 =$ _____
Omitted	10		
Incorrect	50	19	M5 Fill in the values of M in this table according to the equation $M + N = 4$
Omitted	31		

For M5, the table is:

N	0	1	2	3	4
M	4				

when pupils used a trial and error method, guessing the quarter length, the final fold was too long or too short.

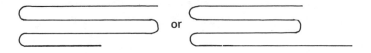

Some pupils changed their strategy at this point but others could not.

Question 3 asked 'what fraction of the whole string that you started with is that little piece?', emphasising the original piece not cut into these bits:

$$\frac{1}{2} \qquad \frac{1}{4} \qquad \frac{1}{8} \qquad \frac{1}{8}$$

The question was about a fraction of a fraction: recognising the required piece as a quarter of a half. The correct answer of $\frac{1}{8}$ was given by 42 per cent of pupils, showing that the notion of multiplying fractions, even with real materials, is not easy. Many pupils said 'a quarter', and a third, a sixth and a tenth were amongst other answers.

The questions about the coloured plastic tiles proved to be difficult:

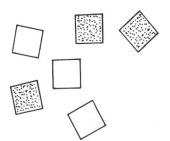

First three red and three yellow square tiles were set out loosely. Question 5 asked 'what fraction of these squares is red?'.

This question was about the basic recognition of fractions, and 61 per cent of pupils gave a correct response. The answer $\frac{3}{6}$ was allowed, and some 12 per cent gave this, but when the testers probed it appeared that some pupils did not appreciate that $\frac{3}{6}$ and $\frac{1}{2}$ were equivalent.

For question 6 the children were shown one red and three yellow squares and asked 'What fraction of these squares is red?'. This time 64 per cent gave a correct response. A frequent wrong answer was $\frac{1}{3}$ where pupils gave the ratio of red to yellow. This demonstrates lack of understanding of set inclusion, that the red square is included in the set of all squares.

Table 2 Topic on fractions: results

Questions		A Unaided success (%)	B Unaided + aided success (%)	C Unsuccessful (%)	D Remainder (%)
1 'Cut this string in half.'	All	86	87	12	1
	Boys	83	85	14	1
	Girls	92	92	8	1
2 Pick up one piece. 'Now cut off ¼ of this piece.'	All	64	68	32	0
	Boys	60	64	35	0
	Girls	71	74	26	0
3 'What fraction of the whole string that you started with is that little piece?'	All	42	48	50	3
	Boys	43	48	49	3
	Girls	40	46	51	2
4 Present 3 yellow and 3 red squares. 'How many of these squares are red?'	All	—	—	—	—
5 'What fraction of these squares is red?'	All	61	65	34	1
	Boys	58	63	31	1
	Girls	66	68	31	1
6 Present 3 yellow and 1 red square. 'What fraction of these squares is red?'	All	64	66	32	2
	Boys	65	68	30	2
	Girls	61	64	35	1
7 Present stapled bag. 'Estimate what fraction of these pegs is white.'	All	61	63	36	2
	Boys	61	63	35	2
	Girls	60	62	37	1
7a 'How did you make your estimation?'	All	48	48	40	11
	Boys	47	47	42	10
	Girls	49	49	37	13

381 pupils took this topic

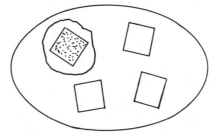

These tests indicated that a third of all 11 year old pupils (61 and 64 per cent correct) do not fully understand the nature of fractions with discrete objects.

Further evidence that pupils find the idea of fractions hard came in question 7. The pupil was presented with a stapled plastic bag containing 15 white and 45 coloured pegs and asked to estimate the fraction of white ones. To be acceptable the pupils' answer had to be greater than or equal to $\frac{1}{10}$ and less than $\frac{1}{2}$. Question 7a: 'How did you make your estimation?', was added at the suggestion of one of the teachers at the briefing conference.

Some answers were succinct and correct:

'¼. It looks like there's 3 reds for every white one'. Other responses illustrate how an answer can be coded 'successful' without being 'correct', e.g. '$\frac{1}{3}$: if you split the red pegs into three parts they'd make about the same as the white ones', or '$\frac{1}{3}$: for every white peg there looked like 3 red ones'.

One boy, while trying hard to give the tester the answer he wanted, showed that he did not appreciate what a fraction was: '$\frac{1}{14}$. 14 white pegs. If you just say 14 it isn't a fraction. You have to say $\frac{1}{14}$, otherwise you break the rule'.

While many pupils answered this test as a whole with confidence and accuracy, a number gave evidence of not understanding some aspects of the notion of a fraction.

The results of the survey

It would be reasonable to conclude from the results of the written and practical tests [. . . those included in previous parts of this chapter, and many others] that most 11 year olds can do mathematics involving the more fundamental concepts and skills to which they have been introduced and also simple applications of them. There is, however, a fairly sharp decline in performance as pupils' understanding of the concepts is probed more deeply and as their basic knowledge has to be applied in more complex settings or unfamiliar contexts. Typical examples of the effect of a deeper probe into concepts are that the reflection of a simple shape in a vertical mirror was drawn successfully by 80 per cent, but by about 20 per cent if the mirror was diagonal. Pupils' grasp of the concept of decimal place value was shown by several items to be tenuous; placing decimals written to one place in order of size was achieved by 80 per cent of pupils but the introduction in some of the numbers of a second place of decimals reduced the facility for the same process to 20 per cent. Fractions could be added by 60 per cent to 70 per cent if their denominators were the same, but by less than 30 per cent if they were not.

Different contexts influence performance on items involving the same processes or operations in various ways and there were a number of examples of this in the survey. An unfamiliar context can induce a tentative approach and this is probably why many pupils appeared to be put off their stroke when asked to calculate Geoffrey Boycott's batting average, although the method of getting the result was explained and the computation involved was not difficult. In another example a division of two numbers $84 \div 4$ was answered correctly by 70 per cent of pupils while the same calculation, written more unusually in ratio or fraction form, $\frac{84}{4}$, obtained a facility value of only 40 per cent. Some pupils may not have appreciated that $\frac{84}{4}$ was an instruction to do anything, and, of those who did, some tried to introduce a fraction into their answer.

All mathematics problems and questions have to be analysed to establish what mathematical knowledge is required to get an answer. At the age of 11 it is difficult for pupils to extract the essential details from more complex contexts. Thus, items on angle properties of figures such as the sum of adjacent angles on a straight line and the sum of interior angles of a triangle became more difficult as the basic figures were more deeply embedded in other diagrams.

Different contexts can also elicit alternative approaches to the same process and this effect may have been responsible for a number of items on proportionality with similar operations receiving widely different facilities. In the practical interviews it was possible to demonstrate this context effect in the topic 'methods of computation' in which pupils were presented with verbal problems and their equivalent computations. A high proportion of pupils used different methods in the two contexts and in addition some testers reported interviewing pupils who did not see the connection between these same computations carried out by the different methods.

An important feature of mathematics is its power to communicate in symbols, graphs and diagrams. The results show that while pupils have had experience of, and understand, the basic ideas and skills, many find translating and manipulating symbols too abstract to deal with and that graphs and diagrams generally communicate only what is immediately evident. Most pupils could read scale and graph points correctly if they were labelled but the interpolation of intermediate unmarked points and extrapolation to points off the graph could be done by just a few pupils. Information which had to be worked out from data extracted from tables, graphs or diagrams generally gained lower facilities than the comparable computations presented in a basic straightforward manner. Inferring information from graphs and diagrams proved difficult. For example, questions on the calculation of perimeters of rectangles showed that some children do not infer the remaining lengths if only one length and breadth are given on the accompanying diagram. Another example occurred in the practical topic 'visualisation', where a high proportion of pupils were able to interpret two-dimensional diagrams of three-dimensional shapes so that they could build the latter with small cubes, but any information which had to be inferred from the diagram (e.g. 'where could you place a cube which cannot be seen in the diagram?') produced lower facilities.

Communicating with symbols is related to communication with ordinary language; while only very few pupils could translate or manipulate mathematical symbols, more were able to describe in words relationships such as those between two sets of numbers. In some instances the use of verbal forms to stand for mathematical symbols substantially improved performance. This happened in the multiplication of fractions (using 'of' for the multiplication sign) and division of fractions (using 'how many halves in $2\frac{1}{2}$' for '$2\frac{1}{2} \div \frac{1}{2}$') where the words make the situation more concrete. However, in some items in computation with whole numbers a slight worsening of performance was the result of using verbal forms like 'what is the sum of' for the addition sign and 'what is 5 times as big as 2' in place of 5 × 2. This was probably because familiar and well understood symbols were replaced by less well-known words and phrases.

Words have other functions in addition to standing for symbols: they can define; they have a classifying function; and they can draw attention to a particular feature of a situation. Pupils may know definitions of mathematical terms like 'prime number' for example, but do not always follow their implications. Thus a non-prime odd number was often selected as a prime possibly because, as prime numbers are also odd (with the exception of 2), odd numbers 'look like' primes. The classifying function of words is employed in the naming of two- or three-dimensional shapes which a high proportion of pupils could do when different ones such as circle, triangle, rectangle or cube, cone and cylinder were contrasted in the same item.

In the practical interview words could be used to probe and draw attention to particular features of the situation under discussion and the pupils' understanding of the terms and expressions used to describe it. In cases where the meaning of a term (e.g. 'estimate') was not understood, or needed to be negotiated, (e.g. 'different' in 'different number pattern') then prompts improved performance. There was a more limited effect where difficult underlying concepts were involved, for example, in relation to fractions of a number of discrete objects.

Finally, as to pupils' attitudes towards mathematics, the main finding of interest was that the four rules are regarded by pupils as the topics which are most representative of the subject. It was also found that pupils' attitude to dividing, in contrast to adding, subtracting and multiplying, is probably a good indicator of their interest in mathematics as a whole.

SECTION 3 Developing mathematical thinking

≪≪

Introduction

The picture of mathematical thinking and a strategy for developing it, painted at the beginning of this book, can be supported and amplified in many ways. This section of the book is primarily concerned with such background. Some of the chapters are to do with the psychology of learning, both in general terms and specifically in mathematics. Others focus upon the nature of problem-solving. A third theme is language, for it is argued that an essential part of the strategy for developing mathematical thinking is communicating one's thoughts, both orally and in written records. Most of the chapters deal with more than one of these three themes, for they are all interconnected. Nevertheless each chapter has one of the themes as its principal focus, and the chapters have been grouped accordingly.

The first three chapters are all mainly concerned with the psychology of learning. In chapter 6, *The Desire to Learn*, Margaret Donaldson discusses motivation. She maintains that the key role of the teacher is to provide children with appropriate challenges – to give them problems that they can solve, but which nevertheless require some effort. She quotes research evidence to the effect that such activity is intrinsically satisfying so there is no need for external incentives. Provided that their confidence has not been destroyed, children and adults enjoy meaningful and manageable challenges.

Chapters 7 and 8 are specifically concerned with the psychology of learning mathematics. In chapter 7 Richard Skemp discusses how mathematical concepts are formed. In essence his argument is that they are formed not by definitions but by examples. That is, children learn about measurement by trying to measure all manner of different things and about general rules for adding by trying to add particular pairs of numbers. They do not learn about measurement so well if they are only given such definitions as the 'area of a rectangle is length times breadth', nor do they understand about adding numbers of two or more digits by merely being given rules about 'carrying'. The common sense of both definition and rule need first of all to be made apparent from the children's own experience.

Chapter 8 lends support to this argument from a rather different perspective. It stems from a large-scale inquiry into children's cognitive development and is very much in the Piagetian tradition. Many years ago Piaget investigated the growth of children's understanding of such fundamental mathematical concepts as number, length, and weight. His conclusion was that children passed through a stage when they believed that the number of objects in a collection might alter if the objects were moved around, and that the weight of a ball of plasticine might change if it were rolled into a different shape. In Piagetian terminology, children at such a stage do not 'conserve' number or weight, nor yet many other basic concepts such as length or area. Piaget also maintained that children's logic was somewhat deficient. They could not use arguments of the form '$A = B$ and $B = C$, therefore $A = C$' or 'If A is greater than B and B is greater than C, A must be greater than C'. Many criticisms have been made of Piagetian methodology and his conclusions have been questioned in a number of ways: nevertheless conservation, and what chapter 8 refers to as 'concreto-logic', continue to be major concepts in research into cognitive development. In that chapter Eryl Rothwell Hughes describes and interprets the results of a large-scale study of the development of children's understanding of the three concepts of area, weight and volume. She argues that the common view that these concepts are only understood in that order has little foundation. The crucial factor determining children's grasp of these concepts is the practical experience that they have had and she considers this to be a powerful argument for involving children in practical activities in which these concepts are implicit. Understanding will stem from a wide range of particular examples in the same way as Skemp describes.

The second three chapters, 9, 10 and 11 focus upon what problem-solving actually involves. Chapter 9 is taken from the writings of that most well-known of mathematical problem-solvers, George Polya. His advice to would-be problem-solvers is couched in the form of a dialogue in which he identifies several phases in the process: getting acquainted with the problem, trying to understand it more fully, looking for helpful ideas, carrying out some kind of solution, and then finally looking back over the experience for any lessons that can be formed. In keeping with the argument that one needs particular examples of an idea in order to fully understand it, Polya's general advice probably makes most sense when seen in the light of personal experiences of problem-solving; in this book that is left as an exercise for the reader, though students of the Developing Mathematical Thinking course will certainly be trying to do this.

Chapter 10, by Bob Samples, describes the nature of the problem-solving that he and two other observers saw happening in a particular classroom. Using the metaphor of left-handed and right-handed knowing — the former being intuitive and the latter rational — he describes how the children oscillated between the two. Given a piece of equipment to explore they spent some of the time playing with it in what seemed to be a fairly disorganised manner, and Samples describes this as getting to know the equipment (here a set of pendula) in a left-handed, intuitive way. However, some of their time was spent in thinking rationally about the way in which the pendula behaved, that is, working in the right-handed mode. To begin with, the left hand predominated, while later on the right hand largely took over, but all the way through the children oscillated between the two.

Chapter 11, by Sandy Dawson and John Trivett, is also centred upon children investigating problems in the classroom. They are firm believers in the value of such activity and advocate it strongly. The picture they paint is very akin to that described at the beginning of the book, in which children are engaged in a variety of investigations and spend much of their time discussing them with each other.

The final two chapters in this section, chapters 12 and 13, pay particular attention to language. Chapter 12 is a very brief account by Dan Slobin of the interactions between language and cognitive development in general. In other words it looks at the way in which the developments of language and thinking influence each other. In Chapter 13, David Pimm focuses entirely upon language and mathematics, and is concerned with what is involved in communicating mathematical ideas. He argues that a prime source of confusion for would-be learners of mathematics is that the way in which symbols are written down and then manipulated can easily become dissociated from anything that happens in the real world. Any talking that then happens about the mathematics then degenerates into rules for moving symbols around, rules like 'take it to the other side and change the sign'. But such rules are not arbitrary; they derive from activities that make sense and which can be talked about. In this way the rules become intuitively obvious. Even so there are pitfalls in seeing mathematics as a language into which activities described in English can be translated. For example, many different activities share a single mathematical formulation: the sign '−' relates to, among other things, taking away and to finding the difference between, which arise in situations that are far from being the same. Many other aspects of considering mathematics to be a language are also explored in this chapter.

6 The desire to learn

Margaret Donaldson

Source: Donaldson, M., Children's Minds, chapter 10, pp 110–120, Fontana, 1978.

≪≪≪

At a very early age, human babies show signs of a strong urge to master the environment. They are limited in what they can do by the slow development of their skill in controlling their own movements. Thus it is fair to call them 'helpless' in the sense that they cannot manage the environment well enough to survive unaided. This makes it all the more interesting to discover that the urge to manage the environment is already there at this time of helplessness and that it does not appear to derive from anything else or to depend on any reward apart from the achieving of competence and control.

For some time past it has been widely accepted that babies, and some other creatures, learn to do things because certain acts lead to 'rewards'; and there is no reason to doubt that this is true. But it used also to be widely believed that effective rewards, at least in the early stages, had to be directly related to such basic physiological 'drives' as thirst or hunger. In other words, a baby would learn if he got food or drink or some sort of physical comfort, not otherwise.

It is now clear that this is not so. Babies will learn to behave in ways that produce results in the world with no reward except the successful outcome. For an example of work which shows this clearly we may turn to some studies carried out by Hanus Papousek.

Papousek began by using milk in the normal way to 'reward' the babies he studied and so teach them to carry out some simple movements, such as turning the head to one side or the other. Then he noticed that an infant who had had enough to drink would refuse the milk but would still go on making the learned response with clear signs of pleasure. So he began to study the children's responses in situations where no milk was provided. He quickly found that children as young as four months would learn to turn their heads to right or left if the movement 'switched on' a display of lights — and indeed that they were capable of learning quite complex sequences of head turns to bring about this result. For instance, they could learn to make alternating turns to left and right; or to make double alternating turns (two left, two right); or to make as many as three consecutive turns to one side.

Papousek's light display was placed directly in front of the infants and he made the interesting observation that sometimes they would not turn back to watch the lights closely although they would 'smile and bubble' when the display came on. Papousek concluded that it was not primarily the sight of the lights which pleased them, it was the success they were achieving in solving the problem, in mastering the skill. If he is right in this — and there is a considerable amount of other confirming evidence — then we may conclude that there exists a fundamental human urge to make sense of the world and bring it under deliberate control.

Papousek argues further that what his babies are doing as they try to achieve this control is matching incoming information about the world against some sort of inner 'standard'. And this amounts to saying that they are already engaged in building some kind of 'model' of bits of the world — some mental representation of what it is like. They then experience satisfaction when the fit between the model and the world is good, dissatisfaction when it is bad, that is, when the expected result fails to occur, when the lights do not go on. Papousek reports 'increased tension and finally upsetness and signs of displeasure' in the latter case.

Now on even the simplest notion of what is involved in adaptation, it can come as no surprise that dissatisfaction arises when prediction fails. As soon as a species abandons reliance on instinctual patterns of behaviour and begins to rely instead on building inner representations and making predictions then it becomes critical for survival to get the predictions right. Thus the realisation of incongruity between our notion of the world and what it turns out to be like should naturally lead us to want to understand it better. And many different theories about the growth of intelligent thought stress that this kind of cognitive conflict is unacceptable to us, that it is something we try to get rid of. After the early stages, the conflict may be between different parts of our world model. If we come to face the fact that we hold two inconsistent beliefs we find this uncomfortable. And so we should. For it is axiomatic that the different parts of a model must fit together.

This argument [. . . indicates] the educational value of becoming aware of error. But there are two further considerations which now need to be added. Firstly it is not only when incongruities are forced on us by events that we try to resolve them. Sometimes we positively seek them out, as if we liked having to deal with things that we do not understand, things that challenge us intellectually. But secondly we may, on the contrary, become afraid of meeting incongruity, afraid of realising that we are wrong, and we may then take steps to defend ourselves against this recognition by avoiding situations that are likely to give rise to it. We may withdraw.

These are sharply contrasted responses and the difference between them is of crucial educational importance. Education should aim to encourage the readiness to come to grips with incongruity and even to seek it out in a positive fashion, enjoying challenge. Equally, it should aim to discourage defence and withdrawal. But often it seems in effect to do exactly the opposite. The reasons for this cannot become clear without consideration of another topic: the development of the self-image.

We are beings who ask questions; we are beings who make value judgements, holding some things good and important, others bad or worthless; and we are beings who build models of the world. In the course of time, these models come to include some representation of ourselves as part of the world. It is thus inevitable that we should arrive at the question: of what value am I? And it is also inevitable that the answer should matter to us a great deal.

When a child first asks this question, how is he to get the answer? One obvious way will be to try to discover what value other people place upon him. With increasing maturity, when he has perhaps managed to develop a more independent value system of his own, the judgements of others may come to matter less. But while he is still a young child they are bound to exert powerful influence on his self-esteem.

I have been arguing that there is a fundamental human urge to be effective, competent and independent, to understand the world and to act with skill. I am reminded of a little girl of eighteen months, verbally somewhat precocious, who, when she was offered help with anything, was given to saying firmly: 'Can man'ge'. To this basic urge to 'manage' there is added in our kind of culture very strong social approval of certain kinds of competence. It is arguable that in some ways we do *not* encourage competence – that we keep our children too dependent for too long, denying them the opportunity to exercise their very considerable capacity for initiative and responsible action. This is perhaps hard to avoid in a complex urban society with a highly developed technology. Yet within the educational system at least there is certainly strong social approval of competence in the more disembodied skills of the mind. So the child who succeeds in coping with these new challenges when he enters school will be highly valued by his teachers – and all too often the one who initially fails will not. In either case the child will quickly discover how he is judged to be doing. That he has often made up his mind about his cognitive competence even before he comes to school is emphasised by Marion Blank, who reports the occurrence of remarks like 'I'm dumb', 'I can't, 'I'm stupid' and 'I don't know how to do things' from certain kindergarten children faced by some cognitive demand.

There can be no doubt that if we decide we cannot cope with a particular kind of challenge we tend to give up and avoid it. Bruner draws a sharp distinction between 'coping' and 'defending' which he likens to the distinction between 'playing tennis on the one hand and fighting like fury to stay off the tennis court altogether on the other'. People do of course differ in the extent to which they persevere in the teeth of persistent failure. Robert the Bruce is said to have observed the tenacity of a spider and resolved to try again. But a spider has presumably no self-image to disturb it, and Robert the Bruce was a mature man who doubtless had a strong and resilient one.

Szasz has this to say on the subject:

> 'Definers (that is, persons who insist on defining others) are like pathogenic micro-organisms; each invades, parasitises, and often destroys his victim; and, in each case, those whose resistance is low are the most susceptible to attack. Hence, those whose immunological defences are weak are most

73

likely to contract infectious diseases; and those whose social defences are weak — that is, the young and the old, the sick and the poor, and so forth — are most likely to contract invidious definitions of themselves.'

If the child is defined as a failure he will almost certainly fail, at any rate in the things which the definers value; and perhaps later he will hit out very hard against those who so defined him.

So we know at least something to avoid. But we must contrive to avoid it not merely at the surface of our behaviour. If we do not genuinely respect and value the children, I am afraid they will come to know.

Yet important as it is to avoid infecting the children with 'invidious definitions', it is not enough. More than this is called for. When it comes to self-esteem, not even a young child depends entirely for his judgements on the views of others. For he can often see quite well for himself how he is doing. Paquita McMichael, in an interesting study of the relation between early reading skills and the self-image, concluded that there was a good deal of objective truth in the children's assessments of their competence. 'When they agreed that they were not able to do things as well as some other children they were admitting to a reality.'

Thus a very important part of the job of a teacher — or of a parent in a teaching role — is to guide the child towards tasks where he will be able objectively to do well, but not too easily, not without putting forth some effort, not without difficulties to be mastered, errors to be overcome, creative solutions to be found. This means assessing his skills with sensitivity and accuracy, understanding the levels of his confidence and energy, and responding to his errors in helpful ways.

Most teachers would accept this, I daresay, but it is not at all easy to achieve in practice and there is no general formula for success. However, a valuable discussion of teaching episodes where just this kind of thing is being attempted is given in Marion Blank's book, *Teaching Learning in the Pre-school*. She argues that it is essential to permit errors to occur but that the effectiveness of any teaching critically depends on how the wrong responses are then handled by the teacher. She makes many specific practical suggestions about this but she acknowledges that it is not possible at the moment to give rules for the exact application of her technique — it remains an art. Obviously much depends on the child's personality. Ways that work with a passive withdrawn child will not work with a hyperactive impulsive one. And if the child is functioning very poorly it is necessary to concentrate on helping him over his difficulties without too much delay.

It should be noted that Blank developed her techniques for use in a one-to-one teaching situation. She fully recognises the difficulties of applying them with a group. It remains true that the kinds of teaching decision with which she is concerned are of pervasive importance and that there must surely be gain from any enhanced awareness of them.

The traditional way of encouraging children to want to learn the things that we want to teach is by giving rewards for success: prizes, privileges, gold stars. Two grave risks attend this practice. The first is obvious to common sense, the second much less so.

The obvious risk is to the children who do not get the stars, for this is just one way of defining them as failures. The other risk is to all of the children – 'winners' and 'losers' alike. There is now a substantial amount of evidence pointing to the conclusion that if an activity is rewarded by some extrinsic prize or token – something quite external to the activity itself – then that activity is less likely to be engaged in later in a free and voluntary manner when the rewards are absent, and it is less likely to be enjoyed.

This has now been demonstrated in numerous experiments with people of ages ranging from three or four years to adulthood.

One study, by M. R. Lepper and his colleagues, was carried out in a nursery school. Some of the children were given materials to draw with and were told that they would get a prize for drawing, which they duly did. Other children were given the same materials but with no prizes or talk of prizes. Some days afterwards all of the children were given the opportunity to use these same materials again in a situation where lots of other toys were available to them. The question was: would the groups differ in the amount of time which they spent in drawing? One might have expected that those who had been rewarded would return more eagerly to the situation which had been 'reinforced'. But the opposite happened. The children who had been rewarded spent a smaller proportion of their time drawing.

If one takes as criterion not the time freely spent on an activity but the person's own statement of how much it has been enjoyed, the same sort of thing is found: extrinsic material reward tends to decrease enjoyment. Children (and adults) who have been given prizes for doing something tend to say that they like it less well than children who have been given none. And there is even some evidence to suggest that the quality of what is produced may decline.

These findings obviously lead on at once to a further question: if you tell a child he is doing well, are you also rewarding him and hence perhaps running the same sort of risk as if you give him a prize? For, after all, verbal approval is a kind of prize. And certainly, like a material object, it is extrinsic to the activity itself – something added on at the end.

The available evidence suggests that the effects of telling someone he has done well are not the same as those of giving him a prize. For instance, R. Anderson, S. T. Manoogian and J. S. Reznick carried out a study very similar to the one by Lepper and his colleagues (see above) except that there were two extra conditions, in one of which the children were praised for their drawings. The results from Lepper's study were confirmed: the giving of material rewards was related to a decrease in time spent on the activity later. But the giving of verbal encouragement had the opposite effect. And this is just as well. If it were not so, teachers would have to face a disconcerting dilemma. For children must know how they are doing. As we have seen, they often have a shrewd idea of this themselves – and some tasks make it very evident [. . .] Young children [. . .] given the task of balancing blocks on a narrow bar [. . . can] see for themselves whether the blocks stay in place or [fall] off. So they [can] develop theories, discover the inadequacies of these theories and develop better theories, all without external reward of any kind. This is part of the justification for 'discovery learning'. But it is not equally possible in all kinds of learning to contrive situations where the child will see for himself the outcome of his efforts. Frequently he must be told. He must be told: 'Good, you've got that right!' or: 'No, that's wrong. Try again.' Notice that, if the child is told 'That's good' whether he has really done well or not, the informational value of the comment is destroyed. It is a subtle art to give genuine information and to encourage at the same time.

Such comments do more, of course, than merely give objective knowledge of results. They are unquestionably not neutral. But perhaps it is relevant to an understanding of the difference between words of praise and gold stars to draw a distinction between reward and recognition and to acknowledge how strong a need we have to communicate achievement to our fellow men and see it confirmed in their eyes. Thus Gerard Manley Hopkins, who considered that his vocation as a Jesuit was incompatible with the publication of his poetry in his lifetime, reveals in his letters — especially his letters to Robert Bridges — how hard this was for him: 'There is a point with me in matters of any size when I must absolutely have encouragement as much as crops rain . . .' He goes on bravely, '. . . afterwards I am independent.' But many of us do not reach this kind of independence ever. And young children are certainly unlikely to have done so.

The final condition which Anderson and her colleagues included in their study [. . .] is relevant here. In this condition the experimenter began by declaring an interest in 'how boys and girls draw pictures' — and thereafter firmly refused to manifest this interest in any way. A child might show a picture, trying, as the report of the study puts it, 'to elicit some recognition or validation'. But he got none. The experimenter ignored all such overtures, turning his face away and saying: 'I've got work to do.' It is not surprising to learn that the children who received this treatment showed the greatest drop of all in the time which they later spent in drawing.

This still leaves us with the question of why extrinsic material rewards tend to produce effects of damaging kinds. The explanation which fits the known facts most nearly would seem to be that we enjoy best and engage most readily in activities which we *experience as freely chosen.* We do not like being controlled, we like controlling ourselves. In so far as reward is seen as a means of controlling our behaviour, it tends to diminish our interest and our pleasure. Of course we may work hard to get the reward at the time and for so long as we expect more reward to be forthcoming but we will be less likely to go on with the activity when the reward is withdrawn.

This is strikingly illustrated by the following story (quoted by E. L. Deci in his book *Intrinsic Motivation*).

> 'In a little Southern town where the Klan was riding again, a Jewish tailor had the temerity to open his little shop on the main street. To drive him out of the town the Kleagle of the Klan set a gang of little ragamuffins to annoy him. Day after day they stood at the entrance of his shop. "Jew! Jew!" they hooted after him. The situation looked serious for the tailor.

He took the matter so much to heart that he began to brood and spent sleepless nights over it. Finally out of desperation he evolved a plan.

The following day, when the little hoodlums came to jeer at him, he came to the door and said to them, "From today on any boy who calls me 'Jew' will get a dime from me." Then he put his hand in his pocket and gave each boy a dime.

Delighted with their booty, the boys came back the following day and began to shrill, "Jew! Jew!" The tailor came out smiling. He put his hand in his pocket and gave each of the boys a nickel, saying, "A dime is too much — I can only afford a nickel today." The boys went away satisfied because, after all, a nickel was money, too.

However, when they returned the next day to hoot at him, the tailor gave them only a penny each.

"Why do we only get a penny today?" they yelled.

"That's all I can afford."

"But two days ago you gave a dime, and yesterday we got a nickel. It's not fair, mister."

"Take it or leave it. That's all you're going to get!"

"Do you think we're going to call you 'Jew' for one lousy penny?"

"So don't!"

And they didn't.'

All of this leads to a central dilemma for those who want to teach the young. There is a compelling case for control. The young child is not capable of deciding for himself what he should learn: he is quite simply too ignorant. And he needs our help to sustain him through the actual process of learning. Whitehead puts it vividly: 'After all the child is the heir to long ages of civilization and it is absurd to let him wander in the intellectual maze of men in the Glacial Epoch.'

On the other hand, we should never forget the children who, having learned to shout 'Jew' for a dime, would not then shout it when the payment came to an end. And there is clear evidence that if we try to exercise the control not by reward but by punishment the negative effects are even greater. If, when they leave us, our pupils turn away from what we have taught them, the teaching has surely been in vain.

Those who are most keenly aware of this latter danger tend to call themselves 'progressive' and to advocate 'freedom'. Those who are most keenly aware of the former danger — the danger of leaving children to wander in the intellectual mazes of pre-history — are the advocates of 'formal education' and of 'discipline'.

I can see only one way out of this dilemma: it is to exercise such control as is needful with a light touch and never to relish the need. It is possible after all for control to be more or less obtrusive, more or less paraded. Also a great deal will depend on what the teacher sees the aim of the control to be. If the ultimate aim of the control is to render itself unnecessary, if the teacher obviously wants the children to become competent, self-determining, responsible beings and believes them capable of it, then I am convinced that the risk of rejection of learning will be much diminished. We come back thus to the question of whether the teacher truly respects the children and lets them see it. If this condition is met, then the guidance of learning within a structured environment will not be seen as the action of a warder behind prison bars.

References

Anderson, R., Manoogian, S. T. and Reznick, J. S., 'The Undermining and Enhancing of Intrinsic Motivation in Pre-school Children', *Journal of Personality and Social Psychology*, vol. 34, pp. 915–22, 1976.

Blank, M., *Teaching Learning in the Pre-school*, Merrill, Columbus, Ohio, 1973.

Deci, E. L., *Intrinsic Motivation*, Plenum Press, New York, 1975.

Hopkins, G. M., 'Letter to Robert Bridges dated 17 May 1885', in Abbott, C. C. (ed.), *The Letters of Gerard Manley Hopkins to Robert Bridges*, Oxford University Press, London, 1935.

Lepper, M. R., Greene, D. and Nisbett, R. E. 'Undermining Children's Intrinsic Interest with Extrinsic Rewards: A Test of the "Over-Justification" Hypothesis', *Journal of Personality and Social Psychology*, vol. 28, pp. 129–37, 1973.

McMichael, P., 'Self-Esteem, Behaviour and Early Reading Skills in Infant School Children', in Reid, J. F. and Donaldson, H. (eds.), *Reading: Problems and Practices*, 2nd edn, Ward Lock Educational, London, 1977.

Papousek, H., 'Individual Variability in Learned Responses in Human Infants', in Robinson, R. J. (ed.), *Brain and Early Behaviour*, Academic Press, London, 1969.

Szasz, T. S. *The Second Sin*, Routledge and Kegan Paul, London, 1974.

Whitehead, A. N., 'Technical Education and its Relation to Science and Literature', in Whitehead, A. N. (ed.), *The Aims of Education*, Williams and Norgate, London, 1932.

7 The formation of mathematical concepts

Richard Skemp

Source: Skemp, R., The Psychology of Learning Mathematics, chapter 2 (abridged) pp 19–35, Penguin, 1971.

Abstracting and classifying

Though the term 'concept' is widely used, it is not easy to define. Nor, for reasons which will appear later, is a direct definition the best way to convey its meaning. So I shall approach it from several directions, and with a variety of examples. Since mathematical concepts are among the most abstract, we shall reach these last.

First, two pre-verbal examples. An infant aged twelve months, having finished sucking his bottle, crawled across the floor of the living room to where two empty wine bottles were standing, and stood his own empty feeding bottle neatly alongside them. A two-year-old, seeing a baby on the floor, reacted to it as he usually did to dogs, patting it on the head and stroking its back (He had seen plenty of dogs, but had never before seen another baby crawling.)

In both these cases the behaviour of the children concerned implies: one, some kind of classification of their previous experience; two, the fitting of their present experience into one of these classes.

We all do these all the time; it is thus that we bring to bear our past experience on the present situation. The activity is so continuous and automatic that it requires some slightly unexpected outcome thereof, such as the above, to call it to our attention.

At a lower level, we classify every time we recognise an object as one which we have seen before. On no two occasions are the incoming sense data likely to be exactly the same, since we see objects at different distances and angles, and also in varying lights. From these varying inputs we abstract certain *invariant* properties, and these properties persist in memory longer than the memory of any particular presentation of the object. In the diagram at the top of page 80, $C_1, C_2, \ldots$ represent successive past experiences of the same object; say, a particular chair. From these we abstract certain common properties, represented in the diagram by C. Once this abstraction is formed, any further experience C_n evokes C, and the chair is *recognised*: that is, the new experience is classified with C_1, C_2, etc. C_n and C are now experienced together; and from their com-

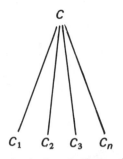

bination, we experience both the *similarity* (*C*) of C_n to our previous experienes of seeing this chair, and also the particular distance, angle, etc., on this occasion (C_n). Awareness of the *differences* between C_n and C_1, C_2, C_3 is (according to this diagram) a more indirect process; and this accords with experimental data — children find it easier to give similarities between, say, an orange and an apple, than differences.

We progress rapidly to further abstractions. From particular chairs *C, C', C''*, we abstract further invariant properties, by which we recognise *Ch* (a new object seen for the first time, say in a shop window) as a member of this class. It is the second-order abstraction (from the set of abstractions *C, C',* ...) to which we give the name 'chair'. The invariant properties which characterise it are already becoming more functional and less perceptual — that is, less attached to the physical properties of a chair. One I saw recently was of basket-work, egg-shaped, and hung from a single

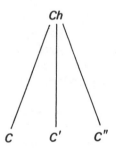

rope. It bore little or no physical resemblance to any chair which I had ever seen — but I recognised it at once as a chair, and a most desirable one too! [. . .]

A concept therefore requires for its formation a number of experiences which have something in common. Once the concept is formed, we may (retrospectively) talk about *examples* of the concept. Everyday concepts come from everyday experience, and the examples which lead to their formation occur randomly, spaced in time. The more frequently encountered objects are, in general, conceptualised more rapidly: but many other factors are at work, which makes this statement an over-simplification. One of these is *contrast*. In the diagram on the right, the single *X* stands out perceptually from the five variously shaped *O*s.

Objects which thus stand out from their surroundings are more likely to be remembered, and their similarities more likely to be abstracted across intervals of space and time.

The diagram also illustrates the function of non-examples in determining a class. The *X*, by its difference from all the other shapes, makes the similarity between them more noticeable. The essential characteristics of a *chair* are clarified by pointing to (say) a stool, a settee, a bed, and a garden seat, and saying 'These are not chairs.' This is specially useful in fixing the border-line of a class — we use objects which might be examples, but aren't.

[...]

The communication of concepts

We can see that language can be used to speed up the formation of a concept by helping to collect and separate contributory examples and non-examples. Can it be used to short-circuit the process altogether, by simply defining a concept verbally? Particularly in mathematics, this is often attempted; so let us examine the idea of a definition, as usual with the help of examples. To begin with, let us choose a simple and well-known concept, say *red*, and imagine that we are asked the meaning of this word by someone blind from birth, who has been given sight by a corneal graft. The meaning of the word is the concept associated with that word; so our task is now to enable the person to form the concept *red* (which he does not have when we begin) and associate it with the word 'red'.

There are two ways in which we might do this. Being scientifically inclined, and perhaps interested in colour photography, we could give a definition. 'Red is the colour we experience from light of wavelength in the region of 0.6 microns.' Would he now have the concept red? Of course not. Such a definition would be useless *to him*, though not necessarily for other purposes. Intuitively, in such a case, we would point to various objects and say 'This is a red diary; this is a red tie; this is a red jumper . . .' In this way we would arrange for him to have, close together in time, a collection of experiences from which we hope that he will abstract the common property, red. Naming is here used as an auxiliary, in the way already described. The same process of abstraction could take place in silence, but probably more slowly: and the name 'red' would not become attached.

If he now asks a different question, 'What does "colour" mean?', we can no longer collect together examples for him by pointing; for the examples we want are *red, blue, green, yellow, . . .* and these are themselves concepts. If (and only if) he already has these concepts in his own mind — their presence in our mind is not enough — then by collecting together the words for them, we can arrange for him to collect together the concepts themselves; and thus make possible, though not guarantee, the process of abstraction. Naming (or some other symbolization) now becomes an essential factor of the process of abstraction, and not just a useful help.

We now need to distinguish between two kinds of concept. Those which are derived from our sensory and motor experiences of the outside world, such as *red, motor car, heavy, hot, sweet,* will be called *primary concepts*; and those which are abstracted from other concepts we shall call *secondary concepts.* If concept *A* is an example of concept *B*, then we shall say that *B* is of a higher order than *A*. Clearly, if *A* is an example of *B* and *B* of *C*, then *C* is also of higher order than both *B* and *A*. 'Of higher order than' means 'abstracted from' (directly or indirectly). So 'more abstract' means 'more removed from experience of the outside world', which fits in with the everyday meaning of the word 'abstract'. This comparison can only be made between concepts in the same hierarchy. Although we might consider that *sonata form* is a more abstract (higher order) concept than *colour*, we cannot properly compare the two.

These related ideas, of order between concepts and a conceptual hierarchy, enable us to see more clearly why, for the person we are thinking of, the definition of red was an inadequate mode of communication; for it pre-supposed concepts such as *colour, light,* which could only be formed if concepts such as *red, blue, green, . . .* had already been formed. In general, concepts of a higher order than those which a person already has cannot be communicated to him by a definition, but only by collecting together, for him to experience, suitable examples.

Of what use, if any, then, is a definition?

Two uses can be seen at once. If it were necessary (e.g. for a photographic colour filter) to specify exactly within what limits we would still call a colour red, then the above definition would enable us to say where red starts and finishes. And having gone further in the process of abstraction, i.e. in the formation of larger classes based on similarities, a definition enables us to retrace our steps. By stating all those (and only those) classes to which our particular concept belongs, we are left with just one possible concept — the one we are defining. In the process we have shown how it relates to other concepts in its hierarchy. Definitions can thus be seen as a way of adding precision to the boundaries of a concept, once formed; and of stating explicitly its relation to other concepts.

New concepts, of a lower order, can also be communicated for the first time by this means. For example, if our formerly blind subject asked 'What colour is magenta?' and we could not find a sufficiency of magenta objects to show him, we could say 'It is a colour, between red and blue, rather more blue than red.' Provided that he already had the concepts of blue and red, he could then form at least a beginning of the concept of magenta without ever having seen this colour.

Since most of the new concepts we need in everyday life are of fairly low order, we usually have available suitable higher-order concepts for the new concepts to be easily communicable by definition; often followed by an example or two, which then serve a different purpose — that of illustration. 'What is a stool?' 'It's a seat for one person, without a back,' is quite a good definition, but even so a few examples will define the concept in such a way as to exclude hassocks, pouffes, and garden swings far more successfully than further elaboration of the definition.

In mathematics, however, not only are the concepts far more abstract than those of everyday life, but the direction of learning is for the most part in the direction of still greater abstraction. The communication of mathematical concepts is therefore much more difficult, on the part of both communicator and receiver. This problem will be taken up again shortly, after certain other general topics have been explored.

One other consequence of this principle, that concepts of a higher order in a hierarchy than those which a person already has cannot be communicated by definition, can now be deduced. This is, that *concept* itself cannot be defined: for any particular concept must be an example of *this* concept, which is therefore of higher order than any other concept. We can however describe some of the characteristics of concepts, discuss how they function, and build up a general understanding of the idea by relating it to other ideas. This is adequate for our purpose, as indeed it has to be. Similarly, I believe that mathematics cannot be precisely defined, but only exemplified. [...]

The learning of mathematical concepts

Much of our everyday knowledge is learnt directly from our environment, and the concepts involved are not very abstract. The particular problem (but also the power) of mathematics lies in its great abstractness and generality, achieved by successive generations of particularly intelligent individuals each of whom has been abstracting from, or generalising, concepts of earlier generations. The present-day learner has to process, not raw data, but the data-processing systems of existing mathematics. This is not only an immeasurable advantage, in that an able student can acquire in years ideas which took centuries of past effort to develop: it also exposes the learner to a particular hazard. Mathematics cannot be learnt directly from the everyday environment, but only indirectly from other mathematicians. At best, this makes him largely dependent on his teachers (including all who write mathematics text books); and, at worst, it exposes him to the possibility of acquiring a lifelong fear and dislike of mathematics.

Though the first principles of the learning of mathematics are straightforward, it is the communicator of mathematical ideas, and not the recipient, who most needs to know them. And though they are simple enough in themselves, their mathematical applications involve much hard thinking. The first of these principles was stated earlier in the chapter:

1 Concepts of a higher order than those which a person already has cannot be communicated to him by a definition, but only by arranging for him to encounter a suitable collection of examples.

The second follows directly from it:

2 Since in mathematics these examples are almost invariably other concepts, it must first be ensured that these are already formed in the mind of the learner.

The first of these principles is broken by the vast majority of textbooks, past and present. Nearly everywhere we see new topics introduced, not by examples, but by definitions: of the most admirable brevity and exactitude for the teacher (who already has the concepts to which they refer), but unintelligible to the student. For reasons which will be apparent, examples cannot be quoted here: but the reader is invited to verify this statement for himself. It is also a useful exercise to look at some definitions of ideas new to oneself, in books about mathematics beyond the stage which one has reached. This enables one to experience at first hand the bafflement of the younger learner.

Good teachers intuitively help out a definition with examples. To choose a suitable collection is, however, harder than it sounds. The examples must have in common the properties which form the concept, but no others. To put it differently, they must be alike in the ways which are to be abstracted, and otherwise different enough for the properties irrelevant to this particular concept to cancel out; or, more accurately, fail to summate. Remembering that these irrelevant properties may be regarded as noise, we may say that some noise is necessary to concept formation. In the earlier stages, low noise – clear embodiment of the concept, with little distracting detail – is desirable; but as the concept becomes more strongly established, increasing noise teaches the recipient to abstract the conceptual properties from more difficult examples, and so reduces his dependence on the teacher.

Composing a suitable collection thus requires both inventiveness and a very clear awareness of the concept to be communicated. Now it is possible to have, and use, a concept at an intuitive level without being consciously aware of it. This applies particularly to some of the most basic and frequently used ideas; partly because the more automatic any activity, the less we think about it; partly because the most fundamental ideas of mathematics are acquired at an early age when we have not the ability to analyse them; and partly because some of these fundamental ideas are also among the most subtle. But it is easy to slip up even when these factors do not apply.

Some African children were learning the theorem of Pythagoras. They had copied a right-angled triangle from the blackboard, and were told to make a square on each side. This they did easily enough for the two shorter sides;

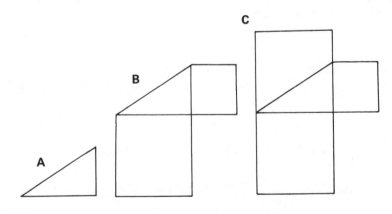

but they were nearly all in difficulty when they tried to draw the square on the hypotenuse. Many of them drew something like figure C. From this, I inferred that the squares from which they had formed their concepts had all been 'square' to the paper, and had included no obliquely placed examples. All too easily done!

The second of the two principles, that the necessary lower-order concept must be present before the next stage of abstraction is possible, seems even more straightforward. To put this into effect, however, means that before we try to communicate a new concept, we have to find out what are its contributory concepts; and for each of these, we have to find out *its* contributory concepts; and so on, until we reach either primary concepts, or experience which we may assume as 'given'. When this has been done, a suitable plan can then be made which will present to the learner a possible, and not an impossible, task.

This conceptual analysis involves much more work than just giving a definition. If done, it leads to some surprising results. Ideas which until recently were first taught in university courses are now seen to be so fundamental that they are being introduced in the primary school; for example, sets, one-to-one correspondence. Other topics still regarded as elementary are found, on analysis, to involve ideas which even those teaching the topic have for the most part never heard of. In this category I include the manipulation of fractional numbers.

There are two other consequences of the second principle. The first is that in the building up of the structure of successive abstractions, if a particular level is imperfectly understood, everything from then on is in peril. This dependency is probably greater in mathematics than in any other subject. One can understand the geography of Africa even if one has missed that of Europe; one can understand the history of the nineteenth century even if one has missed that of the eighteenth; in physics one can understand 'heat and light' even if one has missed 'sound'. But to understand algebra without ever having really understood arithmetic is an impossibility, for much of the algebra we learn at school is generalised arithmetic. Since many pupils learn to do the manipulations of arithmetic with a very imperfect understanding of the underlying principles, it is small wonder that mathematics remains a closed book to them. Even those who get off to a good start may through absence, inattention, failure to keep up with the pace of the class, or other reason, fail to form the concepts of some particular stage. In that case, all subsequent concepts dependent on these may never be understood, and the pupil becomes steadily more out of his depth. In the latter case, however, the situation may not be so irremediable, if the learning situation is one which makes back-tracking possible; e.g. if the text in use provides a genuine explanation, and is not just a collection of exercises. Success will then depend partly on the confidence of the learner in his own powers of comprehension.

The other consequence (of the second principle) is that the contributory concepts needed for each new stage of abstraction must be *available*. It is not sufficient for them to have been learnt at some time in the past: they must be accessible when needed. This is partly a matter, again, of having facilities available for back-tracking. Appropriate revision, planned by a teacher, will be specially useful for beginners; but more advanced students should be taking a more active part in the direction of their own studies, and, for these, returning to take another look at earlier work will be more effective if it is directed by a felt need rather than by an outside instruction. To put it differently, an answer has more meaning to someone who has first asked a question.

Learning and teaching

In learning mathematics, although we have to create all the concepts anew in our own minds, we are only able to do this by using the concepts arrived at by past mathematicians. There is too much for even a genius to do in a lifetime.

This makes the learning of mathematics, especially in its early stages, and for the average student, very dependent on good teaching. Now, to know mathematics is one thing, and to be able to teach it — to communicate it to those at a lower conceptual level — is quite another; and I believe that it is the latter which is most lacking at the moment. As a result, many people acquire at school a lifelong dislike, even fear, of mathematics.

It is good to report that widespread efforts are being made to remedy this, for example by the introduction of new syllabuses, more attractive presentation, television series, and other means. These efforts will all however be of greater value if they are combined with greater awareness of the mental processes involved in the learning of mathematics. This will reduce the danger of new topics being chosen largely according to the current fashion, and taught almost as badly as those they replace. [. . .]

8 A comparative study of the order of acquisition of the concepts of weight, area and volume

Eryl Rothwell Hughes

Source: Hughes, E. R. with Rogers J., Conceptual Powers of Children: An Approach through Mathematics and Science, Schools Council, Research Studies, Macmillan Education, chs 8 and 10, 1979.

One of the main objectives of [. . . this] research was to examine the same children's responses to similar tests in all three concepts.

The order of acquisition of different concepts has been a topic of considerable interest to Piagetian research workers, and the interpretation of their findings has had some influence on the teaching of these subjects in schools. One of the most common interpretations concerns the order of acquisition of the concepts of weight and volume. It is widely held that the concept of weight is understood before that of volume, and also that the concept of area is easier to understand than that of volume. These conclusions have affected the teaching of these topics in primary schools, and many teachers' guides advocate that the teaching of the concept of weight be carried out at seven or eight years of age, or even earlier, and that volume be left until the final years of the primary school. The concept of area, on the other hand, commonly features in the mathematics curriculum of the 7 to 11 year old.

Examination of earlier research on the sequential development of concepts shows that the conclusions were often based on a cross-reference of two different samples, one sample or group experiencing one or two tests on one concept and the other group tests on another concept. These samples were often made up of few children and, in the main, the tests explored the children's understanding of conservation or measurement. More recent researches (e.g. by Beard, Lister, Hyde) have attempted to overcome the obvious weaknesses in these earlier studies and have examined the same children using tests dealing with two or three concepts.

Beard (1963) used five tests in each of the concepts of weight and volume with the same children; Piaget's order of achievement of conservation in the concepts of 'substance' and weight was not borne out. Commenting on these differences, Beard stressed the importance of relevant practical experience and suggested that success or failure in any one concept seemed to be related to the child's degree of experience in that concept rather than to a natural order of development from one concept to another. In another research (Beard, 1963) concerned with a study of the acquisition of number concepts, she suggested that general conclusions on the order of acquisition of different concepts were not so easily deduced:

> 'Two points deserve further mention. First, children differed to some degree in the order in which they understood concepts. Some could count fluently to a hundred or more but failed in simple conservation: by contrast, a child who could not count accurately to twenty succeeded in every other item. Secondly, there was a greater variety in the kind of answers given than Piaget describes.'

[This research therefore sought to find out] to what extent the children would conform to Piaget's pattern of acquisition of concepts, according to which they would tend to understand the concept of weight before area and volume, and their understanding of the concept of volume would prove to be the more difficult.

In order to do this it was necessary to design tests in all three concepts which could be termed 'parallel' items, i.e. having the same basic features and measuring similar conceptual stages, but using different practical materials. The easiest to design of these groups of tests proved to be that concerned with the conservation of weight, area and volume, and the results of this group are considered before those involving the use of concreto-logic and measurement. [. . .]

Table 1 presents the results (as percentages) of all the test items in the three concepts which required only the understanding of conservation for their correct solution. Nineteen tests — five for weight, nine for area and five for volume — fell into this category. For each age group the percentage of correct responses as indicated by correct answers and correct verbal explanation is given alongside the number of incorrect responses of the type indicating that the children were basing their conclusions on simple perception or appearances (other incorrect responses are not analysed [here]).

Four general points emerge from an examination of this table.

1 With the exception of one or two items, the results all follow the same general trend. It is difficult to conclude that the understanding of conservation in any one concept is more difficult for the children than in any of the others. The numbers of fully correct responses range more or less between the same figures from concept to concept. The only clearly observable trend is that fewer children appear to be dominated by visual appearances in the weight tests than in the other two concepts.

2 There is more variation in the numbers of correct responses between similar items in any one concept than can be generally detected between items in different concepts. It should be remembered that, with the exception of the one or two items referred to below, all were carefully designed to be presented in similar fashion. In all these cases the children remained in a passive situation, observing the tester handling the materials. In all these items, too, the children

Table 1 Conservation in weight, area and volume

	7y 5m		7y 11m		8y 5m		8y 11m		9y 5m		9y 11m	
	Correct (%)	Incorrect* (%)	Correct (%)	Incorrect* (%)	Correct (%)	Incorrect* (%)	Correct (%)	Incorrect* (%)	Correct (%)	Incorrect* (%)	Correct (%)	Incorrect* (%)
Weight												
Item 4a	52	28	63	24	66	26	71	19	83	8	80	14
Item 4b	39	37	57	32	60	31	63	25	80	11	77	16
Item 5	41	27	50	19	59	15	75	6	70	6	74	5
Item 6a	59	25	68	17	80	14	88	7	90	7	84	11
Item 6b	68	17	71	17	82	12	87	6	93	6	91	5
Area												
Item 6a	25	47	29	41	43	31	49	29	63	21	55	25
Item 6b	67	19	71	18	85	9	90	7	87	6	87	8
Item 7a	49	38	54	34	71	19	76	21	78	16	83	15
Item 7b	58	29	62	27	75	17	81	14	85	10	86	9
Item 8	8	69	11	70	18	68	20	64	21	66	26	66
Item 9a	58	34	68	24	81	15	83	14	90	7	88	9
Item 9b	70	15	72	18	90	6	89	7	93	2	93	2
Item 9c	61	25	68	17	84	10	83	8	90	4	90	5
Item 10	43	37	43	24	64	18	61	15	69	13	73	9
Volume												
Item 7	51	38	56	28	68	24	71	18	75	20	79	13
Item 8a	43	38	46	32	57	25	62	16	74	11	72	10
Item 8b	35	34	45	29	54	25	63	16	72	15	72	17
Item 9a	51	39	57	33	69	24	70	24	73	24	71	22
Item 9b	52	40	58	28	72	18	75	16	81	12	77	15
Sample size **N (= 100%)**	146		150		150		155		155		149	

*'Incorrect' refers to incorrect responses due to centring; other incorrect responses are not shown.

89

first saw and agreed that the property in question (weight, area or volume) was equal in the two objects. One object was then deformed or rearranged to accentuate a dimension and the children were asked questions of a similar nature to determine whether they understood the concept of conservation.

Test items using discontinuous objects (weight item 6b; area items 9b and 9c) broken up into separate pieces, rather than objects rearranged into continuous, elongated shapes, produce more correct responses than any other. Other variations in the results are more easily explained in terms of variations between actual items rather than of relative difficulty in understanding one concept (say, weight) rather than another (say, volume).

3 In three or four items the results differ significantly from the general pattern. These differences can be explained in terms of individual design.

In area item 6 the children did not first see and agree that the two shapes had similar areas. In fact, the two shapes were clearly seen to be different at the beginning of the test and the children were asked, if they thought that they had equal areas. In contrast to all the other items, they were not encouraged, therefore, to use the mental operation of reversibility by any practical procedure on the part of the tester. The children, too, had to manoeuvre the shapes in order to arrive at an answer and this proved to be difficult, especially in item 6a.

Similarly, in area item 8, the children were given two different shapes and once more asked if they thought the two had similar areas. They had to determine whether they should rely on perception or on arguments based on conservation. The observation that the numbers of correct responses fall dramatically in this item and that the number of reasons based on perception increase correspondingly demonstrates the unstable nature of the children's beliefs and reasoning powers in this age range. Clearly single tests do not give accurate pictures of children's understanding of a particular concept.

4 The concept of conservation of solid and occupied (space) volume is only marginally more difficult than that of conservation of weight. Indeed, one can perhaps detect that conservation of area is generally better understood than conservation of either weight or volume. This slight difference is perhaps to be expected, as 'area' is commonly taught at this age. Indeed, the conservation of volume is surprisingly well understood, even at $7\frac{1}{2}$ years of age, considering that it is rarely taught directly in the classroom. It would seem that there is very little basis for the supposition that the concept of volume is harder to understand than, say, that of area. From the present results, there is much to be said for the introduction of the concept of conservation in all three topics at about the same time. This question of teaching sequence is referred to again later.

As the results throw considerable doubt on the reliability of earlier research, the analysis has been carried further. Two tests in each concept were selected for closer comparisons. All satisfy the three conditions that (a) the children remain in a passive situation; (b) the children first see and agree that the property in question is the same in the pair of objects; (c) the children see a dimension changed and are asked whether the property (weight, area or volume) of the objects is still the same, increased or decreased.

Both area test items use shapes that are broken up and reorientated into a continuous form. Weight item 4a is the familiar plasticine ball and sausage test where one ball is elongated. Weight item 6a is similar to the two area items, in that the blocks are broken up and reorientated into a continuous form. This feature is also seen in volume item 7, whereas volume item 8a is the well-known cylinder-conical flask liquid test (here with container and wider beaker) and has a slightly more complicated practical procedure than the others in that two other (similar) containers are also used. The results are now presented (table 2) as actual numbers of children who gave correct responses (percentages are given alongside).

Table 2 Correct responses to conservation tasks

	7y 5m		7y 11m		8y 5m		8y 11m		9y 5m		9y 11m	
	No.	%	No.	%	No.	%	No.	%	No.	%	No.	%
Weight												
Item 4a	76	52	95	63	99	66	109	71	130	83	119	80
Item 6a	86	59	102	68	119	80	136	88	139	90	125	84
Area												
Item 7b	85	58	92	62	113	75	125	81	132	85	128	86
Item 9a	85	58	102	68	122	81	128	83	139	90	131	88
Volume												
Item 7	75	51	85	56	101	68	110	71	116	75	117	79
Item 8a	62	43	68	46	86	57	96	62	115	74	108	72
Sample size *N* (= 100%)	146		150		150		155		155		149	

The liquid volume item (8a) is more difficult than any of the others. Conservation of liquid volume does appear to be harder to understand than the conservation of other properties. Conservation of area is better understood at all ages than even weight. Again this could be explained in terms of practical experience in the classroom rather than in terms of Piagetian sequence. Comparison of the weight items with volume item 7 shows that the figures for correct responses are almost identical at all ages. Above all else, the results clearly demonstrate that over half of even the youngest children, regardless of their mental ability in intelligence test items, are able to give correct answers and verbally explain their reasons in all six tests of conservation.

If the property of conservation is more difficult to grasp in, say, volume or area than in weight and this understanding is expressed by children in the concept of weight before the concept of volume, as if so often maintained, then it follows that if children display understanding of conservation in volume, these children should also all display understanding in weight. If the evidence is contrary to this thesis, then an order in the understanding of volume and weight cannot be admitted. To test for this it is necessary to ask: 'Of those children who were correct in the volume tests how many of those same children were correct in the weight tests (and, in turn, in area)?' The results of such an analysis are displayed in figures 1—5. The comparisons are made as follows.

Figure 1   Volume 7 with weight 4a : volume 7 with weight 6a.
Figure 2   Volume 8a with weight 4a : volume 8a with weight 6a.
Figure 3   Volume 7 with area 7b : volume 7 with area 9a.
Figure 4   Volume 8a with area 7b : volume 8a with area 9a.
Figure 5   Area 7b with weight 4a : area 9a with weight 6a.

As an example, of this particular method of display, the number of $7\frac{1}{2}$ year-old children who gave correct answers to volume item 7 is examined to see how many of them also gave correct responses in weight item 4a. Reading left to right, 75 children (23 + 52) out of 146 gave the correct answer to volume item 7; *of these*, 23 (31%) gave the correct answer to this item but did *not* give the correct answer to weight item 4a. The remaining 52 (69%) also gave the correct answer to weight item 4a. Alternatively, reading right to left, 76 children (52 + 24) gave the correct answer to weight item 4a. Of these, 24 (32%) gave the correct answer to this item but did *not* give the right answer to the volume item. Obviously the remaining 52 (68% of weight item 4a correct answers) also gave the correct response to the volume item.

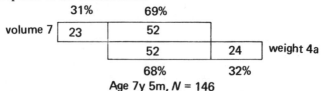

Age 7y 5m, *N* = 146

It is argued that only such an analysis will show whether there is an order in the understanding of conservation of weight, area and volume. Simple examination of numbers of correct responses at different ages does not enable one to arrive at firm conclusions on this question.

Examination of figure 1 (volume item 7 compared, in turn, with weight items 4a and 6a) shows that for weight item 4a there are almost equal numbers of children at all ages who conserved *only* in the volume test and who conserved *only* in the weight test. This result is at variance with the conclusions of most Piagetian research on this question.

The comparison between volume item 7 and weight item 6a shows that, at all ages, there is a definite trend for more children to respond correctly only in the weight item than only in the volume test. However, the proportion of children answering correctly only in the supposedly harder volume item is still considerable, especially at the younger ages.

The trend displayed in figure 1 is confirmed in figure 2, where the more difficult volume item 8a (liquid volume) is compared with weight items 4a and 6a. Although the conservation of liquid volume is more difficult to grasp than the conservation of weight, here too we witness a considerable proportion of children, especially at the lower ages, who gave the correct responses only to the volume item yet gave incorrect responses to the weight items (e.g. 40% of the children at $7\frac{1}{2}$ years who gave the correct responses to the volume item fall into this category). It should be remembered that these children also gave correct reasons for their choices. Once more, the results demonstrate the complexity of the pattern of concept development in children.

Whilst there is a trend for more correct responses in the weight items (supporting Piaget's thesis), the conclusion that the concept of conservation of weight precedes the concept of conservation of volume does not follow. Some children, at all ages, grasp one conservation concept before the other, but it is not possible to determine for certain which they will grasp first. Unfortunately, of those children who showed that they understood the concept of conservation in both weight and volume, it is impossible to determine which they grasped first.

The results of two volume items are also compared with the results of two area items (figures 3 and 4). At all ages, in all four comparisons, a higher proportion of children gave the correct answers and explanations in the area items without giving correct answers in the volume counterpart items than gave the correct answers in the volume items without giving correct answers in the area counterpart items. However, when one examines this difference at its greatest in all four comparisons, it is noticed that this amounts to 16 (volume 7: area 7b); 23 (volume 7: area 9a); 29 (volume 8a: area 7b) and 36 (volume 8a: area 9a) children out of some 150 in each group. Bearing in mind that the test for conservation of liquid and volume (volume 8a) is harder than the other tests, these differences could simply be accounted for by the differences between the children's practical experience in handling area shapes and volumes.

On the other hand, the fact that there were never more children answering correctly only in the volume tests than in the area tests may be taken as evidence for a Piagetian sequence of understanding from conservation in area to conservation in volume. This argument is not favoured here because it is noticed that, at younger ages, the difference between successful answers in one test and successful answers in the other test only are considerably less than at older ages. On Piagetian grounds one would expect the reverse to be true. It seems more reasonable to suppose that the differences increase with age simply because the children gain more experience in carrying out practical exercises dealing with area than they do in the concept of volume. Furthermore, one would not expect any child to grasp the so-called harder concept before the easier concept but in fact a number of children did this. Flavell's (1972, p. 330) point that children 'may exhibit significant asequential features in addition to the obvious sequential ones' is supported by these results.

Figure 5 compares the results of area item 7b with weight item 4a and area item 9a with weight item 6a. Once more there is a tendency for more children to answer correctly in the area items alone than in the weight items alone but these differences are marginal. On the whole, children are just as likely to conserve in one situation as in another. As these items are probably the best matched in terms of design and method of presentation, they seem to demonstrate that it is not so much the order of conservation across the concepts area and weight and volume that emerges from the results but the variations in the individual's responses according to the exact nature of the task set.

For the research worker this section raises a number of questions relating to

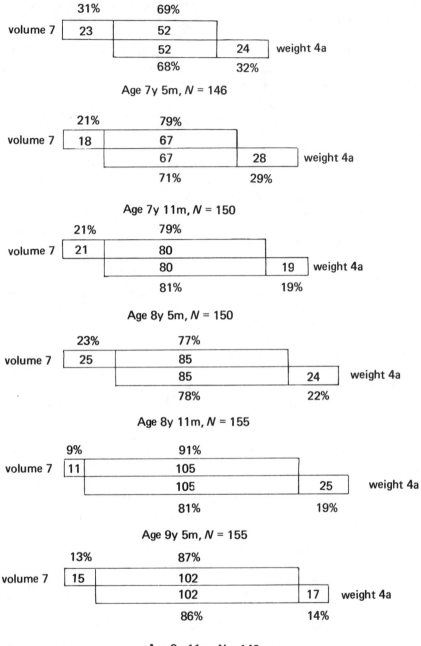

Figure 1a

The order of acquisition of the concepts of weight, area and volume

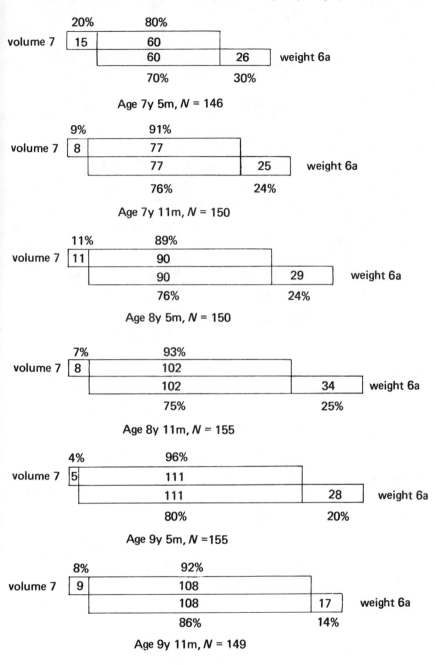

Figure 1b

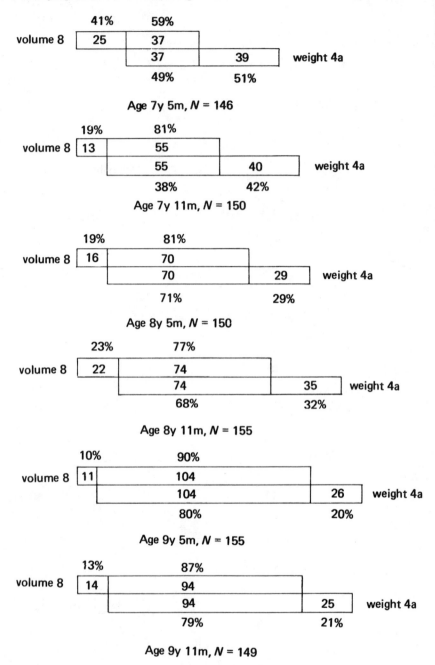

Age 7y 5m, *N* = 146

Age 7y 11m, *N* = 150

Age 8y 5m, *N* = 150

Age 8y 11m, *N* = 155

Age 9y 5m, *N* = 155

Age 9y 11m, *N* = 149

Figure 2a

The order of acquisition of the concepts of weight, area and volume

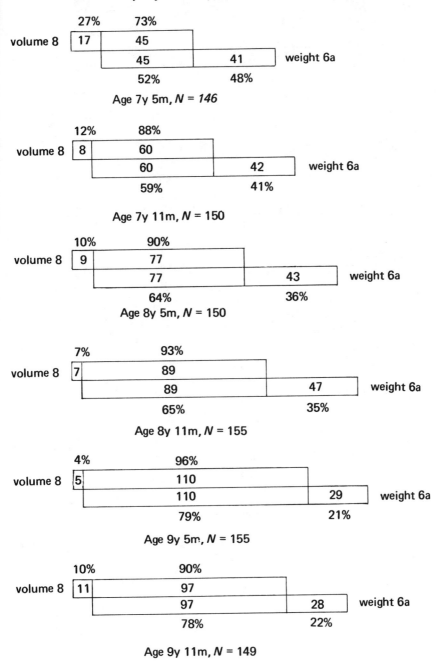

Figure 2b

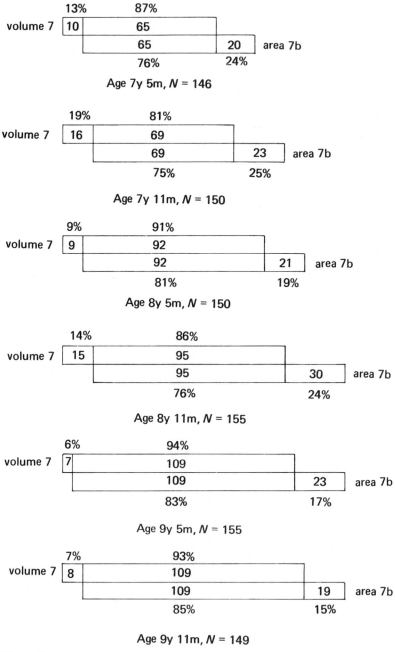

Figure 3a

The order of acquisition of the concepts of weight, area and volume

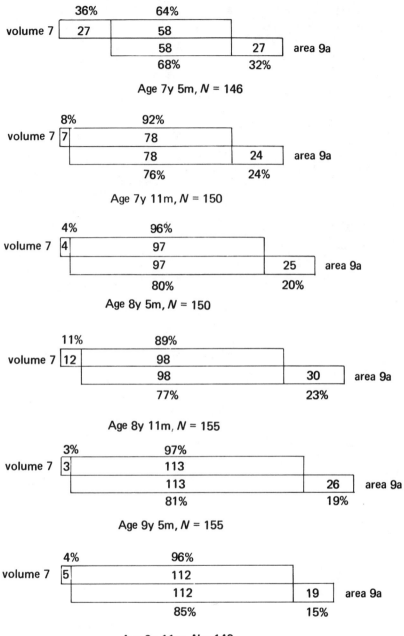

volume 7 | 36% 27 | 64% 58 |
| 58 | 27 | area 9a
| 68% | 32% |

Age 7y 5m, *N* = 146

volume 7 | 8% 7 | 92% 78 |
| 78 | 24 | area 9a
| 76% | 24% |

Age 7y 11m, *N* = 150

volume 7 | 4% 4 | 96% 97 |
| 97 | 25 | area 9a
| 80% | 20% |

Age 8y 5m, *N* = 150

volume 7 | 11% 12 | 89% 98 |
| 98 | 30 | area 9a
| 77% | 23% |

Age 8y 11m, *N* = 155

volume 7 | 3% 3 | 97% 113 |
| 113 | 26 | area 9a
| 81% | 19% |

Age 9y 5m, *N* = 155

volume 7 | 4% 5 | 96% 112 |
| 112 | 19 | area 9a
| 85% | 15% |

Age 9y 11m, *N* = 149

Figure 3b

99

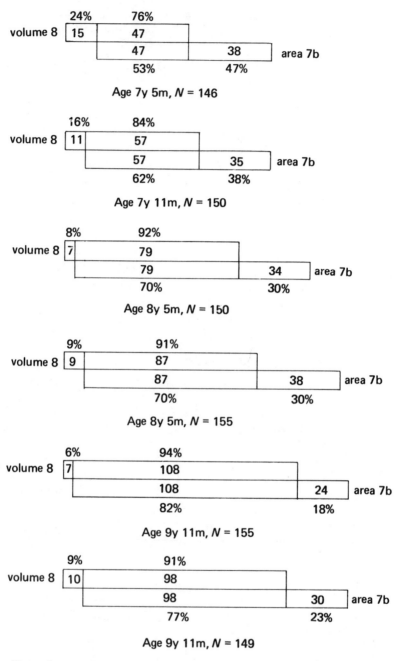

Figure 4a

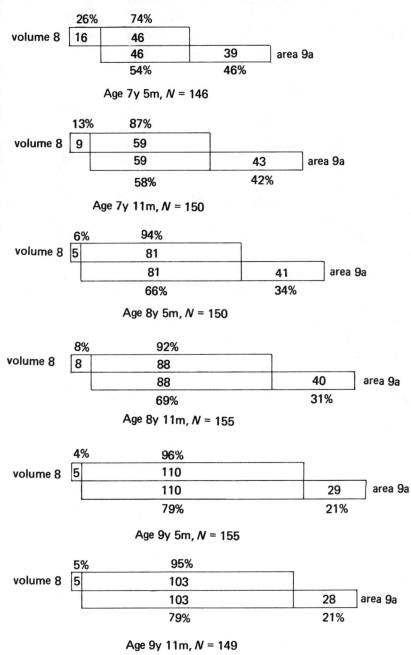

Figure 4b

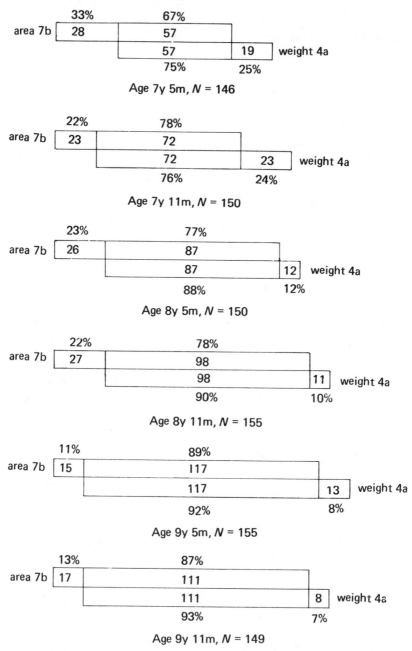

Figure 5a

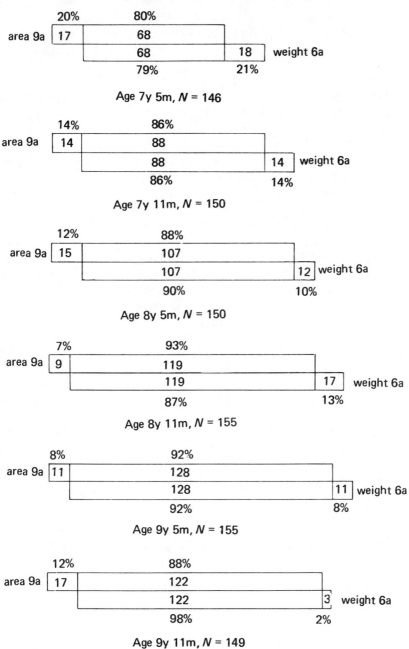

Figure 5b

Piagetian research design and execution. The type of analysis illustrated is rarely carried out, and it seems obvious that much work still remains to be done before the problem of the rate at which children reach the same conceptual stage in different concepts is resolved.

For the teacher the argument that the concept of volume should be taught after the concept of weight or area is clearly too general to have any practical meaning in the classroom. As far as the idea of conservation is concerned, these results seem to indicate that there is much to be said for introducing this idea at about the same time for all three concepts. Conservation is the common property shared by the three topics, and for the child clearly to understand all three concepts it is necessary to focus his attention on the differences between area, weight and volume as well as on the similarities. It can be argued that to do this, comparisons must be made, and that children can only have the opportunity to do this if they examine all three topics at the same time.

Perhaps one of the fundamental differences between area and volume is the way each property is measured. Without a clear understanding of methods of measuring area and volume, children can only become more confused in their ideas about the relationship between area and volume and about the more advanced properties of the concepts themselves.

Figure 6 compares, in the same manner as before, the responses of the children to items testing for the ability to measure area and volume. Area item 12, which uses the irregular shaped pieces and transparent grids, is compared with volume item 16, which uses the solid blocks and unit blocks. Although a small proportion of children did manage to find the volume of the block without being able to measure area in the other item, the results demonstrate that at all ages children had difficulty in measuring solid volume. At first sight this pattern seems to confirm Piaget's idea that the achievement of the ability to measure area occurs before the ability to measure volume, but a closer inspection reveals a possible alternative reason for the results. At the two youngest age levels the difference between the numbers of children who are able to measure in only one or the other concept is small. In other words, if they have to rely on their basic knowledge about measurement and the properties of area and volume, bearing in mind that at this age their practical experience of actual measuring must be limited in both topics, it is just as likely that they will be able to measure area as to measure volume. It is only as they become older that the differences in ability to measure in the two concepts emerge strongly. An alternative explanation could be that the differences are accounted for in terms of degree of actual practical experience of measurement in the two concepts. The differences could be due to teaching rather than natural conceptual development. From the present results it is impossible to decide which is the correct interpretation.

Finally, to complete this particular form of comparative analysis, five items are selected which test the children's ability to use relatively simple concreto-logic forms of reasoning (table 3 and figures 7 to 8).

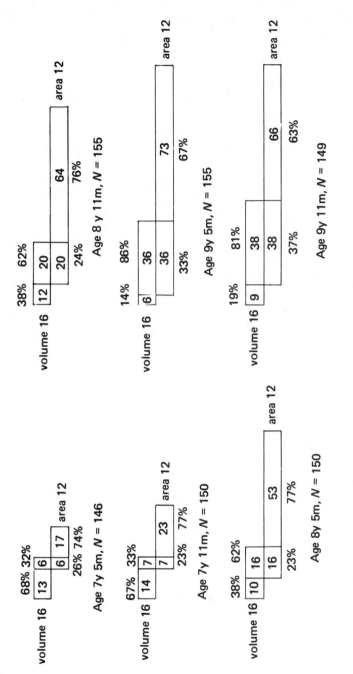

Figure 6

105

Weight item 8 uses the form of logic: since $A = B$ and $B = C$, then A must be equal to C.

Weight item 9 uses the form of logic: since $A > B$ and $B > C$, then $A > C$.

Area item 14 uses the form of logic: since $A + B = C + D$ and $A = C$, then B must be equal to D.

Area item 16 uses the form of logic: since $1A = 3 \times$ units and $1B = 1 \times$ units, then $3B$ must be equal to $1A$.

Volume item 14 uses the form of logic: since $A = C$ and $B = D$ and also $A = B$, then C must be equal to D.

Table 3 Correct responses to tests of concreto-logic

	7y 5m		7y 11m		8y 5m		8y 11m		9y 5m		9y 11m	
	No.	%	No.	%	No.	%	No.	%	No.	%	No.	%
Weight												
Item 8	52	36	65	43	92	61	97	63	115	74	112	75
Item 9	47	32	58	39	80	53	93	60	95	61	101	68
Area												
Item 14	41	28	49	33	82	55	76	49	102	66	97	65
Item 16	27	18	27	18	50	33	57	37	81	52	82	55
Volume												
Item 14	16	11	26	17	35	23	40	26	60	39	59	40
Sample size												
N (= 100%)	146		150		150		155		155		149	

If one is to maintain that the concept of volume in general is more difficult to grasp than, say, the concept of weight, it is necessary to explore the children's responses to tests involving similar logical frameworks for their solution as well as their responses to tests dealing with conservation. Such comparisons are rarely carried out.

It is extremely difficult to design practical tests in each of the concepts which examine the same type of logical thinking. In the present study an attempt was made, not so much to design identical tests, but to design tests which used forms of reasoning which Piaget had identified as being typical for the stage of conceptual development likely to have been reached by a number of the children in our sample. Nevertheless, the items are not exactly identical in degree of complexity and, as a result, exact comparisons are difficult to make.

It is maintained that the logic $A = B$, $B = C$, therefore $A = C$ is easier to grasp than the logic $A > B$, $B > C$, therefore $A > C$, and that these in turn are more difficult than the logic $A + B = C + D$ and $A = C$, therefore $B = D$. The first two of these logical forms occur in the weight test items, whilst the third occurs in an area test item. Table 3 shows the numbers of correct responses which include only those children who were able to explain correctly the reasons for their

The order of acquisition of the concepts of weight, area and volume

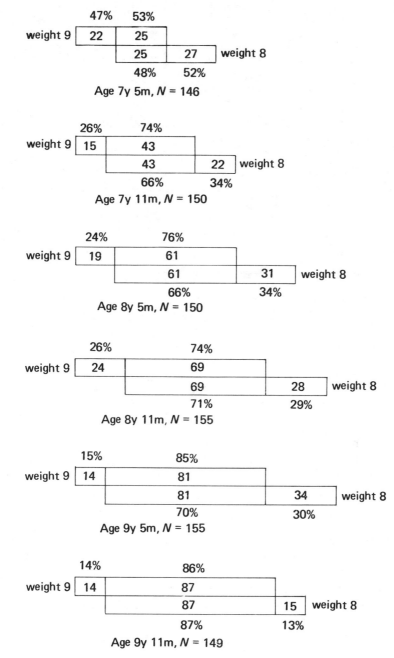

Figure 7

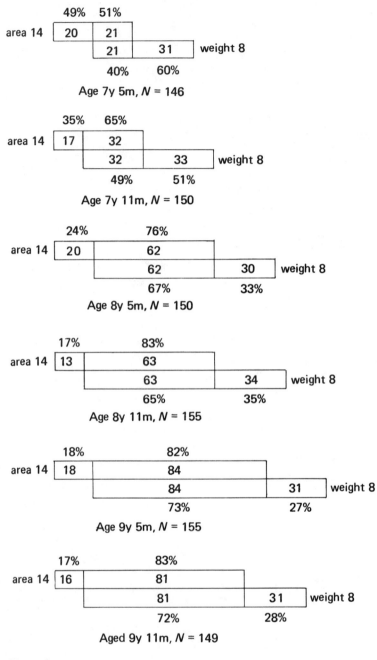

Figure 8a

The order of acquisition of the concepts of weight, area and volume

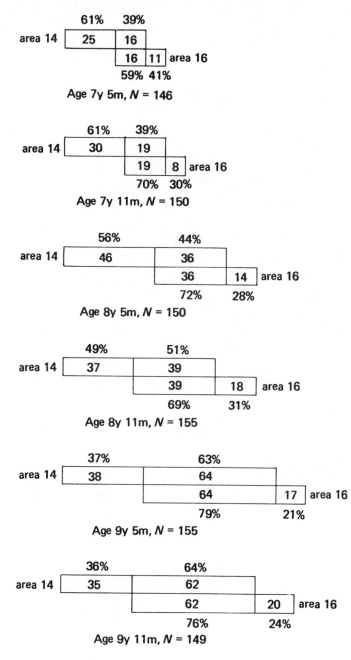

Age 7y 5m, *N* = 146

Age 7y 11m, *N* = 150

Age 8y 5m, *N* = 150

Age 8y 11m, *N* = 155

Age 9y 5m, *N* = 155

Age 9y 11m, *N* = 149

Figure 8b

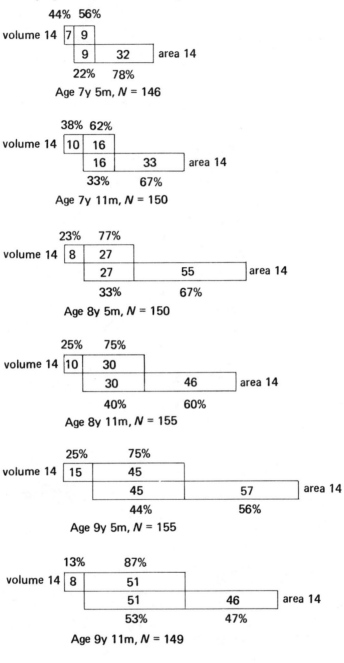

Figure 9a

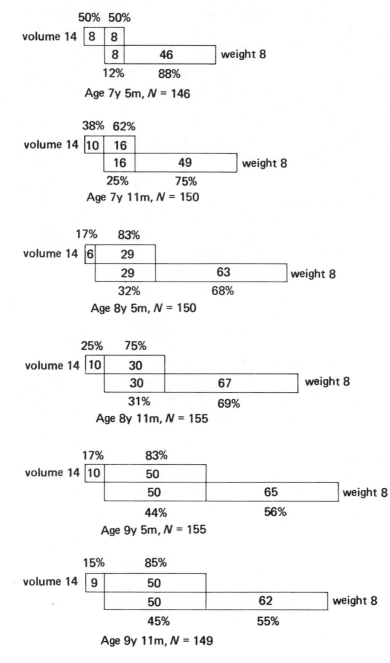

Figure 9b

choices i.e. they clearly demonstrated the power to use the required form of logical reasoning. The results appear to confirm the order of complexity of the logic outlined above. In all the first three items the children remain in the passive situation. Area item 16 calls upon the children to devise practical procedures before they can use the required logic and they have to carry out practical tasks by themselves. This added feature clearly makes the test more difficult and it is difficult to determine whether or not this factor, rather than the form of logic, caused the fall in the number of correct solutions. In volume item 14 the pupil has to remember and relate separate pieces of information and this test proved to be more difficult than any of the others.

This interpretation, if correct, seems to indicate that it is the nature of the logic applicable in any given situation that is the key to understanding rather than the topic (area, weight or volume) in question. To identify conceptual ability with physical 'concepts' such as weight or area or volume is an over-simplification of the conceptual process. It was wondered how the children in our sample would compare in their performances in the items using these forms of logic. Although time did not permit, and test design did not warrant, an exhaustive analysis of these results, a number of such comparisons are presented here, as all highlight, once more, the particularity of individual responses.

Figure 7 compares the results of weight item 9 with weight item 8. The logic of item 8 is easier to understand than the logic of item 9: nevertheless a considerable proportion of the children used one form of logic without using the other. In other words, although one form of logic is generally shown to be used more often than the other form by more children at a given age, the fact that some children are apparently able to use the harder form of logic without demonstrating their ability to use the easier form in the other item complicates the analysis of the conceptual process.

Figures 8 and 9 confirm the pattern of results. The logic required in weight item 8 is seen to be easier than that required in area item 14 and this, in turn, is an easier test than area item 16. Volume item 14 proved to be the most difficult of all. In all these figures, however, it is seen that *a considerable proportion of children continued to display an ability to solve the task generally accepted as harder without being able to solve the task accepted as easier.*

It is this asequential feature witnessed in all the results presented in this chapter that emphasises the need for caution before accepting the principle that *all* children will consistently follow the Piagetian stages of conceptual development. Whilst this study demonstrates that children do display the type of thinking processes described by Piaget, it does not entirely support the interpretation that these processes follow *well-defined* sequential paths. Patterns of performances of groups of children taken together seem to follow Piagetian stages in general, but the responses of individual children do not necessarily correspond to such well-defined stages.

This chapter also emphasises the difficulties encountered when attempting to design tests which allow the research worker to make meaningful comparisons. Very often the introduction of a slightly different practical procedure alters the picture presented to the children to such a degree that their responses vary considerably from one test to another. Research studies which do not include careful analysis of test design are of limited value in Piagetian studies of conceptual development. [. . .]

Summary and conclusions

1 This research has not disproved Piaget's main thesis that the conceptual process follows stages of development. It would seem that, when examining groups of children, this framework provides a more than useful guide for teacher and research worker alike. However, the results of this study emphasise the particularity of the individual and that it is a doubtful practice to categorise the performances of individual children within a rigid framework of stages.

2 Children at younger ages (7y 5m) do not, in the main, display the ability to use concreto-logic forms of reasoning but, on the other hand, more children at the age of ten do display this ability. This finding agrees with Piaget's thesis.

All children tend to rely on perception and the immediate appearances of changes and, if presented with unfamiliar problems, tend to use such observations as a basis for conclusions. This is true even if the same children have earlier displayed the ability to use forms of concreto-logic. This observation emphasises the improbability of ever witnessing the true conceptual ability of children through the use of single test items.

3 Many of the 7 year old children were able to use concreto-logical forms of reasoning, whereas many of the 10 year olds never displayed such ability. This finding suggests that ages should not be used as fine indicators of children's conceptual ability.

4 The relative difficulty of understanding the topics of area, weight and volume is a factor which governs the teaching of these topics in school. As far as the concepts of conservation and use of logic were concerned, the results show that there is little difference in the degree of difficulty of understanding between the three topics. It would appear that the nature of the thinking processes involved at the various levels of achievement within the three topics is more important in conceptualisation than the general nature of the topics themselves.

5 The majority of the children in this research did not fit neatly into one or other of the stages described by Piaget. Most were in a transitional stage. Even those who displayed the ability to use concreto-logical forms of reasoning (e.g. reversibility) often reverted to reasons based on perception when presented with test materials likely to produce conflict in the child's mind between choices based on perception and those based on concreto-logic. [. . .]

It is concluded that a high proportion of the children of average ability in this sample used alternative forms of thinking depending on how they perceived the problem. These children do not fall neatly into one stage or another in *all* situations, although they may appear to do so if the evidence is based on single test items. By its very nature the learning process is transitory, and the children conform to this dynamic principle.

6 It is concluded that there is a relationship between the mental ability of children as measured by a non-verbal intelligence test and their ability to understand the concept of conservation of area, weight and volume as well as their ability to use concreto-logical forms of reasoning.

7 The study has highlighted some of the problems that need to be taken into account when designing Piagetian research. Many of these difficulties were not resolved and, in particular, the problem of measuring the conceptual process through the use of verbal forms of communication remains a fundamental issue in this form of research. It is believed, however, that the results presented here do give good measures of the understandings and misunderstandings of children between the ages of 7 and 11 in the concepts of area, weight and volume.

Many of the results of this inquiry raise issues for further research. An attempt was made to standardise Piagetian testing procedures and to avoid pitfalls caused by ambiguous questions and statements. Nevertheless, the form of the communication between pupil and teacher or tester remains the weakest link in the data-gathering chain. Words or terms conveying real world images in the pupil's mind (e.g. 'grass in a field' to denote area) produced more right answers than when abstract terms ('amount of surface' or 'area') were used. The linguistic form of the question and its relationship to the task set often confused the children so that a slight variation in the wording of the question or in the stress laid on certain words, or even of the practical objects themselves, generated different interpretations of the question by the same children.

Furthermore, a number of children, especially the younger ones, were able to make choices (often correct ones) in the tests and were obviously thinking about the tasks but were quite unable to give reasons for their choices. In other words, their ability to communicate in oral terms was not matched to their conceptual ability. Curiously little reference is made in previous research to such groups of children. There is a need for more research on this problem. It is wondered if there is a relationship between stages of conceptualisation and stages of understanding terms and phrases.

All the test items – in common with other Piagetian researches – called upon the children to listen with understanding, to interpret and respond according to their conceptual powers and to communicate orally their reasons for their responses. It seems clear that these abilities may not be equally well developed in an individual at any given time. Lack of these communication skills obviously masks the true level of conceptualisation of the child.

Even Piaget seems to neglect this problem and all researchers in the field should heed Donaldson's recent comment (1978, p. 61) that:

> 'When [Piaget] does talk about [language learning] he is much more sensitive to differences between what language has become for the adult and what language is for the child in the early stages. However, when he himself, as an experimenter, uses language as part of his method of studying children's thinking, he appears to lose sight of the significance of this issue.'

It seems to be clear, too, that further research in this field should incorporate in its design a number of similar or parallel tests. Many earlier researchers relied on the data gathered from one or two items and the reliability of the ensuing interpretations is open to question. More rigorous techniques need to be developed so that experiments not only test the plausibility of a *particular* hypothesis or explanation but also eliminate all other possible explanations. Recent experiments by Bryant (1974), admittedly in a limited field, have highlighted the necessity for this feature of test design, and this particular age when studying conceptualisation. Mental ability, as measured by a non-verbal intelligence test, appears to be closely related to stages in conceptual ability, and further research needs to be developed in this area.

For the teacher the present research has accentuated the need to use practical materials with young children and, above all else, to structure the resulting activities carefully. A course aiming at developing clear thinking and conceptualisation needs to be related from one school year to the next and calls for close cooperation on the part of the teachers. Primary school teachers have many schemes in mathematics and science at their disposal, and this study indicates that guidance for teachers on the planning of curricular in a structured fashion together with guidance on the evaluation of individual pupils' progress should now be the main objective of curriculum planners over the next decade (*see* the Schools Council Progress in Learning Science Project (1977), directed by Wynne Harlen, for recent work in this field).

Throughout, the variation in the responses of individuals has emerged as the principal observation, and this hinders us from producing a neat and rigid framework for the conceptual powers of our children. Nevertheless, the ability to deviate from the average, from the expected behaviour, is the mark of the intelligent man. It can be maintained that it is only by such deviation, together with the ability to move from thinking about the visual to thinking in terms of mental images, that adults and particularly children can form new ideas and understand the various concepts presented to them.

The measurement of the average ability of an age group or a group of pupils does not supply information of any great worth. Such measurements create a restrictive view of the performances of individuals within a group and tell us nothing about the capabilities of, or the difficulties experienced by, individuals within the group. The strength of Piagetian research lies not in the measurement of average performances but in the recording and measurement of individual responses.

> 'Knowledge is not a loose-leaf notebook of facts. The commonplace of the schoolbooks of tomorrow is the adventure of today, and that is what we are engaged in.'　　　　(J. Bronowski, *The Ascent of Man,* 1973)

References

Beard, R., 'The Order of Concept Development: Studies in two fields, I, II', *Educational Review* vol. 15, (1962–3), pp. 105–17 and pp. 228–37, 1963.

Bryant, P. E., *Perception and Understanding in Young Children*, Methuen, London, 1974.

Donaldson, M., *Children's Minds*, Fontana, London, 1978.

Flavell, J., 'An Analysis of Cognitive-developmental Sequences', *Psychological Monographs: General and Applied*, no. 86, pp. 279–350, 1972.

Harlen, W., *Matching the Learning Environment to Children's Development: The Progress in Learning Science Project*, Schools Council, 1977.

Hyde, *Piaget's Conceptual Development: With a Cross-cultural Study of Number and Quantity*, Holt, Rinehart, Winston, London, 1970.

Lister, R., 'The Development of ESN Children's Understanding of Conservation in a Range of Attribute Situations', *British Journal of Educational Psychology*, vol. 42, no. 1, pp. 14–22, 1972.

9 Thinking about problems

George Polya

Sources: Preface to Part 1 of Polya, G. Mathematical Discovery,
Wiley, New York, 1961; and Polya G., How to Solve it, pp 33–36,
Princeton University Press, 1971.

<<<<<<<<<<<<<<<<<<<<<<<<<<<<<<<<<<<<<<<<<<<<<<<<<<<<<<<<<<<

Introduction

Our knowledge about any subject consists of *information* and of *know-how*. If
you have genuine *bona fide* experience of mathematical work on any level,
elementary or advanced, there will be no doubt in your mind that, in mathematics, know-how is much more important than mere possession of information. Therefore, in the high school, as on any other level, we should impart,
along with a certain amount of information, a certain degree of *know-how* to
the student.

What is know-how in mathematics? The ability to solve problems – not
merely routine problems but problems requiring some degree of independence,
judgment, originality, creativity. Therefore, the first and foremost duty of the
high school in teaching mathematics is to emphasise *methodical work in problem solving*. This is my conviction; you may not go along with it all the way,
but I assume that you agree that problem-solving deserves some emphasis – and
this will do for the present.

The teacher should know what he is supposed to teach. He should show his
students how to solve problems – but if he does not know, how can he show
them? The teacher should develop his students' know-how, their ability to
reason; he should recognise and encourage creative thinking – but the curriculum
he went through paid insufficient attention to his mastery of the subject matter
and no attention at all to his know-how, to his ability to reason, to his ability
to solve problems, to his creative thinking. Here is, in my opinion, the worst gap
in the present preparation of high school mathematics teachers. [The remainder
of this chapter is Polya's advice about problem-solving, cast in the form of a
dialogue.]

How to solve it: a dialogue

Getting acquainted
Where should I start? Start from the statement of the problem.

What can I do? Visualise the problem as a whole as clearly and as vividly as you can. Do not concern yourself with details for the moment.

What can I gain by doing so? You should understand the problem, familiarise yourself with it, impress its purpose on your mind. The attention bestowed on the problem may also stimulate your memory and prepare for the recollection of relevant points.

Working for better understanding

Where should I start? Start again from the statement of the problem. Start when this statement is so clear to you and so well impressed on your mind that you may lose sight of it for a while without fear of losing it altogether.

What can I do? Isolate the principal parts of your problem. The hypothesis and the conclusion are the principal parts of a 'problem to prove'; the unknown, the data, and the conditions are the principal parts of a 'problem to find'. Go through the principal parts of your problem, consider them one by one, consider them in turn, consider them in various combinations, relating each detail to other details and each to the whole of the problem.

What can I gain by doing so? You should prepare and clarify details which are likely to play a role afterwards.

Hunting for the helpful idea

Where should I start? Start from the consideration of the principal parts of your problem. Start when these principal parts are distinctly arranged and clearly conceived, thanks to your previous work, and when your memory seems responsive.

What can I do? Consider your problem from various sides and seek contacts with your formerly acquired knowledge?

Consider your problem from various sides. Emphasise different parts, examine different details, examine the same details repeatedly but in different ways, combine the details differently, approach them from different sides. Try to see some new meaning in each detail, some new interpretation of the whole.

Seek contacts with your formerly acquired knowledge. Try to think of what helped you in similar situations in the past. Try to recognise something familiar in what you examine, try to perceive something useful in what you recognise.

What could I perceive? A helpful idea, perhaps a decisive idea that shows you at a glance the way to the very end.

How can an idea be helpful? It shows you the whole of the way or a part of the way; it suggests to you more or less distinctly how you can proceed. Ideas are more or less complete. You are lucky if you have any idea at all.

What can I do with an incomplete idea? You should consider it. If it looks advantageous you should consider it longer. If it looks reliable you should ascertain how far it leads you, and reconsider the situation. The situation has changed, thanks to your helpful idea. Consider the new situation from various sides and seek contacts with your formerly acquired knowledge.

What can I gain by doing so again? You may be lucky and have another idea. Perhaps your next idea will lead you to the solution right away. Perhaps you need a few more helpful ideas after the next. Perhaps you will be led astray by some of your ideas. Nevertheless you should be grateful for all new ideas, also for the lesser ones, also for the hazy ones, also for the supplementary ideas adding some precision to a hazy one, or attempting the correction of a less fortunate one. Even if you do not have any appreciable new ideas for a while you should be grateful if your conception of the problem becomes more complete or more coherent, more homogeneous or better balanced.

Carrying out the plan

Where should I start? Start from the lucky idea that led you to the solution. Start when you feel sure of your grasp of the main connection and you feel confident that you can supply the minor details that may be wanting.

What can I do? Make your grasp quite secure. Carry through in detail all the algebraic or geometric operations which you have recognised previously as feasible. Convince yourself of the correctness of each step by formal reasoning, or by intuitive insight, or both ways if you can. If your problem is very complex you may distinguish 'great' steps and 'small' steps, each great step being composed of several small ones. Check first the great steps, and get down to the smaller ones afterwards.

What can I gain by doing so? A presentation of the solution of each step which is correct beyond doubt.

Looking back

Where should I start? From the solution, complete and correct in each detail.

What can I do? Consider the solution from various sides and seek contacts with your formerly acquired knowledge.

Consider the details of the solution and try to make them as simple as you can; survey more extensive parts of the solution and try to make them shorter; try to see the whole solution at a glance. Try to modify to their advantage smaller or larger parts of the solution, try to improve the whole solution, to make it intuitive, to fit it into your formerly acquired knowledge as naturally as possible. Scrutinise the method that led you to the solution, try to see its point, and try to make use of it for other problems. Scrutinise the result and try to make use of it for other problems.

What can I gain by doing so? You may find a new and better solution, you may discover new and interesting facts. In any case, if you get into the habit of surveying and scrutinising your solutions in this way, you will acquire some knowledge well ordered and ready to use, and you will develop your ability of solving problems.

10 The metaphoric mind: the gift of beginning

Bob Samples

Source: Samples, B., The Metaphoric Mind, chapter 6, Addison-Wesley, Philippines, 1976.

<<<<<<<<<<<<<<<<<<<<<<<<<<<<<<<<<<<<<<<<<<<<<<<<<<<<<<<<

Bruner had written a fine book called *On Knowing, Essays for the Left Hand*, and he introduced me to this metaphor as a basis for observations I would make that summer and the following year. Although both Bruner and Hawkins were disciples of Piaget, neither insisted that Piaget's models be used. Instead we gathered each day, planned some action assignments, tried them with classrooms full of children, discussed them later, and wrote down our findings. Children of all ages were available to us, so we could run the gamut from Piaget's pre-operational to supposedly formal-operations stages. Because I felt no compulsion at that time to reverify Piaget's logical progression, I chose to discover what I could about left-handed learning.

One of the first things I learned was that it was more like play than work. The children would take the 'problem' we had created and literally play with it. Since our work usually involved some apparatus or some natural materials, the children had something tangible to work on. In a typical beginning, given a series of pendulums hanging from wooden racks, the children were instructed to 'find out what you can about pendulums.'

> 'Children picked up the racks, looked underneath, set them down, and began to swing pendulums. Some started pendulum wars (trying to hit pendulum spheres together). Some chattered about the swings on the playground. Two boys began trying to entwine their pendulum cords by swinging the pendulums. A girl leaned over the frame with her lips on the top, feeling the vibrations as the pendulum swung back and forth. Three boys and one girl tried to make a stack of pendulums so there would be a tower of pendulums that they could get to swing in unison. (This activity took about 40 minutes.)'

At first I noticed a good deal of anxiety on the part of the adults who had written the lessons. Most often they would circulate among the students and ask leading questions — questions designed to 'lead' the children back to where the adults were more comfortable, to a place where the lesson and experience were more closely related to the intent of the lesson as seen by the adults.

In these instances David Hawkins protected the children as they explored. He would weave great rational tales about the sophistication of some of the children's actions, much to the comfort of those whose rational neurosis was being sorely taxed. He invoked everyone from Galileo to Confucius as he guaranteed a space of time for the children to 'mess around' (one of his favourite phrases). Bruner most often agreed and spoke about 'left-handed' knowing. I was enraptured by the lack of structure the children showed until the nervous adults crept in and asked questions or otherwise guided their actions back into 'safe' places.

Thus I was able to observe children playing with science and simultaneously gather several important psychological insights from those participating:

> 'Bruner: The students were involved in play, rich in "left-handed" knowing.
> Hawkins: There were profound rational components being experienced tacitly by the children.
> Other adults: Teachers are generally made nervous by play.
> Samples: Adults (the cultural order) affect the kind of knowing the children are permitted to experience.'

On the basis of these observations I decided to get a group of lesson-makers together. My purpose was to work with children of several ages, in several content areas, and see how they operated through a learning sequence. That is, I chose to observe them until they were really 'finished' with a problem. I did not know whether comprehension or boredom would finish the learning. We worked with third graders (7–8 years old), sixth graders (11–12 years old), and eighth graders (13–14 years old). The content areas included physics, natural science and astronomy. The results were remarkable.

All the students indulged in play for a long period of time at the onset of the lesson. This play was facilitated by the degree of 'trust' we had established with the children. They would often cue in on the adults to see how much we intended to interfere before they got comfortable with the play. The older students always took longer to be convinced of our 'non-intervention' policy. We mapped the excursions of individual students into play–work areas. Work was defined as that activity with obvious rational components. Play was that which lacked these components. The results of several dozen observations that summer and several hundred in the following year are shown in the illustrations that follow.

Generally the students would spend most of their early time within a problem sequence in play. Then, as they reached saturation with the play, they would shift to right-handed or rational knowing. At this point the teacher-observers typically became noticeably more comfortable. The children were operating within the context of their prejudices. They asked questions, performed tasks, and generally conformed to behaviors that were consistent with Piaget's criteria.

The students, however, were quickly satiated with rational discourse. They often gathered their newfound data and then whipped back into metaphoric play in the left-handed mode. After exhausting their rational fix in metaphor, however, the students again excursioned into the right. This always delighted the teachers. But they became bewildered again as the students frequently whipped once more into metaphor. I began to realise that the teachers were exhibiting a form of neurosis consistent with the cultural order . . . rational neurosis. *The teachers were made anxious when the children moved away from the structures the teachers had chosen to accept.*

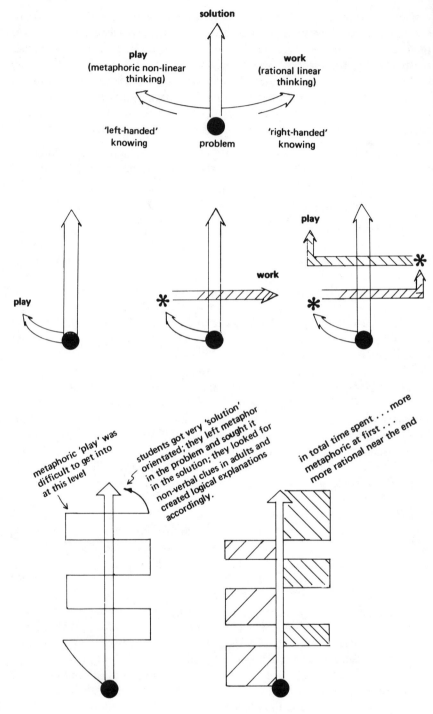

solution

play
(metaphoric non-linear
thinking)

work
(rational linear
thinking)

'left-handed'
knowing

problem

'right-handed'
knowing

play

work

play

metaphoric 'play' was
difficult to get into
at this level

students got very 'solution'
orientated; they left metaphor
in the problem and sought it
in the solution; they looked for
non-verbal clues in adults and
created logical explanations
accordingly.

in total time spent . . . more
metaphoric at first . . .
more rational near the end

Back and forth the pattern went, with alternating excursions from right to left on the part of the students and into and out of anxiety on the part of the teachers. But gradually it got better for the teachers. We began to notice that about two-thirds of the way through a problem—solution sequence, the right-handed knowing began to dominate. That is, the closer the children got to a rational solution, *the more difficult it was for them to return to metaphor.* This difficulty was demonstrated by the students consistently choosing linear and logical explanations and routes for exploration. Even when led in less logical directions, the students clung tenaciously to their rational conclusions. [. . .]

11 And now for something different: teaching by not teaching

Sandy Dawson and John Trivett

Source: specially written for this volume

≪≪≪

Yes, now for something different. We suggest to you that there are *alternative* and feasible ways of structuring what can take place in *your* classroom, that these ways can be initiated by you *now*, tomorrow if you wish, and yet you need not stop anything you do normally, at least not necessarily so.

Consequently, we issue you an invitation — no RSVP required — an invitation to grasp the opportunity now, little by little:

1 to look at and use what students really do,
2 to examine why they do it, and
3 to comprehend what needs to be done — by you — in response to your students' activities.

In other words, we invite you to join with us in exploring how learners can joyfully assume much, much more responsibility for their own learning. In the process of this exploration, we will introduce you to ways of working with children in which *you* subordinate your teaching to the learning of the children with whom you work, so that not only the responsibility for the learning but also the awareness of how learning occurs rests where it must, namely, with the children.

We suggest that you begin this exploration by setting aside one lesson in five, say, to try some of the activities which we will detail shortly. We contend that there will be some very valuable by-products which arise from these explorations, by-products which will affect the remainder of your lessons.

Not the least of these by-products will be the introduction of a variety of approaches as to how mathematics may be taught and learnt, perhaps a variety of topics for the children and for you; an opportunity for an empirical study by you to diagnose whether your children are very much affected by lessons of a new kind; a renewed recognition of the individuality, sincerity, and originality which all children are capable of displaying in classroom settings if given the chance to do so.

However, this is not where we are in maths teaching today. We have had the *old* math and the *new* math, worksheet maths because of the proliferation of photo-copiers, ditto masters, and laminating machines; manipulative aids, maths projects of millions of pounds, maths centres, the back-to-the-basics movement, hand calculators, programmed learning, Tractenberg and Chisanbop, and now micro-computers. But don't you get the feeling that we are still where we were, that the more things seem to change, the more they remain the same? Various national and international reports attest to this.

Are we to be content to produce mathematicians only? We've always done that, and probably always shall. Or are we to do more than that, and thereby help all children be joyful at their own maths for general living purposes, spiritually and practically? We choose the latter. If we did not, we would not bother to write this article.

We allege that significant changes are not occurring because we don't see the proverbial woods for the trees. We contend that people in general and most maths teachers in particular are still not aware that maths is a birthright of *all* human beings.

Everyone, by virtue of being human, has what is needed for some maths. Everyone abstracts, relates, connects, makes models, solves problems, generalises, specialises, and so on, and, moreover, has done so since birth, if not before. The newborn child must do many of these things in order to direct and control its bodily functions. Most certainly, children teaching themselves to talk do each of these things. Teachers need to become aware, if they are not aware already, of just what capabilities children bring with them to classrooms. They should be aware that they need *not* teach children how to do these things. Teachers need, rather, to become aware of how to present maths to children so that these capabilities can be exercised naturally by children. In short, teachers need to educate themselves first to what it involves to teach oneself anything, and secondly to educate themselves of how to assist learners to educate themselves, in our case, with respect to mathematics.

What we presently do with children in classrooms does not, we would argue, allow teachers to educate themselves in either of these ways. The prevalent way of teaching maths in Europe and North America is based, in our view, on a misguided view of the formal nature of mathematics.

None of the maths now reflected in texts, and perhaps by teachers , came into existence in formal ways. The maths inventors doodled, made mistakes galore, agonised over problems for hours, days, weeks, even years, disposed of hoards of paper and chalk, and made haste slowly. Unfortunately, we now pressure children to work hard without suggesting very clearly what they should work hard at or in what way they should work. More often than not, what we teachers have in mind is the final, formal product of many mathematicians' work. This is what we seem to want children to know, and not the excitement and disappointment or struggle with a problem which children could experience until they have found a solution which is correct for them, at least for the moment. This situation is analogous to wanting children to *know* a dictionary, but not ever allowing them to use the words in that dictionary for their own investigations and creations, let alone to communicate with one another.

It has been said (one of the authors of this article said it!), 'Rather than think of maths being integrated with other subjects, maths *is* the integration itself.' Language learning is one of the greatest evidences of that, and *we have all learned language.*

This gives rise to what for us are four absolutely basic questions. If significant changes are to be made in the teaching of maths, then we contend that these questions, as they pertain to maths teaching, must be answered by each teacher, and answered in such a way that teachers know the answers are true based on their own experience, on their own authority.

The questions are as follows:

1 Who is the authority for what is spoken in any language, in particular, the language of mathematics?
2 What help do we as teachers have for learning and teaching the mathematical language? What barriers are there?
3 What kind of learning do we want?
4 Where is the authority for our answers to the above?

Briefly, and later in more detail, our answers to these questions go something like this:

1 The individual learner has to be responsible, because self-speaking and self-education are not avoidable despite what anyone thinks or does. For example, we cannot learn the multiplication table for you. You must do that yourself. That is not to say we cannot help you, but in the final analysis you must do the learning yourself.
2 The spoken and written language is itself a great aid for the teaching and learning of mathematics. However, the native language has barriers built into it, and as teachers we must know how to avoid these. More on this later.
3 The learning we want is for children to use their own individual thoughts, their own direct experiences, their own sense of truth, their own time, their own doubts and queries and so on. This all implies quite a different approach to the teaching and learning of maths than is common today.
4 Our authority for the above answers rests on our own experience in teaching ourselves something new, and also from our close observations of children learning new things if allowed to do so using the powers and capabilities they all possess.

Your answers to these questions must come from *you*. You have done *all* your own learning; you had no choice even if someone else helped considerably in some way.

You are your own authority for what *you* deem to be correct. You use a multitude of aids to help you. You are constantly working at processes.

You don't think so? Examine your daily experiences. For example, examine the way you use language fluently, whether you cook, drive, type or whatever. You are responsible for all this regardless of what anyone else says about the way it seems to them!

The one lesson in five which we suggested to you at the outset can be a great opportunity for you, the teacher, to become aware of all of this, because no matter how clearly we may write, our words are part of the barrier to your learning. Your learning must be based on your experience. It cannot be based on our words. So try that one lesson in five.

Here are some suggestions of things you might try. In making these suggestions we hope also to give more detailed answers to the questions posed above, as well as to give some illustrations of what we are talking about.

1 Who is the authority?

If the learner is the ultimate authority, then you must ease up on the correction of learners, or don't correct at all. Place the responsibility for correction on the learners. Allow the children to talk to one another, to check with each other. After all, that is what they do when learning a new game, or new skill, or even in learning to speak!

Assume, at least during this one lesson in five, that everyone is correct, *not* in what is said or written, *but* in the intent behind such outward evidence. Each of us have had the experience of not being able to say or write exactly what we mean, but our intent is clear. So it is with children. Suspend *your* judgement about what you think was said or written. Try to get at the meaning behind the words and symbols.

Accept, but do not necessarily agree with, what is done. As far as possible for you, become neutral.

All of this may be quite foreign to the way you usually operate, but remember, it is only one lesson in five, and it does provide you with a unique opportunity to stand back and observe what children can do. You may be surprised, but at the very least be acutely observant.

2 What help do we have?

It seems in all but mathematics lessons children are encouraged to talk with each other and to discuss what they are doing. For some reason, teachers tend to view maths as something that children should do by themselves and preferably in silence.

We suggest a reversal of this situation. Encourage two-way conversation in pairs, or with everyone, talking about *what is* not what should be. In this, *you* should remain silent, at least initially, so that you can *watch* the children's eyes, heads, and hand movements, and *listen* to their tone of voice. We say you should be silent, because if at each instance you are thinking about what you are going to say you are preoccupied with *your* thoughts and thereby miss the chance of really seeing and hearing what the children are doing and saying.

Moreover, encourage the children to watch and listen to each other as well. Both for you and the children, try to extract what is meant rather than just noting what is said or written. *And stop being in a hurry!* Be patient, suspend your judgement, and be as silent as possible.

Now, you won't or shouldn't be totally silent all the time. When you do intervene, adopt such phrases as 'Are you saying . . . ?' rather than 'No, it's wrong', or 'Yes, that's right'.

At some point you might even wish to have a discussion with the children about the difficulties of language expression, and the barriers to communication. Someone once said (it might have even been one of us, but it wasn't! It was Caleb Gattegno.) 'Verbalisation is relatively easy. Communication is a miracle.' Yet all of us try to communicate our meanings to others. Indeed, we want to do so, we want to tell others about our findings, our insights, our feelings, our discoveries, and we wish to have others communicate with us. The difficulty is that the content of our meanings – the sum total of our cognitive, affective, and psychomotor knowledge of some subject – is usually far greater than the words or time we possess to convey these meanings. As a result, our verbal descriptions are always less than the content of our meanings. Hence, to communicate our total meaning when lacking adequate time or words is truly miraculous!

There are, of course, aids other than language which can be used. In fact, the use of manipulative aids and physical objects will provide something about which to talk. Allow the children to use their fingers, pebbles, coloured rods, attribute blocks, geoboards and so on. Not only can the use of such materials provide the content for conversation, they can also be valuable tools for self-correction, that is, the materials can be used as models which can establish which of various claims made by children are correct. Teacher does not need to do that. Often, the materials and one's eyesight can take the place of the teacher as authority figure.

3 *What kind of learning do we want?*

We've already indicated that we want children to use their own individual thoughts, observations, experiences and so on. Perhaps the question now is, what is it that we want them to think about, observe, and experience?

As a beginning, for your very first one lesson in five, we suggest you select some standard arithmetic problem, some *old* math perhaps, from a commercial textbook, say, or some new problem you've come across in a journal or at a conference. The topic does not particularly matter, because it is the process – what happens during the lesson – that you should be intent on observing.

You might, for example, ask the children if they can invent new ways to add or multiply. Or you might ask them if they could add from left to right (right to left is the usual way!), get the 'correct' answer, and then teach this new way to someone else.

For younger children, you might simply ask them to write as many names for eight, say, as they can using only addition and the whole numbers. Do you think every child in a class of 35 children could get a different answer? Try it yourself. Then maybe extend the quest so that subtraction could be used as well. Or try the same exercise again, this time for six. Or have groups of children work on different numbers. Finally, if all the names for 4, 5, 6, 7, and 8 using the whole numbers and addition only have been found and counted, is it possible to predict how many names there would be for 9, or 3 or 2? Encourage the children to look for patterns. (There is definitely a pattern here. In fact, more than one pattern. Try to find some of them yourself, *and watch yourself while you are doing it.* You are the learner in this situation. How are you educating yourself? What processes did you go through? Did you make mistakes, grope around, doodle, use hoards of paper, get confused or frustrated, and finally, joyfully, reach some answer satisfactory to you?)

And don't rush the children. Time is not of the essence here. Initially, it may seem like the children are taking a long time to do what is so obvious to you, but it is not necessarily obvious to them. If it was, they wouldn't have to do it, would they? For children not accustomed to searching for patterns and relationships during maths lessons, it will take a while for them to get used to working in this way. Once they begin to function in this fashion, however, we can almost guarantee an explosion of work, because it is a natural manner for all humans to work. It is not usually encouraged in schools, so children need time to become used to doing in schools what comes naturally in the rest of their lives.

Nor should you try to force undue sophistication to their work at the beginning. Maths in the making — pattern seeking, relationship building — is a game-like activity, and premature formalism or written or verbal sophistication is inappropriate. That can come later, and will come naturally as part of the process of refinement and consolidation of results which the children will seek. So once again, be patient and suspend your judgement.

4 *Whose authority?*
Yours, of course.

Here, try this, and after you have finished, decide who you needed to decide if your answers were correct.

Write a name for each of the whole numbers (0, 1, 2, 3, . . .) from 1 to 50 using the numerals 1, 2, 3, and 4 once and only once in each name. You can use the operations of addition, subtraction, multiplication, division, powers, and factorials.

For example, one way to write 10 would be $1 + 2 + 3 + 4$; another way would be $(4 \times 3) - (2 \times 1)$; yet another way could be $[(4 \times 2) + 3] - 1$. One way for writing 17 would be $4^2 + 1^3$, and for 37 one way would be $3[4! \div 2] + 1$. Try it, and then decide who was the *author*-ity for your learning.

Once more, through those questions, now, but let's get even more specific this time. You see, it is difficult to convey with *words* what we suggest you *do* with yourself and with the children whom you will teach.

1 *Who is the authority?*
Most 6 year olds have no difficulty picking up this phrase and its meaning:
two apples plus three apples equals five apples,

or: two bananas plus three bananas equals five bananas,
or: two elephants plus three elephants equals five elephants,
or: two globs plus three globs equals five globs,

or: (watch it now, these are 6 year olds)
two hundred plus three hundred equals five hundred,
or: two thousand plus three thousand equals five thousand,
or: two million plus three million equals five million,
or: two billion plus three billion equals five billion.

Here we use our language, the English language, and the patterns it has to aid us in making children *aware* of some patterns. We are in a sense 'forcing their awareness' in order that they may educate themselves. The above example can be extended so that 6 and 7 year olds can easily handle:

two billion, two million, two thousand, two hundred, two
plus
three billion, three million, three thousand, three hundred, three
equals
five billion, five million, five thousand, five hundred, five

Even if they can't write the symbols of any of these numbers or have any idea how much a billion is! Moreover, they will know that they are correct. You won't have to tell them.

2 *What help do we have?*

Try this with older children — 9 or 10 or older.

Have the children construct the familiar 10 × 10 multiplication table on the chalkboard. Then ask them to identify any patterns they see in the table. Your role is to remain silent except as to clarify what the children describe or point out — *not* to correct, or to say we've had that one before. Here is such a table.

X	1	2	3	4	5	6	7	8	9	10
1	1	2	3	4	5	6	7	8	9	10
2	2	4	6	8	10	12	14	16	18	20
3	3	6	9	12	15	18	21	24	27	30
4	4	8	12	16	20	24	28	32	36	40
5	5	10	15	20	25	30	35	40	45	50
6	6	12	18	24	30	36	42	48	54	60
7	7	14	21	28	35	42	49	56	63	70
8	8	16	24	32	40	48	56	64	72	80
9	9	18	27	36	45	54	63	72	81	90
10	10	20	30	40	50	60	70	80	90	100

It is impossible to say what the children might pick out initially. They may, for instance, note that each vertical *column* increases by the number at the head of that column, that is, the 2s column goes up by twos, the 3s by threes, and so on; or that horizontal *rows* do the same thing.

Study the table yourself. See what patterns you can discern. Focus, for a moment, on the 9 column or row. What things do you notice about the numerals in that column? Is it the same for the corresponding row? Would the pattern hold if you extended the column downward? upward? What further awarenesses would children require for that pattern to assist them in learning their 9 times table?

Are there any similar patterns in other rows or columns?

Study any two adjacent rows or columns. What awarenesses did you gain from this study which might help you teach/learn *fractions*?

The point of all this is that the staid, old multiplication table can be an aid to new and exciting studies. If children are allowed to explore this table, individually or in small groups, then their teachers can, with careful listening and looking, gain a wealth of insights as to how children learn, how they correct themselves and others, how they make guesses and check them, how they formulate hypotheses and test them, all without direction or correction by the teacher. It is not only insights the teacher may gain, but also a renewed respect for the individuality, sincerity, and originality of their students. Try it. You have nothing to lose and so much to gain.

3 *What kind of learning do we want?*

Let's examine a topic in which children might be even more inventive: simple, traditional addition of three-digit numbers. Could we add from left to right — the usual direction for reading English — instead of from right to left as in the traditional algorithm? Let's try.

$$\begin{array}{r} 425 \\ 143 \\ 331 \\ \hline 899 \end{array}$$

(In our usual way, we say something like 5 plus 3 plus 1 is 9. Put down the 9. Now add the tens column. 2 plus 4 plus 3 equals 9. Put down another 9. Now the hundreds. 4 plus 1 plus 3 is 8. Put down the 8. Aha! 899.)

Now, from left to right. The hundreds first. 4 hundreds plus 1 hundred plus 3 hundreds is 8 hundreds or 800. Then the tens. 2 tens plus 4 tens plus 3 tens is 9 tens or 90. Finally the ones. 5 ones plus 3 ones plus 1 one is 9 ones or 9. 800 plus 90 plus 9. Aha, 899!

So, it makes no difference! We could even start from the middle column. Are there other ways to add? Could you invent some? Would either of these patterns work?

$$\begin{array}{r} 425 \\ 143 \\ 331 \\ \hline \end{array} \qquad \begin{array}{r} 425 \\ 143 \\ 331 \\ \hline \end{array}$$

The point is *not* that we want children to know all these ways of adding. There are many points to this illustration. First, we want children and teachers to know — to be aware — that there is not just one right way of doing something in maths. There are usually many ways, and the way which is best depends on the situation.

Second, we want teachers and children to become aware that these processes are created by human beings, and that it is entirely possible for new ones to be invented. Even children can do it! Third, we want teachers to know and children to experience that mathematics is the study of relationships, and not the memorisation of predetermined processes and answers. Maths is something people *do*, all the time, though perhaps unconsciously. People create, examine, modify, adjust, eliminate, create anew, vast numbers of relationships. Maths is the study of these relationships. We all do it. However, what we usually study as mathematics is the final written product of a mathematician's work. We are urging here that maths for children and their teachers, as it is presented in classrooms, should come closer to its true nature. To do so, children need to do maths, that is, they need to study patterns and relationships in an atmosphere which supports their successes and failures, and celebrates their individuality, sincerity, and originality.

4 *Whose authority?*

Recall now, as you sit there in your comfortable chair reading this, what you yourself do in other non-maths lessons. Go ahead. Do it *now*!

In art, for example, do you have an emphasis on correction? Do you have children only copy the art of others?

In science do you enquire, with lots of discussion? Whose authority do you rely on for what each individual *sees*?

In physical education is there only one way of kicking the soccer ball?

In language lessons do you accept only one detailed form for everything your children write? If letters to the Queen are taught in their particular formal way, is there only one form for thanking grandma for a birthday present?

When children talk to us do we stop them every moment to correct their speech, their accents, their intonations? Do we encourage them to speak like us? (Pygmalion!)

Should I correct in detail what you say to me? Do you benefit from it if I do?

In summary, think of teaching maths in ways *you* teach other subjects and try to use the same processes in maths, at least, for starters, during that one lesson in five which you are going to try out tomorrow!

Throughout what you have just read, we've made frequent reference to *awareness* and to *educating oneself.* To us, these notions of awareness and self-education are fundamental to all of education, whether or not it is in maths lessons.

When we try to teach children or adults something, we are at a very basic level trying to get them to become *aware* of patterns and relationships which they had not noticed before. Further, we are trying by emphasising certain approaches — conversations, guessing and testing, conjecturing, use of manipulative aids and physical objects, use of language and so on — to draw the learners' attention to how they go about learning in a natural setting. It is our experience that children welcome such approaches, because they view them as part of what they do all the time when not in schools. They don't see them as different, just natural!

Consequently, when working with learners of whatever age, we attempt to create situations which will *force their awareness* to what it is that we want them to learn. If we do not succeed, we do not assume that there is something wrong with the learner. Rather, we look for other ways to bring whatever awareness it is we are after to the learner's attention.

In order to be able to do that reasonably successfully, however, we have had to educate ourselves not only to be aware of what the children must learn, but to also be aware of those awarenesses. Confused? Let us try to clarify this a bit.

To learn something new requires, in our view, the education of one's awareness. One must become aware of the pattern in the 9s column, for example, if a connection is to be made with the multiplication by 9. To learn the 9s table, this is sufficient. To teach this to someone else requires something more. The something more is the recognition − the awareness − of what the children must do with themselves in order to see that initial pattern in the 9s column. The teacher has to be aware of what awarenesses are requred for someone else to learn. The teacher needs to be aware of the awarenesses.

Moreover, though we have focused here on mainly arithmetic awarenesses, with a bit of language patterning thrown in, the range of awarenesses of which a teacher must be cognisant is not limited to subject matter alone. Perhaps even more importantly, it includes an awareness of what learners must do for and with themselves in order to conquer some new subject, or skill, that is, some new awareness.

Above all it requires the recognition that all of us, young or old, have no choice but to educate ourselves. It is only each of us who can be aware of what we are aware. Someone else cannot be aware for us. Because of that, each of us must teach ourselves, though it is obviously a tremendous help to have someone else close by who is sensitive to us and to what it is we are trying to learn. Are not good teachers those who can put challenges directly in front of their students so that they are hooked immediately, and who then let students take over by getting out of their way? So easily said, so hard to do, all the time, with all students.

The purpose, then, of encouraging you to try different ways in your maths lessons − one in five of them, anyway − was to provide you with the opportunity to first of all become aware of what is required to learn something new, and second to alert yourself to the many awarenesses children must acquire before you and they can proudly say, 'We've mastered it!'

If you try any bit of this, you are giving yourself permission to flounder, at least for a while, but the children won't know that. They will be involved and busy in doing something different and unusual.

You will be researching into how maths can be considered differently, without having to change dramatically, without having to take the two recommended courses.

You will begin to answer for yourself those questions about maths teaching you may have held for a long time, and hopefully begin to be secure, in a few small ways, about improving the situation.

You have the opportunity for doing this each time that one lesson in five comes around, perhaps while you wait patiently for more outside help in the form of better courses, better books, better aids, and for people who may think they know better what you require than you do yourself.

You have an advantage over those folks. You have your children and yourself, and in the last analysis that is all you need, because all that needs to be done has to be done by you and your children in the ways you and they decide is most appropriate for all of you.

Good luck with that first of hopefully many, many one lesson every five.

12 Language and cognitive development

Dan Slobin

Source: Slobin, D. I., Psycholinguistics, ᶜ

≪≪≪

Language is one of several means of representation. Taking this last term quite literally, we see that we are concerned with re-presentation, that is, the problem of presenting ourselves with experience again at some later time. As in the discussion of memory, the matter is one of internal coding of experience. The psychologist Jerome Bruner (1966) has pointed to two other major modes of representation, contrasting them with linguistic representation.

A primitive but often useful means of representation is through action. Some things are best demonstrated by doing – as, for example, using tools, tying knots, and other motor skills. Probably many things we know how to do are represented by some sort of muscle imagery. Children learn much about the world through active manipulation, and there is a good deal of evidence that 'enactive' representation is an early means for representing objects.

Enactive representation is limited, however, in that it is sequentially ordered and not easily reversible. If you learn your way from home to work by remembering a series of left and right turns, you will have difficulty in finding yourself if you get lost, for you have no overall representation of the route. If you have a map (or a visual image) of the route, however, you can scan it back and forth and find your place and your way. Thus there is another, more compact mode of representation which uses visual imagery as its mode. This mode allows for action-free representation.

The most supple mode of action-free representation, however, is language (and the other symbolic systems invented by man, such as mathematical systems). Systems such as language make it possible to invent new symbols to represent anything – even things which cannot be felt or seen. And, given rules of combination and recombination, such as grammar, we can deal with all manner of possibilities, going far beyond things and events we have experienced directly.

Thus there are at least three major means available for representing experience: action, imagery, and language. No one mode serves all human purposes: we must learn manipulative skills, visual configurations, social customs, science, history, and so on. The three modes are used separately and in interaction. Furthermore

135

[. . .] there must be inarticulate forms of thought which precede the production of acts, images, or utterances.

Bruner, Piaget, and others have presented evidence that the modes of representation develop in the order in which we have discussed them. We do not have the means here to evaluate this complex issue, but a few examples may be illuminating. As for the enactive mode, Piaget provides us with valuable observations from his own children during their first year of life (1954). At first it seems that objects are, to a great extent, represented in terms of action. Consider the following example, taken from Piaget's observations of his seven-month-old son (p. 22):

> 'Laurent . . . loses a cigarette box which he has just grasped and swung to and fro. Unintentionally he drops it outside his visual field. He then immediately brings his hand before his eyes and looks at it for a long time with an expression of surprise, disappointment, something like an expression of its disappearance. But far from considering the loss as irremediable, he begins again to swing his hand, although it is empty. After this he looks at it once more! For anyone who has seen this act and the child's expression, it is impossible not to interpret such behavior as an attempt to make the object come back. Such an observation . . . places in full light the true *nature of the object peculiar to this stage: a mere extension of the action.'*

Several months later, action and object are not so closely tied. Earlier, the child would not show signs of missing an object when it was removed – unless he had already begun reaching for it. But later he will cry and search for an object which is presented for a moment and then hidden, even if he had not begun to reach for it. He no longer repeats a movement to restore the object, but seems to have an inner image of it. Development seems to go from a direct momentary prehensive definition of an object to a definition which is increasingly less reliant on action and more reliant upon visual representation (although certain basic characteristics of visual representation are, of course, built-in at birth).

With age, visual imagery seems to play a more and more important role. There is a considerable literature on children's use of imagery. This literature points to interesting conclusions about differences between children and adults in use of imagery:

1 children use more *imagery* in carrying out intellectual tasks;
2 their imagery is more *particularistic*, rather than generic and schematic;
3 children's images seem to have *greater vividness and detail.*

In the book, *Studies in Cognitive Growth*, 1966, Bruner and his co-workers report a number of studies carried out at the Harvard Center for Cognitive Studies documenting the use of imagery by children in intellectual tasks, and the shift with age from visual to linguistic means of dealing with these tasks. For example, if children are given a collection of pictures to be sorted into categories, the younger children sort on the basis of visual features, such as colour, size, pattern, and so on, while the older children sort on the basis of some superordinate linguistic concept. A 6 year old may group together *boat, ruler, doll, bicycle, scissors, saw, shoe, gloves, barn, candle, pie, nails, taxi* because: 'Some are red, some are gold, and some are yellow. One is white, some are brown, and some are blue.' Or he may group together *screw, ruler, nails, candle, hammer, taxi, coat, scissors, sword, bicycle* because: 'They have a part that you get dressed with, or they have holes in them, or you use them for tools, taxi goes with bicycle.' By age eight the picture is different. Bruner reports:

> 'Increasingly with development the child isolates one or more attributes that are common to all the items in the group: "They are all tools," or "You can eat with them," or "They can all move," and so on'.
>
> (pp. 83–84, 1966).

The child may be so struck by vivid perceptual details which attract him from moment to moment that he is prevented from discerning common features. Bruner suggests that the growth of linguistic skills gradually allows the child to code and compare attributes of objects verbally, thus freeing him from the momentary perceptual impact of one attribute or another.

The picture is not as simple as this, however. Note that both 6 and 8 year olds have well-developed linguistic systems, but their means for sorting pictures into categories are quite different. Simply having language is not enough: something else must change with growth. The old 'nature–nurture' debate rages strongly in this domain, and we are far from clear answers. The Americans and the Russians tend to stress the role of training and instruction in cognitive development: whereas Piaget and his school stress the role of naturally developing cognitive growth as the child interacts with his environment. Bruner's book suggests that children must be trained – chiefly through formal school instruction – to use language in ways which free them from attending to concrete, perceptual attributes of things. In regard to the picture-sorting task, for example, he says that the shift from the use of perceptual cues to more abstract, superordinate grouping criteria 'is *not* a universal property of "growing up" ' (p. 85, 1966). A number of the experiments in *Studies in Cognitive Growth* were carried out in a variety of cultural settings, leading to the conclusion that:

> 'the "natural" terminus of growth depends to a very considerable extent on the pattern imposed by the culture. The techniques used [here] have, in modified form, been used in studies of children in Alaska, Mexico, and Senegal . . . and it is plain that school children in Dakar or Mexico City look very much like the school children of [suburban Boston]. But it is equally plain that the village child of rural Mexico and the unschooled Wolof of Senegal seem very different . . . much more perceptually oriented.
>
> (Bruner *et al.*, p. 85, 1966)

Bruner *et al.* thus suggest that the school is a very important determiner of the use of language to facilitate cognitive growth. In school children must learn to use language in the absence of immediate context. This is true especially of learning to read and write, but it applies to a broader range of linguistic tasks which a child must learn to perform in a school setting. Bruner's cross-cultural studies suggest that the sort of intellectual training a child receives is more important than the particular language he happens to speak – as far as the general course of his cognitive growth is concerned. [. . .]

Another important consequence of the use of language is that the child does not have to perform direct tests to acquire knowledge. By dealing with a problem verbally, he can act on *possible information* in addition to actual information — that is, he can eliminate possibilities through reasoning, and can devise intelligent tests of a situation to replace random probing or trial-and-error.

We still do not have sufficient information, however, to determine the extent to which such reasoning abilities require language or schooling. We must know much more about the level of intellectual development reached by individuals deprived of language or deprived of formal education. The work of Piaget's school strongly suggests that language more often *reflects* than determines cognitive development. He and his colleagues have made careful attempts to train children in problem solving by teaching them new ways of talking about particular tasks and concepts. [. . .] The general finding has been that special linguistic training will be of no avail to a child unless his level of cognitive development has already reached the point at which it can embrace the relevant concepts represented by the words. [. . .]

In *Studies in Cognitive Growth*, Bruner discusses five possible sources of language-influenced intellectual development:

1 Words can serve as 'invitations to form concepts.' That is, the very occurrence of unfamiliar words stimulates the child to discover the meanings of those words.
2 Dialogue between adult and child can serve to orient and educate the child, providing an important source of experience and knowledge.
3 School creates the need for new uses of language — particularly context-free and elaborated uses.
4 Scientific concepts are developed in a culture and are conveyed verbally.
5 The occurrence of conflict between modes of representation can be a source of intellectual development.

We have touched upon these major issues briefly. These five aspects of language use in cognitive development vary with culture and social class, interact with one another, and can influence intelligence in many ways. Given these multifarious questions about the role of language in human behavior, we must, of course, accept the platitude that language is an important component of the psychological nature of man. But we are still a long way from understanding the specific aspects and functions of this component in all of human behaviour and cognition. [. . .]

References

Bruner, J. S. *et al.* (eds.), *Studies in Cognitive Growth*, New York, John Wiley, 1966.

13 Mathematics? I speak it fluently

David Pimm

Source: specially written for this volume

<<<<<<<<<<<<<<<<<<<<<<<<<<<<<<<<<<<<<<<<<<<<<<<<<<<<<<<

Introduction

As teachers, our primary concern should be encouraging and improving the communication of mathematical meanings, both between teacher and pupil, but also among pupils themselves. Such communication about a situation or an idea can be verbal, pictorial or in mathematical symbols, where I assume the latter two to be written. Mathematical ideas are often conveyed using a specialised, highly condensed symbol system which attempts to reflect relationships among the ideas by means of relationships among the symbols. In so doing, the symbol system acts as a kind of filter, dispensing with all but the essential elements involved, as by no means all the relationships among the ideas can be simultaneously represented. The pupils must therefore come to understand this filtering process and become confident users of it.

Thus we can see the dual nature of mathematics, at once medium and message. Any mathematics classroom will provide many examples of the medium influencing, and sometimes distorting, the intended message. As a consequence, one role for any maths teacher is the encouragement of fluency, both oral and written, in the language of mathematics. But that the emphasis must always remain on meaningful communication of experiences and ideas is the main point of this introduction.

I want to take the commonly heard statement that mathematics *is* a language as a starting point for this essay and explore in part what arises if this claim is taken seriously. It could be taken to mean that mathematical language is a part of English (or French, German, etc.). Another interpretation could be that it is a universal shorthand, while a third might be that maths is a language in its own right. However you interpret it, I think the main point for the teaching of mathematics is the importance of meaning to mathematical activity, rather than the mere manipulation of symbols to which it so often degenerates. Therefore the aim of mathematical language should be to help construct, express and communicate these mathematical meanings. I hope this point will become clearer through the examples as the chapter unfolds.

My approach throughout is to look to natural language itself for certain key ideas which we can then try to identify within mathematics itself. As a brief overview of what is to come, the second section focuses on the basic notions of *vocabulary* and *grammar,* and possible differences in these regards between what I shall contrast as ordinary English and mathematical English. Moving away from surface features, I shall look at metaphor, a common yet powerful phenomenon in ordinary English. Does it arise in mathematics, and if so what are some of the consequences? In the last section, I deal with the question of the readability of mathematical prose. Many children's difficulties with mathematics may be due more to the complexity of wording of written material than to the express mathematical task being posed or explained.

In this introduction, I have tried to provide some idea of what this chapter contains as well as a sense of some more general questions which can be posed concerning the role of language in mathematics. This discussion is by no means exhaustive. I have, for example, made no reference to the increasingly vexed and important question of children for whom English is a second language. Any reader who wishes to pursue further one of these areas may care to consult the article by Austin and Howson listed in the references which reviews much of the literature on the topic of language and mathematics.

Mathematical English and ordinary English

What does it mean to say that mathematics is a language and how does it differ from English? If it is a shorthand, a shorthand is learned as a language, and not just translation, for you can't translate shorthand without learning the language. Does it make sense to refer to mathematics as a language in its own right? Is it not merely English with the addition of a few specialised terms, such as any professional group might employ? Most mathematical classes actually take place in a mixture of ordinary English and a mathematical English in which ordinary words are used with a specialised meaning (Kane, 1968). It is important to distinguish these as failure to do so can result in incongruous errors.

For example, in response to 'What is the difference between 30 and 7?' answers often include '30 is a big number and 7 is a small number' or '30 is even while 7 is odd'. Halving, indicating a process of division into two (not necessarily equal) pieces allows us to speak of (and ask for!) 'the larger half'. Many confusions can occur as a result of differing linguistic usage with the teacher, most often, speaking mathematical English, while the student interprets it as ordinary English. Mathematics is notorious for attaching specialised meanings to everyday words, words which already have meanings. Thus one set of problems arise from two people using the same words but understanding different things by it.

Mathematics, when written, often employs its own symbols (e.g. $2 + 3 = 5$) yet, when spoken, comes out in English sentences. There are conventions developed over the centuries governing the construction of symbolic mathematical sentences. In what ways do they differ from the structure of English? Are there many examples of conflict? For instance, we write $8 - 4$ but sometimes say 'four from eight' where the written left-to-right order is the opposite of the spoken order. (Another example of this is seventeen for 17, where the seven comes first, compared with twenty-seven for 27). This can cause particular problems when tens and units are reached, for example

$$38$$
$$\underline{-\ 14}$$

The direction of the operation must be indicated (top to bottom or conversely, rather than left to right) for if you mix both expressions ('eight take away four' and 'four from eight') you will only encourage the children's natural tendency to take the smaller from the larger. This problem becomes acute with

$$34$$
$$\underline{-\ 18}$$

With corresponding addition problems the choice is irrelevant due to commutativity of addition which only encourages the problem.

A second difficulty thus arises from the lack of synonyms in mathematical language. Many different processes and operations in the real world come under the one heading 'subtraction', for example, as a result of the filtering process I mentioned in the first section. Many different English words and phrases have a single mathematical expression, as all the differences reflected in the English have been filtered out. As further instances of how the richness (and structure) of English is not necessarily a useful guide to its mathematical equivalent, consider some of the ways we speak about basic arithmetic operations in English. (I shall not concern myself here with words like *more, extra, altogether,* which seem to indicate particular operations).

1 *Addition: 3 + 2*
This can be rendered in English as: the sum of three and two, add three and two, add two to three, two added to three, three plus two. Only the last version is a straightforward, term for term transliteration preserving the order of the mathematical symbols.

2 *Subtraction: 3 − 2*
The difference between three and two (but *not* subtract two and three), take two from three, three take away two, two from three, three minus two.

3 *Multiplication: 3 × 2*
Three times two (two is the operator, three the operand), multiply three by two (the reverse), the product of three and two, take two three times.

4 *Division: 2 ÷ 3, 3$\overline{)2}$, $\frac{2}{3}$*
Three into two, divide two into three (i.e. three pieces), divide two by three, two over three.

Notice that we have three different ways of symbolising the same operation, yet with entirely different orders. We have broken with the left to right order for our notation when we use $\frac{2}{3}$. (Something more involved has happened since from a verb phrase, we now see a noun, a number. What sense can be made of $2 \div 3, \frac{2}{3}$?)

In each case, the English has at least two forms where the order of the numbers is reversed. Unfortunately only two of the operations, addition and multiplication, are commutative, that is, the order of operation is unimportant with regard to the result. For many children, however, the other two operations, subtraction and division also only have one permissible order: subtract smaller from larger, divide smaller into larger.

As a final instance of ways in which mathematical English and ordinary English differ, consider the grammatical function of number words themselves. Cardinal numbers in everyday usage seem to function more as adjectives in that they describe one property of a set. But in mathematical English, numbers function as nouns, entities with properties of their own for instance, *odd, square, prime*. This confusion can be seen in multiplication tables where both arise together. One four is four, two fours are eight and so on. We have an entity, a 'four', of which we can have any number. Notice this is usually called the four times table, whereas the four times table might more logically run four ones are four, four twos are eight and so on.

The third main point will comprise the remainder of this section and concerns the differences in various conventions employed in mathematical symbolism, differences within the supposedly consistent language of mathematics itself. My focus is on the symbols themselves, but also on the uses to which they are put as well as the conventions governing that use. Mathematical symbols occur predominantly on paper and hence are two-dimensional, spatial entities which have different meanings dependent on their position in relation to other symbols. Thus the 2 in 23 differs in meaning from the 2 in 32, as does the 3 in $\frac{3}{4}$ from the 3 in $\frac{4}{3}$. Possible relationships among symbols include above/below, to the left/right of and not many more.

Orientation in the plane is also important in the interpretation of symbols, (at the most basic level, that of distinguishing between 6 and 9 or 2 and 5). I was once in a classroom talking with a 6 year old. He had just drawn a 7 on his paper and commented that to him it looked like a seven, but to the girl opposite it looked like a nose! Yet children see numbers in all directions and angles, for example 8 on a bus, 8 on a gatepost (*see Higginson*, 1980).

Consider powers such as 2^3. A common misinterpretation of 2^3 is 2×3, fairly reasonably as the operation does involve multiplication (in fact, 2×3 is three times two as opposed to 2^3, multiply two by itself three times). With powers, in most books, there is a size relationship between the numerals (the exponent is smaller). Thus relative size is another possible relationship among symbols. Compare the requests, 'draw a larger 2' and 'which is larger, 2 or 5?'. At some level, a distinction between the symbol and the concept needs to be drawn, yet it is difficult to indicate a desirable level of awareness at all clearly.

Symbols can only be confidently interpreted within a given context. Sometimes the same spatial relationship reflects a different meaning according to that context. In algebra, for example, juxtaposition of certain symbols denotes multiplication, whereas in arithmetic it denotes place value. What is $3pq$ if $p = 4$ and $q = 2$? In arithmetical terms the answer would be 342, but in algebra a different convention provides with the interpretation $3 \times 4 \times 2$ which is 24.

We know multiplication is commutative, so $ab = ba$, yet $23 \neq 32$. Our conventions have changed regarding the interpretation of symbols yet you often hear comments to the effect that, 'algebra is just like arithmetic only you are operating with letters rather than numbers.' We need to ensure that the original convention is made very explicit and secondly that we are changing it (and are free to do so) in algebra. Although $23y$ does not mean $2 \times 3 \times y$.

Another example comes from juxtaposition and the often subtle gap relationship involved. Consider the sequence 891011. Why is 11 seen as *a* number and not 'one one' or even 'two ones' (*see* Higginson again for a lovely exploration of this point). Initially, number meant *digit*. Yet in algebra when we refer to an entry in a matrix, for example, a, we revert to 'a one one' and not 'a eleven'. A further cause for concern comes from reading decimals aloud. 2.57 is often referred to as two point fifty seven. One not unreasonable conclusion from this is that two point fifty seven is bigger than two point seven since fifty seven is bigger than seven. As a final example of symbol interpretation, look at the complexity of place-value notation. The meaning we attach to each digit depends precisely on its location within a string of digits. Yet even within the context of arithmetic itself we write 32 to imply the invisible power of ten and addition, $32 = 3 \times 10 + 2$, whereas we also write $2\frac{5}{8}$, where we just imply addition.

So far, I have been dealing primarily with the vocabulary of mathematics, both its place within spoken English and its written, symbolic form. Any mathematical expression can be written out as a sentence of English and this is one way to gain an appreciation of exactly how compact is our contemporary notation. But, just as knowing French is much more than knowing the contents of a French dictionary, knowledge of mathematical language is far more than an awareness of individual symbols and their meanings. One of the essential characteristics of doing mathematics is not only *forming* grammatical mathematical sentences which describe something, but also *transforming* them to gain further knowledge of the situation. Mathematics is action, it is operating on the given to produce new things. The most commonly asked question in a maths class is, I suspect, 'how do I *do* this one?'. Listening to a child performing (!) a long multiplication, one hears, 'I do this ... then I go like this ...'. Any algorithm in arithmetic consists of an ordered sequence of such actions.

But maths, as a transformational activity, comes into its own with algebra. So often, sadly, learning algebra consists solely of learning the appropriate 'moves' to apply in particular situations, and how to discriminate among different situations. Even with a verbal arithmetic problem, the question often asked is 'is it an add or a times?' What happens is that there are a few basic sequences of operations to apply and all that is required is a cue to clue pupils in to which one. Because meaning, in the sense of an understanding of the situation which gave rise to the problem, is so often absent for pupils in mathematics, it cannot guide them (as it does in English) to 'correct' sentence construction. They have to fall back on trying to learn 'the rules' directly. In learning to speak English, they have acquired the rules governing formation of a question, a negative, the passive construction and so on without having to be taught them. Algebraic transformations are analogous to some degree, but are taught consciously. Because the manipulations are necessarily transacted at the symbolic level, most of the guidance tends to be phrased in terms of how to obtain the desired surface features. For example:

1 Take it over to the other side and change the sign.
2 Cross multiply.
3 Move it one space to the left. This implies an absolute spacing on paper, so we know how far 'one space' is.
4 To multiply by ten, add a nought. But adding a nought doesn't change anything?
5 Put down a zero, carry the one down (over).
6 You must always do the top what you do to the bottom. One instance would be

$$\frac{xc}{yc} = \frac{x}{y}, \quad \text{yet} \quad \frac{x+c}{y+c} \neq \frac{x}{y}$$

$$\text{However} \quad \frac{x+x}{y+y} = \frac{x}{y}$$

(where we broke the injunction), while

$$\frac{xx}{yy} \neq \frac{x}{y}$$

7 Turn it upside down and multiply.
8 Collect all the xs on one side of the equation. Yet see Brown (1976) for an exploration of a situation where he deliberately ignores this maxim.

I'm sure you can come up with other examples. These are all instructions (actions, note) on how to move symbols around on a piece of paper, guides of greater or lesser efficacy, with no indication as to why they work. Nor is there any feeling for what the effect is of these transformations at the level of meaning, which is after all what should be guiding these manipulations. In other words, we are unconscious of changing the underlying reality which these symbols represent as well.

What are the transformations linking $7 - \square = 4$ to $4 + \square = 7$? One possible sequence could be:

1 add $\square$ to each side,
2 recombine via distributive law for addition,
3 if $a = b$, then $b = a$.

Difficulties arise with 1 as pupils say 'but we don't know what □ is. How can we add it to each side?' and 3 as pupils are so used to seeing derivations which end up '. . . , so $x = 2$,' when confronted with '. . . , so $2 = x$,' they declare 'but you've solved for 2, not x'. Reading left to right and word order mattering for meaning (e.g. Mary hit John *v.* John hit Mary) may be powerful reasons underlying difficulty in grasping this sort of order invariance of meaning.

In conclusion, in this section I have outlined three possible sources of difficulty from the interaction of ordinary English with mathematical English, at the level of individual words and conflicting meanings, at the level of grammar and conflicts within the mathematical symbolism itself. There are undoubtedly many more instances of these phenomena and I would be most interested to hear of them.

Metaphor

Moving away from the question of grammatical structure, what are some constructions, figures of speech which make natural language so expressive? Metaphor comes to mind as a technique for creating new meanings, often by transfer of meaning by means of an analogy. One's initial inclination is to view mathematical language as clear and precise, while metaphors seem fuzzy, and, at best, suggestive. One could be forgiven for thinking them unsuited to mathematical work. I think, however, there are important cases of metaphor to be found in arithmetic and algebra and that metaphor is as central to the expression of mathematical meaning as it is to the expression of meaning in ordinary language (*see* Lakoff, 1980).

Before trying to identify instances of metaphor in mathematics, let us look at a straightforward everyday example: George is a lion. There are a number of senses in which this could be meant. For instance he may be brave, he may have a tremendous head of hair ('a mane'), he may roar a lot, or some combination of these. What is important to realise is that not everything which is the case about lions will be transferable. The context of use will usually determine which features are intended to be carried over and which are not. We will also understand or make sense of the statement 'George is a lion' very differently according to the situation. Often the force of a metaphoric statement comes from the strength of the claim, that is 'George *is* a lion', compared with 'George *is like* a lion' (simile).

So if we are looking for metaphor in mathematics, we need statements of equality where the two things being equated are not the same. Then we can look at which features are being transferred and which are not. My first example comes from arithmetic. Contrast the statement $3 - 2 = 1$ with $2 - 3 = -1$. The latter involves an unexamined metaphor which leads us to presume that the meanings of certain symbols, for instance, 2, $-$, $=$, are the same as had been used previously. There are however conflicts which often arise as they are not the same. The metaphor involved identifies 2 with the directed number $+ 2$ (just as George was identified with the lion) and so on, very soon after the introduction

145

of directed numbers. The same notation is used for subtraction of directed numbers as for subtraction of counting (unsigned) numbers. But the results disagree, for whereas $2 - 3$ is impossible within the counting numbers, $(+2) - (+3) = -1$ within the system of directed numbers. The problem of taking a metaphor literally, which I shall examine for this example in the next couple of paragraphs, is increased by its existence being concealed through using the same symbols.

Discussions of metaphor often hinge on the distinction between literal and metaphorical meaning. Let us look at the basic situation with the counting numbers and the operations on them. From where does the meaning arise? One approach, rich in meaning, is that counting numbers arise as possible answers to the question 'how many', addition from conflating two sets of distinct elements, subtraction from take away, multiplication from repeated addition and division from equal sharing. Yet $- 1$ makes no sense as an answer to 'how many', any more than $+ 2$ does. $- 1$ is often referred to as 'minus one', a verb without a subject. Yet previously, in all earlier work, the verb had always been flanked on both sides by a number. We have switched systems while keeping the language the same, yet not all of the properties of the old system are carried over by the metaphor $2 = + 2$, etc. particularly not the specific meanings involved. The central issue is that although the symbolic statements equated by the metaphor may behave in analogous ways, their meanings are not compatible.

Consider the case of multiplication of directed numbers (integers). I can find no corresponding real-world situation to which we can refer. One force of making $+ 2$ into 2 is that it permits the literal meaning of multiplication of counting numbers to be used metaphorically (*transferring* an old meaning to *construct* a new meaning) with integers thus $+ 2 \times + 3$ takes on the meaning $2 \times + 3$ or $+ 3 + + 3$. Having made sense of $+$ in terms of movement to the right on a number line (a fairly surface meaning) we obtain $+ 6$. $+ 2 \times - 3$ is acceptable also without too much stretching (assuming our view of addition works on all the integers). $- 3 \times + 2$ we can approach by means of commutativity, though justification of this is flimsy due to the absence of any situational meaning guiding our actions. What can we do with $- 2 \times - 3$? Our metaphor cannot help us here and this is, I believe, one of the causes of problems of multiplying negative numbers together.

Turning to the algebra of indices produces further instances of precisely this extension of meaning, in one direction to negative numbers and in the other to fractional numbers. a^2, a^3, . . . can be seen as a shorthand notation for repeated multiplication (just as multiplication itself started out life as repeated addition) where the index is the number (in the sense of 'how many') of times it is to be repeated. What can be made of a^{-1} in this light? What sort of statement is $a^{-1} = \frac{1}{a}$? The metaphor $2 = + 2$ gives us $a^2 = a^{+2}$ and then, presuming we wish to preserve the law of exponents for counting numbers, namely that $a^m . a^n = a^{m+n}$, we can give a meaning to a^0, a^{-1}, ... But just as with falling back on commutativity of the extended operation of multiplication, the question *why* should we accept this as justification is a difficult one to answer. In the same way $a^{\frac{1}{2}} = \sqrt{a}$ can extend the range of indices to fractions and then in a double move, produce $a^{-\frac{1}{2}} = \frac{1}{\sqrt{a}}$ and so on that is, allowing directed fractional numbers as indices).

Why is this a problem? If the metaphoric quality of certain conceptual extensions in mathematics is not made clear to children, then specific meanings and observations (whether intuitive or consciously formulated) about the original setting will be carried over to the new setting where they are often inappropriate. The identification, which is at the basis of the metaphor, guarantees only that certain structural properties are preserved in the extended system, not the meaning. Consider the observation that subtraction produces something less than either of the two starting numbers. Then think about $4 - (-2) = 6$. Or, for example, that multiplying two whole numbers together results in a number larger than each of the original pair. This is a correct concommitant of viewing multiplication as repeated addition. This no longer holds with fractions. Why do we call $\frac{2}{3} \times \frac{4}{3}$ multiplication anyway? What is the root meaning of this operation? The extension of concepts in this fashion can result in the destruction of meaning, presuming no distinction is made between the literal and metaphorical use, because the confusion arising from seeing such (often unanalysed) truths fail contaminates not only the extended system but also the one from which it grew. The old concept resists expansion precisely because it is the literal, and hence, the most basic meaning. There is no trace in the symbolism to indicate that a metaphor is in use, the same symbols and words are used throughout. A metaphor skims over a lot and a polished notation permits this riding on the surface. If students are not used to mathematics making sense, then having tried and failed to make literal sense of a statement they are likely to give up. But this experience also undermines their faith in situations where the original meaning is the most sensible one.

[For an extended version of this section, *see* 'Metaphor and Analogy in Mathematics', *Journal For the Learning of Mathematics,* vol. 1, no. 3, March 1981.]

Other work on language and mathematics

Consideration of mathematics as language has almost always focused on the obvious interaction of English with mathematics, namely text books in general and verbal problems in particular. An example of the latter would be, 'John has seven sweets, Sally has nineteen. How many more does Sally have than John?' The unquestionable difficulty pupils often encounter reading mathematical prose in texts in general (at all age levels), and in contending with such problems in particular has often been remarked upon and, as a result, verbal problems have been singled out as an item of research interest as if it formed a coherent topic. (Though, in fact, they cohere only in the uncommon form, namely prose, of problem presentation). This provides another instance of the problem due to the filtering from many forms of expression in English to one in mathematics.

The adopted approach to both problems has been to explain why certain passages in texts or certain problems are difficult to read or interpret in terms of the construct of text readability. As this area forms the overlap of reading and mathematics, and readability measures abound for ordinary prose, the first step was an attempt to modify the ubiquitous 'cloze' procedure in an attempt to measure the reading difficulty level. I suspect this process will be familiar to you, but there is a difficulty in applying it to mathematics, as the redundancy patterns are very different and what constitutes a unit of mathematical prose is a very difficult question.

There is also a reasonable, general assumption that a poor reader is going to have problems reading mathematics — although the extent to which the converse is true remains unclear. Certainly the intervention strategies in this area have focused on improving specific reading skills. An approach to difficulty in work problems themselves (particularly arithmetic ones) has involved an attempt to find a number of contributory factors (both linguistic and non-linguistic) which would allow the difficulty level of a problem to be predicted.

Among examples of the sorts of things the researchers thought might be relevant can be listed the length of the problem, the number of words and sentences, the average sentence length, and some grammatical measures — for instance, the presence of relative clauses, uncommon question forms, unusual vocabulary. In some cases up to seventy different contributory factors were examined at one time! It is, however, assumed that the variation in a problem's difficulty is within the problem itself and that an objective level of difficulty can be assigned to any given problem. No discussion or importance is assigned to the strategies the students actually use! The concern is merely whether or not they correctly solve the problem so as to enable average success rates to be calculated for a group of problems.

One general belief is that a straightforward translation technique from English into arithmetic equations is the method to follow. As a result of this there has been a lot of teaching based on verbal cues to be used as clues. Once again we see surface features being used as a guide for action. 'If the word *more* appears, then the problem is a take away'. How can this be reconciled with 'Charles earns four times more than Steve?' Pearla Nesher and her co-workers have investigated the topic thoroughly (1975, 1976, 1977), and come to the conclusion that it is impossible to make a one-to-one translation from ordinary language to arithmetical language solely on a linguistic level. Thus it is inappropriate to teach by means of the presence or absence of certain key words. Once again we see a move away from the surface level to a focusing on the meaning inherent in the situation behind the problem. This is essential to a successful *mathematical* formulation of the problem, one which depends on knowledge of the real world and how to represent it mathematically as well as how to mirror the relevant relationships through the choice of an appropriate mathematical model. If you wish to follow up the brief discussion of the work on text readability, I suggest you write for a copy of Rothery *et al., Children Reading Maths*, 1980.

Summary and conclusions

In this article I have tried to outline some of the many fascinating interactions that there are between mathematics and ordinary language, as well as what sense might be made of the claim that mathematics is a language. There are many different levels on which one can operate. One is to focus on the particular English words which crop up in mathematics classes (and the uncommon meanings they have there). Another involves the different symbols we employ as part of the representation system of mathematics and the conventions implicit in our use of them both in understanding them as they stand (such as place-value notation) and the transformations of mathematical phrases and sentences in arithmetical computation and algebra. A third is to focus not on the words (or symbols), nor on the *grammar* of mathematics at all, but on the meanings that we are trying to convey through our language and how that meaning changes and expands even though we may use the same words and symbols (the examples of subtraction and multiplication were discussed).

Metaphors deny distinctions between things; problems often arise from taking metaphors too literally. Because unexamined metaphors lead us to assume the identity of non-identical things, conflicts can arise which can only be explained by understanding the metaphor which requires its recognition as such. Teachers will often cease to use the term consciously in a metaphorical way when their concept is an expanded one. This will not mirror the situation in most of their pupils' minds. The unexplained extension of concepts can too often result in the destruction rather than an expansion of meaning. It is important to *tell* children when we are using words with either an expanded or restricted meaning and we underestimate children's ability to understand that words can have different meanings in different contexts.

Lastly I discussed the question of reading mathematical prose and the particular problems involved with mathematical (especially arithmetical) problems posed in ordinary language. Many children's difficulties with mathematics may be due more to the complexity of wording of written material, rather than the mathematical task being requested. This is something which has attracted a good deal of attention of people professing an interest in the area of language and mathematics. In fact, the two are often equated, though I hope that this is a limited view and there are other possibilities of importance and interest. Lastly, may I make a plea for you, as teachers of mathematics, to listen with an open ear for what your children are trying to say. It is surprising how often there is a comprehensible basis for mistakes and misunderstandings and one which has a linguistic origin.

Bibliography

Austin, J. L. and Howson, A. G., 'Language and Mathematical Education' *Educational Studies in Mathematics,* vol. 10, pp. 161–197, 1979.

149

Brown, S. I., 'From the Golden Rectangle and Fibonaca to Pedagogy and Problem-Solving', *Mathematics Teacher*, vol. 69, no. 3, pp. 180–188, March 1976.

Higginson, W., 'Berry Undecided: A Digital Dialogue', *Mathematics Teaching*, vol. 91, pp. 8–13, June 1980.

Kane, R. B., 'The Readability of Mathematical English', *Journal of Research in Science Teaching*, vol. 5, pp. 296–298, 1968.

Lakoff, G., *Metaphors We Live By*, University of Chicago, Chicago, 1980.

Nesher, P. A., Three Determinants of Difficulty in Verbal Arithmetic Problems', *Educational Studies in Mathematics*, vol. 7, pp. 369–388, 1976.

Nesher, P. A. and Katriel, T., 'A Semantic Analysis of Addition and Subtraction Word Problems in Arithmetic', *Educational Studies in Mathematics*, vol. 8, pp. 257–269, 1977.

Nesher, P. A. and Teubal, E., 'Verbal Cues as an Interfering Factor in Verbal Problem-Solving', *Educational Studies in Mathematics*, vol. 6, pp. 41–51, 1975.

Pimm, D. J., 'Metaphor and Analogy in Mathematics', *For the Learning of Mathematics*, vol. 1, no. 3, 1981.

Rothery, A. *et al.*, *Children Reading Maths,* a working paper of the Language and Reading in Mathematics group. Obtainable from A. Rothery, Dept. of Mathematics, Worcester College of Higher Education (unpublished).

SECTION 4 Some particular topics

>>>

Introduction

Many of the ideas about developing mathematical thinking that this book and its associated course are seeking to convey are implicit in many articles that have been written over the years concerning the teaching of particular mathematical topics. This section is a collection of some of these.

Between them they describe a wide range of activities which children can engage in and discuss with each other and their teachers. Some of them are also concerned with the transition from doing the activity to recording it in some way. A key notion that several of those articles use in this connection is 'informal mathematics'. By this is usually meant almost any means of calculating other than by using one of the standard procedures. Calculating $35 - 19$ by reasoning 'if it were $35 - 20$ the difference would be 15. The answer I need is one more than that, so the answer is 16' is an example of a piece of informal mathematics. Such mathematics is not usually taught, but is commonly used. Several of the chapters suggest that these informal methods should be built upon whenever possible. This is particularly true of the first five chapters. The remaining eight are more concerned with different kinds of investigation.

In Chapter 14, the first of the four chapters that are particularly concerned with the role of informal mathematics, Kathy Hebbeler gives an account of her study of young children's addition. She found that in this respect children were 'good informal mathematicians' before they ever entered a classroom. Herbert Ginsburg found that children who were having great difficulty with formal mathematics were often surprisingly capable at the informal level, and in chapter 15, he describes four such children. Both chapters advocate building on informal methods whenever a standard (formal) method is the ultimate goal.

In chapter 16, Stuart Plunkett questions the central role that the standard methods of adding, subtracting, multiplying and dividing play in the curriculum and proposes a way of teaching basic arithmetic that lays much less stress on the usual formal written procedures so that informal methods are used whenever they are appropriate.

The last of these four chapters describes the way in which children in a Russian classroom are helped to tease out the formal arithmetic it is necessary to do in order to solve word problems, by coming to understand just what the problems are about.

Chapter 18 is the first of the chapters primarily concerned with the role of investigation in developing mathematical thinking and in it Alistair McIntosh suggests a new approach to 'tables', in which they would be seen as patterns with rectangles that children can explore. In chapter 19 Daphne Kerslake discusses the teaching of time in which a number of possible investigations are suggested. Chapter 20, by David Hale, is concerned with algebra, in which he advocates that the foundations of algebra are most usefully laid by looking for number patterns of various kinds. Chapter 21 by David Fielker and chapter 22 by Marie Kuper and Marion Walter, both feature ideas for investigations in geometry. Chapter 23 is an account, by Christine Billinge, of a number of different investigations of spatial patterns. In the final chapter in this section, Seymour Papert describes what children could do when given the opportunity of trying to make a computer work for them. He argues forcibly that working with computers is a very powerful means of developing mathematical thinking.

14 Young children's addition

Kathy Hebbeler

Source: Journal of Children's Mathematical Behaviour, vol. 1, no.4, pp. 108–121.

A 4 year old girl is playing with coloured beads. The girl has two red beads in her hand and five more on the floor. The girl's older brother asks her how many she has altogether. The girl responds by placing the beads in a row and counting them off, '1, 2, 3, 4, . . .'. She tells him she has seven.

This story is hypothetical but it does not seem too far removed from the simple kinds of quantitative problems which must present themselves to young children as part of their everyday lives. One mother has recorded how her young son delighted in creating and solving mathematical problems for himself.

> 'For instance, when there were apples in a problem, he would convert his fingers to apples. He would thus use the fingers for any objects mentioned in the problem. . . The next stage of abstraction consisted of his counting on his fingers only the numbers to be added. He would wave his hand and say: "I have three apples there: now, here are four more (his fingers); three (over there), four, five, etc." (pointing to his fingers).'
>
> (Court, 1925, pp. 79–80)

This little boy was 4 years old at the time. He had not been to school but he had learned how to solve simple addition problems.

Although all children may not know how to find sums at such a young age, they do not wait for a teacher to hand them their first text book before they start acquiring mathematical knowledge. Indeed, in many important ways, what children learn in school about mathematics is not the beginning but the continuation of the development of mathematical thinking. Some aspects of the preschool child's quantitative skills are already well known. Young children are actively involved with quantity in the world around them: they count, they divide wholes into parts, they add objects to make 'more'. Through actions such as these, children acquire basic knowledge about the effects of certain operations upon the objects around them (*see* Ginsburg, 1977, for a review of research on young children's mathematics).

When the child enters school, he or she will begin to learn mathematics in a more formal way set apart from the context of daily activities. Here the child is introduced to mathematical symbolism such as written numerals (which many children know before beginning school) and signs such as 'plus' (+) and 'minus' (−) to be performed on the quantities those numerals represent. In school too, children's counting skills are expanded and perfected.

Hopefully, what the child learns in school will be useful for solving numerical problems encountered out of school. While many of these problems could be solved by counting − something the child has known how to do for years − it is not a particularly efficient strategy. Written numbers and memorised sums can make calculating an easier process. Part of the development of mathematical thinking is the acquisition of more sophisticated procedures for dealing with quantities. The child's informal procedures are gradually replaced by the strategies children learn in school. Numerous observations and interviews suggest that the child's informal counting procedures predominate as a reliable method of solution for a number of years after the child enters school (Ginsburg, 1977). Observations also suggest that children often have difficulty in integrating their informal procedures with school learning: many children seem to be unaware that there is a connection between the two.

In order to present to children the mathematics of the classroom in a way most compatible with what they already understand, we need to know what children learn about quantities and relations before the onset of schooling. This study looks at the development of one mathematical skill: the solution of addition story problems. It is an investigation of how young children who have and who have not been instructed in mathematics perform when they are presented with tasks similar to those found in the 'problem-solving' section of any mathematics achievement test. The question asked is not only *'can pre-school children do addition problems?'*, but *'how do they do them?'* and *'what kind of mistakes do they make when they don't get a correct answer?'* Addition problems may be dealt with in any one of several ways. Young children may not have any idea of how to solve an addition problem. They generally know how to count but they may not realise that counting can be used to solve addition problems and so they may just guess. Or they may count so poorly that they come close but seldom get the problems exactly right. Or they may use methods other than counting. Children's strategies and errors are the keys to understanding their early work in arithmetic. The child's answer is the product of a complex process, and errors often give insight into that process. It is also important to consider how mathematical thinking develops. The study examines what both younger and older children do with the same problems. The development of addition problem-solving is followed from the pre-school years through second grade to learn how this process changes as children are introduced to mathematics in a school setting.

Description of study

To examine the development of the quantitive problem-solving process, 128 children were asked to solve nine addition problems. Thirty-two children were from each of the four grade levels: pre-kindergarten, first grade and second grade.

The average age of the groups ranged from 5 years 2 months for the pre-school children to 7 years 10 months for the second graders. All of the problems involved stories about animals. For example:

'The elephant and the owl went shopping. The elephant brought along five pennies and the owl brought along seven. How many pennies did they bring altogether?'

Interspersed among the addition problems were subtraction problems and problems requiring 'more' or 'less' judgements. These were included to prevent the child from blindly adopting the same operation and strategy for all the problems. As the interviewer read the problem, stuffed animals to represent the characters in the story were placed in front of the child. Half the children at each grade level were also shown objects described in the stories. Thus, for the problem above, five pennies were placed by the elephant and seven by the owl. The other half of the children saw only the animals. These two conditions of administration were used to examine how much of the children's difficulties with the problems could be attributed to a lack of representational skills. The objects should make the problem more concrete and make a strategy easier to execute as the presence of objects precludes the need for representing the quantities to be combined.

Each child was interviewed individually. After the child was read a problem and gave an answer, the interviewer asked questions about how he or she got the answer. Generally, a question such as 'How did you get that?' was sufficient to elicit a detailed description of what the child did. Sometimes, especially with the younger children, more direct questioning was required. In this case, the interviewer might suggest a method: 'Did you count?', 'Were you using your fingers?', 'Did you already know that one?'. All sessions were videotaped. The children's strategies and errors were later coded from the videotapes by two judges working independently. Reliability was high.

What young children can do

Accuracy

The pre-school children who were not shown the objects averaged 2.86 (of 9) problems correct. If the children were just responding randomly by picking any whole number from one to ten (pretesting had established that all the children could count to at least 10), the chances of getting three problems out of nine correct is 0.046. The mean score for these children does not tell the entire story. The number of problems correct ranged from 0 to 9. Some children were very good at solving addition problems while others, in fact most of the children, could hardly do any. This contrasts sharply with the performance of the pre-school children who were presented with the objects. The mean score for these children was 5.43. The difference between the two means is significant at less than 0.05. The probability of a child responding randomly and getting five problems correct is 0.0074. Even with the objects present, the variability in the children's performances is great, with the scores again ranging from 0 to 9. Most of the children solved five or more of the problems although a few children were unable to do the problems even with objects present. The way in which the objects help the children will become clear when we examine strategies and mistakes. The pre-school children's scores do show that some children understand and can solve addition problems before they have learned mathematics in a school setting. More children can do addition problems when they are given the objects to which the problems refer.

Table 1 gives the mean scores of the pre-school groups and each of the older grade levels. The scores continue to improve as children get older.

Table 1 Mean scores on addition problems

	P-K	*K*	*G*1	*G*2
No objects (*N* = 16)	2.86	6.63	6.94	8.63
Objects (*N* = 16)	5.43	7.56	8.06	8.38

By kindergarten, the children are averaging seven problems correct. After only one year of school, simple addition problems are easily understood and solved. At each of the three older grade levels, the children who saw the objects do not score significantly higher than those who did not. The older children do not need the objects nor do they benefit from having them.

Children's strategies

The methods of solution were classified as one of six possible types:

1 counted (the child counted to find the sum),
2 looked (the child looked at the objects and then answered),
3 used number fact (the child solved the problem by using a number fact, like 2 + 2),
4 guessed,
5 ambiguous,
6 no answer.

A ratio was calculated for each child as a measure of the relative use of counting and number facts. The 'counting ratio' was defined as the number of problems on which the child counted divided by the number of problems on which he used non-ambiguous strategies (#1/#1−4, 6). For the 'number-facts ratio', the number of times the child used number facts appeared in the numerator.

In regard to counting, when the youngest children are not given the objects they use their counting skills on only 37 per cent of the problems. These two groups differ significantly in their use of counting ($p < 0.02$). This was not true of other groups. Kindergarten children, whether or not they saw the objects, counted on about 70 per cent of the problems; first graders counted on about 50 per cent of the problems; and second graders on about 40 per cent. Thus, counting peaks at kindergarten and declines thereafter.

Consider now use of number facts. This means the child was able to give the sum of two or possibly three numbers without counting. Unlike the use of counting, the use of number facts continues to increase as children get older. This is expected as it is a more sophisticated problem-solving strategy than counting. The pre-school and kindergarten children make a very limited use of number facts (about 10 per cent of the problems) although some children can use them. By first grade, children make considerable use of number facts (about 40 per cent) and by second grade the use of number facts has become the predominant mean of solution of the problems (about 60 per cent). At all grade levels, the presence of the objects has no effect on the children's use of number facts. This demonstrates that it is not necessary to force children to give up counting as a strategy. They readily adopted the more efficient procedures of using number facts when they could, even though the presence of the objects would have made counting quite easy.

A more complete picture of the development of problem-solving can be obtained by examining the ratio of 'useful' strategies the children employed. The 'useful-strategy ratio' measures the total proportions of counting, number facts and looking strategies used by each of the children. Counting is slower than using a number fact but either strategy can produce the answer. Looking means the child simply looks at the representation of the problem and gives the answer. It is effective only for problems involving small numbers of objects. The pre-school children who were not shown the objects were the only group who did not employ a useful strategy on a majority of the problems. The presence of the objects seems to allow the pre-school children to understand the problem and to realise the applicability of their skills. Without the objects, many of the youngest children did not undertake any useful strategy to solve the problem. Children continue to improve as they get older and by second grade, the children are doing something that could result in a right answer on 99 per cent of the problems.

The pre-kindergarten children who did not employ useful strategies preferred another way of answering: they guessed. The mean guessing ratio for the children who did not see the objects is 0.38. This is as high as their counting ratio which means the children were just as likely to guess to find the answer as they were to count. Seven of the sixteen children guessed on four or more of the problems. Three of these guessed on eight or more problems. There were five pre-schoolers in this group who did not guess at all, so guessing is not the only thing young children do when asked to solve addition problems. It is, however, a very popular method of getting an answer when the problem is not physically represented for the child. Guessing is used very little by the kindergarten children and it is a practically non-existent strategy among the first- and second-grade children. This doesn't mean these children don't guess; it just means they have no need to on problems which are this simple for them.

Children's mistakes
One other way to understand children's problem solving is to look at the mistakes children make. Wrong answers do not necessarily mean a complete failure to

understand the problem; they could mean instead that the child counted clumsily or made use of an incorrect number fact. All children's errors were classified as one of two types: execution errors or conceptual errors. An execution error occurs when a child understands the problem but does not give the correct answer because of an error made while carrying out a reasonable strategy. Conceptual errors are more serious and mean that the child did not realise how to go about solving the problem. This distinction is essential for helping children improve their mathematics skill. A poor counter can practise counting but a child who doesn't understand the problem needs a different kind of help.

The data on the kinds of mistakes the children made can show if children understood the problems even when they didn't get the right answers. The percent of the total errors which were execution errors was calculated for each child. For this analysis, grades one and two were combined because of the small number of second-grade children who made errors. The pre-school children who were not given the objects stand apart from the other seven groups. For these children only 20 per cent of their errors are execution errors which means that 80 per cent are conceptual errors. When pre-school children see the objects, about 75 per cent of their errors involve execution. Thus, without the objects, the pre-school children do not understand the problem. With objects, they do understand. For all the other children, the overwhelming majority of the mistakes are due to the poor execution of good strategy.

Summary of results

1 Some pre-school children were able to use their informal counting skills to solve addition problems even though they had never been instructed in school mathematics. Their ability to solve problems was greatly enhanced when they were shown a physical representation of the problem. After only one year of kindergarten, the solution of simple addition problems was no mystery to most of the children and they do as well without the objects as with them.

2 The children's strategies for addition problems change drastically between the pre-school and the early school years. The kindergarten children counted more than the pre-schoolers, but after kindergarten, counting skills are used less and less. Counting is replaced by a quicker procedure: number facts. When the pre-school children don't count, they are generally doing something less useful such as guessing. When the older children don't count, they are doing something more sophisticated and efficient like using number facts. At no grade level do children make less use of number facts when given objects which could be easily counted.

3 The analysis of children's mistakes revealed that only the pre-school children in the no-objects condition made predominantly conceptual errors. The difficulty for these children in solving addition problems was in understanding the nature of the task. By contrast, the mistakes made by the other pre-schoolers and the older children resulted mostly from an incorrect execution of a good strategy.

Discussion

Children's understanding of addition seems to involve two key developments: acquisition of the requisite representational capabilities and the development of increasingly efficient strategies.

Consider first the problem of representation. The results showed that when objects are present pre-school children generally understand this kind of addition problem and solve it by use of counting skills. Schooling is not necessary for this. When preschool children are not given the objects, they are unable to conceptualise the problem and of course do not solve it. The difference between the two groups indicates that pre-school children are able to understand addition problems but that they do not yet possess the representational skills necessary for solution in the absence of the problem's objects. By kindergarten, however, mental representation of the quantities presents no difficulty: now children are as successful on addition problems without objects as with them. We do not know what is responsible for this new-found representational ability: perhaps general cognitive development, perhaps schooling, perhaps some combination of the two.

The second thing that children learn is how to use more efficient strategies. The development of problem-solving does not stop once children have learned how to find an answer. Counting is the first problem-solving strategy that children learn and it is the procedure they initially use to find solutions. Gradually, the slow counting procedures are replaced by a quicker and more efficient procedure, the use of memorised sums. The children's school or other experiences apparently provided them with sufficient practice with numbers so that they acquired a repertoire of memorised sums. These sums were not isolated bits of meaningless mathematical knowledge; the children were able to put them to good use as a strategy for solving problems. After learning how to interpret and represent addition problems children continue to improve through the acquisition of more sophisticated methods.

The purpose of mathematics instruction in school is to foster the development of mathematical thinking by helping children to achieve a greater understanding of quantitative phenomena and to learn more sophisticated procedures for dealing with quantity. To best promote that development, it is essential that the process of growth be understood. This means considering what children already know about quantity through their everyday experiences and describing precisely what school must teach. This study has shown that pre-school children do understand addition problems at least when concrete embodiments are employed. These children may need practice at using the calculation techniques of addition and at employing representation, but their spontaneous use of effective solutions procedures indicates that they do not need help in understanding the basic concept of addition.

Describing and explaining the process of mathematical development is particularly important for helping children with problems in mathematics. We need to know what most children do in order to understand how and why the child who has problems with mathematics is different and can best be helped. If a child doesn't give a correct answer for '3 + 4 =   ' or '6 + 10 =   ' or even '28 + 33 = ', is this because the child doesn't understand addition or because he or she doesn't understand the symbols and rules of written mathematics? The impressive performance of the kindergarten children, many of who had not yet learned how to do written 'addition sentences', suggests that young children are good informal mathematicians: they can easily adapt their counting skills to story problems. (Actually, all of the school children were in a curriculum which does not have story problems. None of the children had been taught to use their number knowledge in this way, but the children had no problems figuring out how it could be done.) Addition is not difficult for children to understand, although mathematical symbolism might be.

The study of strategies and errors is especially relevant for children who have trouble with mathematics. Not all children who were given the addition problems solved them in the same way. The older children who give correct answers to these simple problems all look equally competent if only their success rate is examined. Yet the information on strategies paints a slightly different picture. A few of the second graders resembled kindergarten children in their solution procedures. These second graders were capable of getting the right answers but for them the road to solution was much longer than it was for most of their classmates. While most children could use memorised sums, a few children had to count out every problem. It is not difficult to see how these children could become tired of mathematics. The simplest problem is tedious and mistakes can occur as the problem solving process drags on. My own experiences from interviewing and tutoring a child who was falling behind in his classroom work support this conclusion. This boy, a third grader and not one of the children in this study was having trouble with all kinds of written operations. By observing him working problems, I began to understand some of his difficulties. The child knew few sums from memory so that even the simplest problem involved counting. Although he understoond the mechanics of two-digit addition, his answers rarely showed it. In the process of solving a problem by the only way he knew, counting, he became bored and careless. He was well on his way to becoming a maths hater at the ripe old age of nine. Where their classmates have adopted short-cuts, this boy and some of the children in the study were still clinging to counting. Use of number facts is not just frosting on the cake. This strategy may be necessary to allow children to move on to bigger accomplishments.

As this research has shown, the normal course of developments is for children to shift spontaneously from counting to the use of number facts as a problem solving strategy. Children who don't adopt number facts on their own might benefit from explicit instruction in using them in order to make their problem-solving easier.

The significance of this study rests not only in what was found but also in what was investigated. Studies of children's mathematics cannot be restricted to the correctness or incorrectness of answers. This applies equally to a researcher interested in the mathematics of children in general and to a teacher in her students. In both cases, it is crucial to investigate the process of mathematical problem-solving. Changes in the process of mathematical problem-solving are as accessible to study as changes in test scores and are considerably more informative. Through the close examination of what makes up the development of problem-solving we can come to understand why children are getting better — or why they are not. This knowledge in turn can be used to foster that development by building on what children can understand through the presentation of what they need to learn.

References

Court, S. R. A., 'Numbers, Time, and Space in the First Five Years of a Child's Life', *Pedagogical Seminary*, vol. 27, pp. 71–89, 1920.

Ginsburg, H., *Children's arithmetic: the Learning Process*, Van Nostrand, New York, 1977.

15 Learning difficulties

Herbert Ginsburg

Source: Ginsburg H., Children's Arithmetic: the Learning Process, Van Nostrand, New York, 1977.

≪≪≪

This chapter examines in detail four children experiencing severe difficulties in the learning of arithmetic [. . .]

Three of the children (Bob, Patty, and Stacy) were selected in this way: I asked a third-grade teacher in an elementary school serving both middle- and lower-class children in Ithaca, New York, to choose the students having the most trouble in arithmetic. I wanted to know nothing about them except that they were having considerable difficulties learning arithmetic. I did not want to be told their test scores, their IQs, their home situations, or anything else. I did not want myself or the other interviewers to be biased in any way; we wanted to discover the child's weaknesses − and strengths − for ourselves. by our own methods of informal interviewing. While I requested no information, the teacher could not keep from telling us that all of these children suffered from perceptual problems. At the time, there seemed to be a virtual epidemic of this disease in the Ithaca schools. No doubt it has lately been supplanted by something else. Finally, George was selected when a parent asked for help with her child.

The children were receiving an eclectic form of instruction. For example, Patty sometimes worked in her classsroom on Suppes's Sets and Numbers text. As the name suggests, this is a new math approach, based heavily on set theory and logic. Sometimes she went to the learning centre where she worked on a programmed learning system. This involved a procedure that attempted first to diagnose children's level of arithmetic knowledge and then assigned them to specific lessons that they had to get right before being sent on to the next topic.

Consider now four ordinary children doing badly in school.

Bob and George

Bob, a fifth grader, exhibits a pattern that seems typical of children expriencing difficulties in school mathematics.

[. . .] Bob had trouble with standard written algorithms, but at the same time possessed effective informal procedures. There was a profound gap between his formal and informal knowledge.

Consider first his work in addition.

> I: Now we'll do some written problems. How much is 8 plus 11?
> B: (He wrote 8 + 11 = 19.) 19.
> I: How did you do it?
> B: I counted, just take the largest number and add on 8.
> I: So you went: 11, 12, 13 . . .?
> B: Yeah.

Bob had used the common strategy of counting on from the largest number, and could even describe his method in words.

> I: What about 22 plus 19?
> B: (He wrote 22 + 19.) 41?
> I: Did you count from 22 by ones?
> B: I took the 10 and that's 32, and then I took the 9, and that's 41.

Bob had used regrouping to facilitate his addition. He rearranged the problem into (22 + 10) + 9. He knew immediately that 22 + 10 = 32 and then added on the 9.

In the same way, when given 22 + 26, he did (22 + 20) + 6. 'I added the 20, got 42; then took 6 and added it.' We see that Bob used sensible, economical methods to do simple addition. From his performance to this point, he does not seem to suffer from fundamental difficulties in understanding arithmetic.

The interviewer then wanted to see if he could do standard written problems like

$$
\begin{array}{r}
158 \\
265 \\
+98 \\
\hline
\end{array}
$$

[. . .] Bob had trouble with problems like this.

> I: Can you do this problem with carrying?

He began by adding 8 + 5 + 8 to get 21. He wrote:

$$
\begin{array}{r}
\overset{1}{1}58 \\
265 \\
98 \\
\hline
2
\end{array}
$$

> B: I take the 2 and write it down here [in the units column] and carry the 1 . . . I carried, so I put the big number down here.

Bob's rule was always to carry the smaller of the two numbers obtained by adding the units column. Although this rule has sensible origins, it leads to consistently wrong answers.

Given 18 + 5, he did:

$$
\begin{array}{r}
{}^{3}18 \\
+\ 5 \\
\hline
41
\end{array}
$$

He got 8 + 5 = 13, put down the 1 in the units column, and carried the 3.

I: Do you think that's the right answer?
B: Yeah.
I: If you had eighteen candies and you got five more, how many would you have altogether?
B: (He counted on his fingers) 18, 19, 20, 21, 22, 23. (Then he looked at his previous answer, 41.) That's wrong!

Unlike many other children. Bob placed greater confidence in his informal, finger counting method than he did in the written algorithm. He relied on his own intuition, rather than on his misinterpretation of what had been taught in school.

Bob's work with subtraction showed a similar gap between informal and formal knowledge.

I: Do you want to write a take-away problem for yourself?
B: (He wrote 9 ÷ 5 = .) 4?
I: Right. How did you do it?
B: I counted backwards.

The gap is evident at the outset: Bob could not write a proper symbol for minus; and at the same time he solved the problem by a sound informal procedure, namely counting backwards.

As in the case of addition, he used a regrouping procedure when the numbers were relatively large.

I: If you had ninety-eight dollars and you gave away twenty-nine, how many would you have left?
B: OK. 88, 78, and 9 would be 67.
I: Almost.
B: I mean 69.

Bob had transformed 98 − 29 into [(98 − 10) − 10] − 9. He first subtracted or counted back by tens − 98, 88, 78 − and then counted back by ones to subtract the final 9. At first he made a minor error in the last step, but he soon corrected it.

Asked to do written subtraction, Bob did poorly.

I: If you had 158 and you took away 96, how many would you have left?

Bob wrote

$$
\begin{array}{r}
158 \\
96 \\
\hline
\end{array}
$$

Then he corrected it to

$$158$$
$$96$$
$$\overline{}$$

He did 8 minus 6 by counting backward from 8. Then he said '9 minus 5 is 4'. This gave him

$$158$$
$$96$$
$$\overline{142}$$

Next the interviewer gave him a simpler problem.

I: Let's see, now, 21 take away 5.

Bob did

$$21$$
$$-5$$
$$\overline{24}$$

I: Do you think that's the right answer?
B: (He checked his work.) Yes
I: If you had twenty-one candies and gave away five, how many would you have left?
B: Oh! I think I added.

He seemed to mean that since he got more than 21 he must have added.

I: Do you still think that's the right answer?
B: No. 'Cause five take away from 21 is 16.
I: (He pointed to his written 21 − 5 = 24.) But why isn't that the right answer?
B: I don't know.
I: You had 21 and you took away 5. and you had 24 left. What's wrong with that?
B: Oh! I know! It's from this one (the 1 in 21) that it was supposed to taken away from.

In other words. Bob recognised that he should have subtracted the 5 from the 1 rather than the 1 from the 5.

In brief, Bob first used an incorrect written procedure for subtraction. This gave him 21 − 5 = 24, where the result is larger than the number he started with. He could easily do the same problem in his head by counting backwards and in this way got the right answer. Bob then realised that his written answer was wrong. 'Oh! I think I added'. This shows that he knew that in subtraction you should end up with less, not more, than you started with. Then he saw why he was wrong in the first place: he had reversed the order of subtraction.

George, a fifth grader too, was also typical in displaying a gap between informal and formal knowledge.

After investigating George's counting, the interviewer said, "Now I'm going to give you some arithmetic questions. You write them down yourself. How much is 4 plus 2?'

George wrote: $4 \times 2 - 8$.

The interviewer thought that perhaps he did not understand the word plus.

I: How much is 3 *and* 1?

George wrote: $3 \times 1 - 3$.

I: How much is 3 and 4 more altogether?

George wrote $3 \times 4 =$, and then hesitated.

I: Perhaps you could figure this out another way. Would using these clips help?

George took three paper clips, then another four, and counted them all to get the correct answer of 7.

I: O.K. Now try writing this one: 5 and 2.

George wrote: $5 \times 2 = 10$.

I: What happens if you do it the other way?

George took five paper clips, then two, and counted to get 7.

George's responses illustrate a dramatic gap between the informal and formal. Given a spoken addition problem (5 and 2), George used either informal counting to get a correct answer or formal written multiplication to get a wrong one. In his informal mode of operation, he used concrete aids, counting and combining paper clips. In the formal mode, he converted the spoken addition problem into the corresponding multiplication formula and in general (with the exception of 3×4, which he did not complete) solved it. A strange gap indeed.

The cases of Bob and George illustrate some very fundamental points, which we stress even at the risk of repetition.

1 The child's errors often derive from systematic but incorrect written procedures. In adding, Bob always carried the smaller number; in subtracting, he always subtracted the smaller number. Both methods are systematic but wrong. Neither is capricious nor random. In adding, George always multiplied on paper. Again, wrong but systematic.

2 The child often possesses sound informal techniques for arithmetic. Bob and George added by counting and by regrouping. Bob subtracted by counting backwards. These informal techniques led to correct answers.

3 There often exists a gap between the child's informal and formal knowledge. Using formal, school-derived techniques, both Bob and George did poorly; relying on informal knowledge, they did well.

4 Understanding a child's methods for doing arithmetic often leads to suggestions for helping him. Since Bob's informal counting methods were powerful, and since he himself placed confidence in them, they could serve as a useful basis for instruction. For example; Bob spontaneously made use of regrouping.

Given 22 + 19, he regrouped into (22 + 10) + 9. This informal knowledge could be used to teach the standard carrying algorithm. The latter regroups 22 + 19 into (20 + 10) + (2 + 9), which is not very much different from Bob's invented method. Similarly, George could be taught addition through counting. *School mathematics should be built on the child's intuitions.*

Patty

Patty, a 9 year old, illustrates another kind of difficulty. She was first given a subtraction problem, which she did correctly by using the standard algorithm with borrowing. She wrote:

$$9^5 \not{6}^1 2$$
$$-4 \ 3 \ 9$$
$$\overline{5 \ 2 \ 3}$$

Then she did an addition problem correctly $\begin{array}{r} 226 \\ +421 \\ \hline 647 \end{array}$. Again she used the standard method, except that her procedure was to count out loud and on her fingers when she could not remember the relevant number facts. Thus, she added from right to left, remembering that 2 and 2 are 4 and counting to determine that 4 and 2 are 6.

Next she did $\begin{array}{r} ^1 29 \\ +39 \\ \hline 68 \end{array}$. Again this involved the standard algorithm, with carrying, and was done in part by counting on the fingers. Patty could give no rationale for the carrying of the 1. Her only response was that it was wrong to place the 1 on the bottom with the 6 and the 8.

These first few incidents show that Patty had a few basic skills. She was familiar with the common borrowing and carrying methods for subtraction and addition, respectively. She could execute these fairly smoothly, at least under certain conditions — specifically, when relatively small numbers, each having the same number of digits, were involved, and when she could count on her fingers and therefore did not have to rely on memory for number facts. She showed one common and minor weakness: she did not seem to know much about the theory of place value and hence could not explain why one carries, although she could do it.

So far it did not seem as if Patty had any particular difficulties, perceptual or otherwise, with arithmetic. But [. . . children often show complex patterns] of skills and weaknesses.

I: I'm going to give you another problem. You seem to be doing pretty well adding. Suppose you have 29 again and 4.

Patty wrote: $\begin{array}{r} 29 \\ +4 \\ \hline \end{array}$.

Before placing the 4 under the 2 her hand hesitated under the 9; apparently she could not decide where to place the 4. Patty then said, 'You put the 4 over here . . . that would be . . . that's 9 . . . (she whispered) 2, 3, 4, 5, 6 . . . 69.' She had counted to get the sum of 2 and 4. She wrote

$$\begin{array}{r} 29 \\ +4 \\ \hline 69 \end{array}$$

    I: What does it say right here?
    P: 29 and 4.
    I: Are how much?
    P: 69.

This was Patty's first error in the interview. She got a wrong result (69) because she employed a wrong strategy. When there were unequal numbers of digits she lined them up from left to right and then applied the standard addition algorithm, with counting on the fingers, from right to left. This systematic but incorrect strategy, which we have seen in other children, leads to predictable errors.

At this point one might wish to intervene and straighten out Patty's incorrect method. But there was still much to learn about her.

    I: You're sure that 29 and 4 are 69?
    P: Altogether?
    I: Altogether.
    P: No.
    I: How much are 29 and 4?

Patty made a large number of tallies on the bottom of the page. She appeared to count them, at least sometimes using her fingers. Then she announced the result: 33.

This seemed to show a gap between sound informal methods and faulty formal ones. Patty had an incorrect strategy for written addition, as described above. At the same time, she had an effective strategy for performing addition when real objects — here tallies — are involved. The correct strategy for objects is essentially to combine the two groups and count the aggregate. There is a gap between written work and arithmetic with real objects.

The interviewer wanted to determine whether Patty placed more confidence in the written procedure than in the counting one.

    I: 33. O.K. How come this says 69 [She pointed to the written work] ?
    P: Oops! Because you're not doing it like that [she pointed to the tallies].
       Oh, this (the 69) is wrong.

Apparently Patty saw that her answer of 69 was wrong, and that it differed from that result obtained by counting. She changed the 69 to 33. Patty seemed to have greater confidence in her informal method than in written addition.

At this point, the interviewer decided to challenge Patty's new response (33) in order to see how firm was her belief in the counting-derived result.

I: How can you put a 3 here [referring to the second 3 in 33] if it says 9 here (referring to the 9 in 29)?

Patty looked at what was written
$$\begin{array}{r}29\\+\,4\\\hline 33\end{array}$$
and changed it back to
$$\begin{array}{r}29\\+\,4\\\hline 69\end{array}$$.

P: That's 9 and that's gotta be 6. It's just that you're doing it differently than that.
I: So you get a different answer.
P: Yeah. 'Cause you're adding all of this up together [meaning the tallies]. You're not adding it all up altogether this way (she pointed to the written work). You're putting the 9 by itself and that's 69.
I: So when you do it on paper you get 69 and if you do it with the little marks you get how many?
P: 33. Because you're adding all of it altogether. And you're not doing it over here.

For Patty, written work was a world apart from the addition of real objects.

I: Suppose we had 29 of these little chips and put out 4 more. Would we get 33 or 69?
P: 33.
I: How do you know?
P: Because I did it down here and I added 4 more on to it (she pointed to the tallies on the bottom of the page).
I: O.K. So that means these chips would be like these lines.
P: Yes.
I: What would be another thing that would be like this [the written problem] where I could get 69?
P: There ain't no other way. I don't think.

So Patty knew that several ways of counting objects (tallies, chips) were equivalent, but could think of nothing real that corresponded to the written problem.

I: Let's see. You have 29 and 4 and you get 69. Suppose you had 30, so you had 1 more here, and 3, so you have 1 less there. Would you still get 69?

The interviewer's intention was to present Patty with a situation producing a contradiction. 30 + 3 should yield the same sum as 29 + 4. Patty should easily see that 30 had 1 more than 29, but 3 had 1 less than 4. Yet by Patty's method,
she should get a different result for
$$\begin{array}{r}29\\+\,4\end{array}$$
than
$$\begin{array}{r}30\\+\,3\end{array}$$. Would Patty see the contradiction?

P: No. You'd get bigger than 69.

She did 30 + 4 instead of 30 + 3 and wrote
$$\begin{array}{r}30\\+\,4\\\hline 70\end{array}$$

P: Yep. I told you you'd get more than 69.
I: What about on your fingers? Show me how you do it on your fingers. You can use my fingers too. Put out your fingers too.
P: You put the zero on.

I: No. I don't see any zeros. All I see are these little fingers. Never mind zeros.

P: That's hard. (She looked as though thinking intently.)

I: Now you have all kinds of fingers to work with. Patty. Now you figure out how much is 10 plus 1.

P: You have to put a zero underneath.

I: I don't see any zero at all. All I see are these fingers.

P: O.K. If you want zero you have to take those ten away (she pointed to the interviewer's fingers). You put zero then you have 1 and 1 left and you add them up and you get 2. So it's 20.

I: Can you do it without zeros?

P: No.

Patty was most persistent. She could not seem to get away from using the incorrect written algorithm, even when finger counting was suggested.

I: How about with little marks on your paper like you did here? How can you make 10 and 1 on the paper?

In other words, could Patty use tallies to solve the problem of 10 and 1? Patty made ten tallies.

P: (She whispered) 1, 2 ... 10, and then you put 1 (she made another mark).

I: How many do you have altogether?

P: 11.

She made a sweeping motion with her hand as if to indicate that she meant to combine the two sets.

I: 11.

P: Yeah. Altogether.

This incident seemed to show once again that Patty used one procedure (the incorrect algorithm) for written numbers and even fingers and another procedure (combining and counting) for tallies. The gap between the two seemed considerable. On the other hand, there was something strange going on with the word *altogether*.

I: Eleven altogether ... Let's do this ... There are 10 of these (chips) and here's 1 more. How many do you think altogether?

P: Altogether, it would be 11.

I: O.K. What about 10 *plus* one, not *altogether* but *plus*?

P: Then you'd have to put 20.

This was very interesting indeed. Even when real objects were involved, Patty responded to the word *plus* with her incorrect algorithm. And she used the sensible procedure of combining and counting only when the word *altogether* was used. What would she do if written numbers were used?

At this point, it seems clear that Patty has been using two separate methods: a combining and counting method to get correct sums when real objects are involved and an incorrect written algorithm — lining up on the left with uneven numbers of digits — when written numbers are involved. Now the interviewer wondered whether Patty would continue to employ her written method in extreme cases.

    I: O.K. Let me try something. Patty. Can you write down for me 100 plus 1?

            100

Patty wrote + 1   and said. 'Zero, zero, and 2. It would be 200.'

            200

    I: 100 plus 1, huh? Do you think that's right? Got any other way of doing it?

    P: No. Unless the 1 is on the wrong side. Unless the 1 is supposed to be there [she pointed to the ones column].

    I: Where's the 1 supposed to be?

    P: I think it's supposed to be there [pointed to the hundreds column].

    I: You think it's supposed to be there, huh? O.K. Let's do another one. What about 10 plus 1?

            10

Patty wrote + 1 and said, 'That's zero and that's 2. 20.'

           20

    I: 20, think that's right?

    P: Yeah.

    I: Got any other way of doing it?

Patty indicated no.

At this point, it was clear that Patty's written method generalised widely, even to extreme cases like 100 + 1. Now the interviewer wanted to get Patty to see the discrepancy between her written and counting methods.

    I: Well, suppose you couldn't use paper at all and I said how much is 10 plus 1?

    P: I'd count on my fingers.

    I: Why don't you do it?

Patty held up all ten fingers and stared at them.

    P: You have 10 (she looked at the fingers). You put the zero on the bottom [draws a zero with her finger].

    I: Just use your fingers now.

    P: Then you put 2 and you add 1 and 1 and it's 2.

Patty seemed unable to count 10 on her fingers! Instead she persisted in using the written procedure, apparently doing in her head something very much like

   10
 + 1
  20

    I: What if we write down on paper, here's 20, now I write down another 1, and you want to find out how much the 20 and 1 are altogether.

The interviewer wrote 20 1 placing the numbers side by side. He had used the word *altogether,* which should help her.

P: It's 21.

I: O.K. Now what would 20 *plus* 1 be? [The interviewer pointed at the wr:
numbers.]

P: 20 *plus* 1?　She wrote $\dfrac{\begin{array}{r}20\\ +\,1\end{array}}{30}$.

The interviewer's first interpretation was wrong. It was not true that Patty used
counting strategy with real objects and the incorrect algorithm with written numl
Unlike many other children. Patty did not simply show a gap between her infoi
methods and her written arithmetic. Instead, matters were far more complex.
Patty, language was crucial. Given the word *plus*, she applied an incorrect addi
method to both objects and written numbers. Given *altogether*, she used a sen:
counting procedure, again for both objects and written numbers. *Altogether*
natural word for addition: Patty probably used it in everyday life to talk about ad
things. *Plus* is a school word that Patty seems to have associated with a wi
algorithm that she did not understand.

The case study of Patty teaches us several things.

1 As we have seen over and over again, a child's mistakes are seldom capricious: t
are instead the result of systematic but wrong strategies. Patty got wrong ans\
because she lined up numbers from left to right when the word *plus* was used.

2 The artificial (albeit carefully defined) language of mathematics can present
child with considerable difficulties. *Plus, congruent, minus*, and the like are unfam
words that children frequently misunderstand. Defining the artificial words does
guarantee comprehension. The statement that subtraction is a binary operation
relation among ordered pairs may be crucial for the mathematician but of little l
for the child. Perhaps a greater effort could be made to relate the artificial terms to
child's familiar words like *take away* and *altogether*.

3 The child often displays unsuspected strengths. There were several things P:
could do quite well. Despite frequent failure in school, she could add correctly w
she used her informal counting strategy. It is crucial to locate areas of strength in
problem child. Apparently, Patty's teacher was either unaware of her strengths or ▪
unable to exploit them.

4 The *individual's* particular constellation of difficulties often takes a unique fo
Patty's problem with *plus* was unusual. This very uniqueness leads to doubts about
value of standard tests. It is hard to see how they can be sufficiently sensitive
subtleties of this type. In addition to standard tests — and perhaps *instead* of then
we require flexible techniques for interviewing individual children.

5 Sound knowledge of children's difficulties leads to ways of helping them. ‎
teacher could try to help Patty by making the connection between her word *altoget.*
and the arithmetic word *plus*. Also, the teacher might assist Patty by building on :
strength — the counting and combining strategy. Instead of merely *telling* her to l
up numbers differently, the teacher might help her to see that her 'altogether strate
makes sense, and that it is related to the written algorithm. If Patty could be led to ‎
how the written algorithm is in some ways equivalent to combining and counting ◂

then perhaps she could learn to appreciate why one needs to line up numbers properly in the algorithm.

Stacy

Stacy, also a third grader, seemed almost retarded at the outset.

    I: Can you tell me first what kind of work you are doing in math now?

Stacy responded, and continued to respond throughout the session in a slow, quiet voice. Her manner was extremely diffident — even lethargic and depressed.

    S: Lots of things.
    I: You write stuff on paper. Can you show me what stuff you write?
    S: Papers like maths [she then began to write a sentence in words as well as numerals].
    I: Can you read that?
    S: Jimmy had 8 cats; he gave Brian 2 cats.
    I: What comes next?
    S: How many does Jimmy have?
    I: How many do you think he has?
    S: 5.
    I: How did you know that?
    S: He had 8, and 2 and 1.

It was very hard to get Stacy to respond — to indicate how she had done the problem.

    I: How did you do that, Stacy? He had eight cats, and he gave Brian two cats. How many did he have left?
    S: 5. He had 5 and 2 others got away.
    I: So how many did he have left?
    S: Eight cats and I count back.
    I: How do you count back?
    S: 8 and I got 3 more and then I took 2 away.
    I: What do you mean 3 more? Let's start from the beginning. Show me how you count back.
    S: 8, 7, 6, 5, 4. He had 4 left.
    I: How did you know how to stop at 4? You went 8, 7, 6, 5, 4. How did you know to stop at 4?
    S: Because there's 7.

This initial episode gives the flavor of interaction with Stacy. She posed herself a very simple problem with which a third grader ought to have no difficulty. Indeed, the problem was in words, rather than written numerals, and involved a simple story: If Jimmy had eight cats and gave away two, how many would be left? In response to this problem, Stacy did several things. The most obvious is that she gave several *different* wrong answers. She changed her response several times. She indicated that her method of solution was by counting backwards. But her behaviour did not seem to be a simple product of this or any other strategy. Indeed, her responses were so disorganised and chaotic that it is hard to see how any underlying rules could have produced them. In brief Stacy gave wrong answers to an extremely simple problem and seemed to have no organised method for producing answers.

The remainder of the first interview showed that Stacy's work was on a very low level. The interviewer gave her a very simple problem: If there were four dogs and two ran away, how many would be left? Stacy gave the correct answer. When asked how she did it, she replied, 'Because 2 and 2 is 4'. So Stacy seemed to do subtraction by remembering some relevant addition facts. Asked to solve this problem by counting backwards, she could not do so: she merely persisted in the addition or produced apparently chaotic, senseless behaviour.

Next the interviewer gave Stacy some simple addition problems. First, 'How much are three apples and four apples?' Stacy answered, 6 'because 3 and 4 is 6.' The wrong answer was apparently the result of faulty memory of the addition facts. Asked to do the problem by counting, Stacy merely shrugged her shoulder and shook her head − behaviour that she often displayed when she did not know what to do. Next the interviewer asked Stacy, 'How much are two oranges and one more?' She got the answer right, apparently because she remembered the number facts. That was the end of the first interview.

Stacy could do very little. She was struggling with problems that should have been trivially simple for a child her age. Her only achievement was occasionally to remember some number facts. She seemed unable to use counting procedures − which, as we have seen, are usually children's method of preference.

After the first interview, we were very discouraged. We seemed to have encountered a child − the first we had seen − who had almost nothing going for her. The initial episode led us to formulate the following questions: Is she retarded? Can she hear properly? Was she very nervous or intimidated by the interviewer? Can she count? Can she conserve number? How would she do with concrete objects? Some of the questions referred to her motivation and some to her intellectual abilities. We wanted to know, essentially, whether the testing situation failed to uncover her true competence or whether she had much of any competence to begin with.

In the next session, the interviewer first established that Stacy could count as high as 80. Also, Stacy could solve Piaget's conservation problem: she recognised that a row of seven elements had the same number as another row of seven, regardless of whether the rows were the same length or whether one was bunched up.

Then the interviewer asked Stacy to get seven chips from a large pile of chips. Stacy took seven, one at a time, and put them in a straight line. The interviewer asked her to get three more. Stacy did so, putting them in a line below the first. Thus:

Figure 1 Stacy's chips

I: O.K. How many do you have altogether now?

174

S: Ten.
I: Ten. Very good. How did you figure that out?
S: Just counted them.
I: Counted them up. O.K. Now suppose we have one more. Can you get one more chip? How many do we have altogether now?
S: Eleven.
I: Eleven. And how about one more. How many do we have now?
S: Twelve.
I: How come you did that so fast?
S: There's 11, then I count 12.
I: You count 12. O.K. How about getting two more?
S: (quickly) 14.
I: 14. O.K. How are you doing that so fast? What are you doing in your head? Are you doing something, saying some numbers to yourself?
S: I say 13, 14, like that.

Stacy could count collections of objects; she could remember from one situation to the next; she could add by counting on when real objects are involved and when the numbers are small. Stacy had stopped shrugging her shoulders; she looked more lively. Later in the interview she demonstrated an ability to work with larger numbers. She was able to add ten and twelve chips.

Next, the interviewer wanted to see if Stacy could do addition in the absence of real objects. The interviewer took four chips, one at a time, and placed them behind a screen. The interviewer did the same with another three chips, and said that there are three chips behind the screen here and four there. All Stacy could see was each chip going behind the screen. How many altogether? Stacy answered correctly. Then the interviewer presented Stacy with four and five chips in the same manner. Again, she answered correctly. How did she do it? Previously she had denied counting on fingers. Probably the denial was the result of her teacher's strong opposition to such methods. Now, however, Stacy admitted to solving the problem by counting. She was able to do $6 + 5$ (after an initial error); $10 + 4$; $14 + 6$. She seemed to count on her fingers, sometimes starting from 1, and sometimes counting on from the larger number. Apparently, Stacy could solve problems involving absent objects, at least when she had the opportunity to see them, however fleetingly, before they were hidden.

These episodes bring out the following points.

1 Even children who fail badly seem to possess some kind of intellectual strengths that can be used as a basis for learning. At the outset, Stacy's behaviour seemed chaotic; she appeared to be retarded. Everything she did confirmed the teacher's judgment that she had the most difficulty of anyone in the class. She could not do anything right, and we felt quite hopeless about helping her. Nevertheless, subsequent interviewing showed that she had some basic skills, especially for dealing with concrete objects. I believe that if you dig deep enough you will find in virtually all children a core of arithmetic skills on which they can build. At least that has been our experience with every child we have seen.

2 The child's hidden strengths usually involve some form of counting. Stacy could add by counting sets or by counting on from the larger number. We have

seen repeatedly that children frequently use some variant of counting in their arithmetic work. Do we stress counting enough in our curricula?

3 Intellectual success helps to alleviate emotional difficulties. At the outset, it was abundantly clear that Stacy was depressed. She was lethargic, she seemed miserable, it was hard to get her to say anything. All this was typical of her ordinary classroom behaviour. We do not know the reason for her depression: perhaps it was linked to some events at home; perhaps it was the result of her failure to learn in school; or perhaps it stemmed from some combination of the two. Whatever its causes, her depression seemed to have been alleviated by her improved performance in arithmetic. When the interviewer succeeded in discovering some of Stacy's competencies and in getting her to use them, her entire manner changed: she seemed more alert, more lively, she had some sparkle. Stacy seemed to enjoy seeing herself as a child with ability. Children's self-concept is usually bound up with their intellectual achievements. In some cases, helping children to improve their schoolwork may do more for their emotional health than well-meaning attempts to analyse and treat their emotional disturbances directly.

4 Informal methods often play a key role in getting to know and in helping children with problems. On discovering how badly Stacy did on ordinary arithmetic problems, the interviewer introduced concrete tasks, phrased them in ways that Stacy could understand, and attempted, in a deliberately non-standardised way, to tailor the testing of her strengths. This procedure seemed to relax her, to reduce her anxieties about being tested, and provided her with opportunities to show and discover what she could do. The interview also suggested some very specific ways of helping her – for example, by developing her finger counting.

By contrast, standard tests are of little value in a case like Stacy's. They often frighten children doing badly. They yield unhelpful labels like 'low mathematical aptitude'. And worst of all, they fail to reveal children's strengths. The tests say nothing specific about what the child can do and about how instruction should proceed. All this is positively harmful to the child who has trouble learning.

16 Decomposition and all that rot

Stuart Plunkett

Source: Mathematics in Schools, vol. 8, no. 3, pp. 2—7, May 1979.

⋘⋘⋘⋘⋘⋘⋘⋘⋘⋘⋘⋘⋘⋘⋘⋘⋘⋘⋘⋘⋘⋘⋘⋘⋘⋘⋘⋘⋘

How do people calculate?

Well, it varies rather a lot. Here are just three stories:

> Me: Do you know what 7 lots of 8 are?
> Peter (7): No.
> Me: Could you work it out?
> Peter: (Long pause) 56.
> Me: How did you do that?
> Peter: Well . . . I knew 10 8s so I took away 8, that's 72 and another and another — 56.

> Me: What's 213 take away 188?
> Ray (adult): 25.
> Me: How d'you do it?
> Ray: Well it's 12 up to 200 and 13s 25.

> Me: What's 213 take away 188?
> Student (19): Silence
> Me: What happened when I asked?
> Student: Panic.
> Me: Did you see anything in your mind . . .
> Student: Yes. I saw 213 written down and 188 underneath, and then a line . .

Ask people how they calculate, and indeed observe yourself at work, and you will soon find a fascinating variety of idiosyncratic methods.

How are calculations taught?

In contrast to the diversity of methods people actually use, there is very little variation in the methods taught in schools. At the present moment, it is a fair bet that almost all children in this country are taught standard written algorithms for the four rules of number. By this I mean processes for addition, subtraction, long and short multiplication and division which are laid out something like this:

177

$$
\begin{array}{r}
5\ 7 \\
+\ _1 3\ 8 \\
\hline
9\ 5
\end{array}
\qquad
\begin{array}{r}
^4 \cancel{5} \,^1 7 \\
-\ \ 3\ 8 \\
\hline
1\ 9
\end{array}
\qquad
\begin{array}{r}
5\ 7 \\
\times\ \ \ 8 \\
\hline
4\ 5\ 6 \\
{\scriptstyle 5}
\end{array}
\qquad
\begin{array}{r}
1\ 9 \\
3\overline{)5\,^2 7}
\end{array}
$$

There are minor variations, of course, concerning whether you multiply first by the units or by the tens in long multiplication, and whether the quotient goes above or below the dividend in short division, and there is the relatively major distinction between decomposition and equal additions. But that's about the sum of it. The vast majority of children are taught these methods as the primary way of dealing with whole number (and decimal) calculations; and for the majority, I suspect, these are the *only* methods they are taught.

The nature of standard written algorithms

Why should this be? The reasons lie largely in the nature of these algorithms. It is worth attempting to summarise them.

1 They are *written,* so the calculation is permanent and correctible.

2 They are *standardised:* it is possible to arrange that everyone does the same thing.

3 They are *contracted* in the sense that they summarise several lines of equations involving distributivity and associativity.

4 They are *efficient.* For instance, it's less efficient to add the tens first, because you might need to make a subsequent amendment to their total after you've added the units.

5 They can be *automatic:* they can be taught to, and carried out by, someone who has no understanding of what is happening.

6 They are *symbolic.* One does one's calculations entirely by symbol manipulation, with no reference to the real world, or any other model. At the last stage the answer appears with, usually, no previous approach to it.

7 They are *general* in the sense that they will work for *any* numbers, large or small, whole or decimal, with few or many digits. This is perhaps their greatest attraction, and it comes from their exploitation of place-value.

8 They are *analytic.* They require the numbers to be broken up, into tens and units digits, and the digits dealt with separately.

9 They are *not easily internalised.* They do not correspond to the ways in which people tend to think about numbers.

10 They encourage *cognitive passivity* or suspended understanding. One is unlikely to exercise any choice over method and while the calculation is being carried out one does not think much about why one does it in that way.

Possibly the most significant of these characteristics is the eighth. By breaking a number up into hundreds, tens and units digits, and dealing with these as digits, we develop methods which can be applied to all numbers, however large or small, and which can be applied efficiently. However, such an analytical approach detaches the methods from the area of complete numbers (i.e. numbers not split into digits) where people are more at home. Thus even if the rules can be remembered they are learnt largely without reasons and are not related to other number knowledge. They are far from aiding the understanding of numbers; rather they encourage a belief that mathematics is essentially arbitrary.

As has often been stated, training in these methods may be a good idea if you want to produce clerks, and others, who are quick and accurate at doing large numbers of difficult calculations by hand. Also, teaching these methods leaves you with work which is easy to manage and to mark.

Perhaps a further point should be added to the list above: they are *traditional*. For a lot of non-specialist teachers of mathematics, as for the general public, the four rules of number are the standard written algorithms. Concept and algorithm are equated. So to teach division you teach a method rather than an idea. And the method will be the one you were taught, and in this area, at least, you can perpetuate your own knowledge with some confidence.

The use of standard written algorithms

One of the most remarkable things about these methods is that *they are used so little*. In some research directed to quite other ends, D. A. Jones, 1973, investigated the methods used by each of 80 11 year olds to calculate $67 + 38$, $83 - 26$, 17×6 and $116 \div 4^2$. The questions were written in this form, and the children were free to use written or mental methods. Over *half* of the 320 calculations were successfully completed by *non-standard* methods, such as $83 - 26$: 83, 73, 63, 60, 57; 17×6: $12 \times 6 = 72$, $72 + 30 = 102$. Thus despite the heavy teaching of standard algorithms, they are not necessarily chosen for calculations of this order of difficulty. This suggests, at the least, that the standard methods are not suitable for mental work. Casual enquiry amongst both adults and children into how they do their 'sums' yields similar results.

At the same time, the standard algorithms are *not understood* by children. Any teacher of maths to children between 8 and 16 will recognise these:

$$
\begin{array}{cccc}
\begin{array}{r} 3\,5 \\ +\ 4\,7 \\ \hline 9\,1 \\ \hline \scriptstyle 2 \end{array}
&
\begin{array}{r} 4\,5 \\ -3\,7 \\ \hline 1\,2 \end{array}
&
\begin{array}{r} 3\,5 \\ \times\ \ 3 \\ \hline 9\,1\,5 \end{array}
&
\begin{array}{r} 2\lfloor 2\,1\,6 \\ \hline 1\ \ 8 \end{array}
\end{array}
$$

and probably quickly add to the sad collection. The situation is highlighted if the child who has failed on paper is asked the question orally and is able, as so often, to do it in his head. Mary Harris writes about the two different spaces in which the child operates: the space of written numbers and the space of spoken numbers. She conjectures that there is only the most tenuous connection between the two.

The standard algorithms are also *misused*, like sledge-hammers to crack nuts. How many children have recorded calculations like these?

$$1 \; {}^{1}0 \; {}^{1}0 \, {}^{1}2$$
$$-_1 \quad {}^{10}\!\!\!\not0 \; {}^{10}\!\!\!\not0 \; 5$$
$$\overline{0 \quad 0 \quad 7}$$

$$26$$
$$\times \, 100$$
$$\overline{00}$$
$$000$$
$$\underline{2600}$$
$$2600$$

$$10|6\,{}^{6}2\,{}^{2}7\,{}^{7}0$$
$$6 \quad 2 \quad 7$$

Either being required to conform, or not expecting to think for themselves, they apply standard methods as though they were always the most appropriate.

The nature of mental algorithms

Work these in your head, or better still ask a child, and try to determine how they were done:

$$57 + 24 \qquad 83 - 69 \qquad 3 \times 24 \qquad 112 \div 4$$

Here are some of the characteristics of mental algorithms. They contrast with those in the list above, but there has been no attempt to match them point for point.

1 They are *fleeting* and often difficult to catch hold of.
2 They are *variable*. From his 80 children, Jones recorded 16 different methods altogether for finding $83 - 26$. Of these, three were standard written algorithms.
3 They are *flexible*, and can be adapted to suit the numbers involved. Do you have different methods for $83 - 79, 83 - 51, 83 - 7$?
4 They are *active* methods in the sense that the user makes a definite, if not always very conscious, choice of method and is in control of his own calculations.
5 They are usually *holistic,* in that they work with complete numbers rather than separated tens and units digits, e.g. $4 \times 35 = 2 \times 70 = 140$; 4×28: $4 \times 30 = 120, - 8, 112$.
6 They are frequently *constructive,* working from one part of the question towards the answer, e.g. $37 + 28$: $37, 47, 57, 67, 65$.
7 They are *not designed for recording*. So written down they tend to sprawl, as in the example above. But they can of course be recorded where this is desirable.
8 They *require understanding* all along. A child who gets his mental calculations right almost certainly understands what he is doing. Equally their use develops understanding. But on the other hand they cannot be used to achieve performance in advance of understanding.
9 They are often *iconic*. Either they relate to an icon such as the number line or a number square, or they depend upon serial enunciation as in $32 + 21$: $32, 42, 52, 53$. In either case some overall picture of the numbers is being used.
10 Often they give an *early approximation* to the correct answer. This is usually because a left-most digit is calculated first, but in the context of complete numbers, e.g. $145 + 37$: $175, 182$; $34 \times 4 = 120, 136$.

11 They are *limited* in the sense that they cannot be applied to the most difficult calculations, such as 269 × 23. Nevertheless they are suitable for a greater range of problems than a casual observation of school number work might lead one to suspect.

It is fairly clear that mental methods are the ones to foster if you wish to use and develop children's understanding of number, and any teaching of them would obviously be accompanied by other means to this end. You would have to accept that children would not be able to do calculations before they had a pretty clear idea of what was going on. You would have to be able to provide them with alternative ways of dealing with difficult calculations. And a teacher of these methods would obviously expect a degree of independence and individuality in his pupils.

So teachers, or schools, or society, have a choice in the methods which might be taught, and the choice can be made on the basis of previously determined aims in number education. Either standard written algorithms for efficiency and order and because that is what we have taught for 100 years, or mental algorithms for independence and understanding and because they are the methods people actually use. Or both: 'Ah, mental algorithms are all very well, but they must learn the standard methods sooner or later.' Must they?

A spectrum of calculations

In order to discuss what we should teach, it helps to take a look at the range of calculations we can do with numbers. It is easy to include 'the four rules of number' as a basic skill for all citizens without considering exactly what this entails. The general applicability of the standard algorithms makes us forget the enormous width of the spectrum (*see* table 1). For convenience, I have divided the range into five rough bands. They are approximately in order of decreasing frequency of use, and I suspect the relationship is a negative exponential one. (When did you last need to do a long multiplication, other than in your professional work?) Needless to say the order is also one of increasing difficulty. This is very convenient: the calculations we use a lot are the easy ones. It should also give us occasion to pause before spending a lot of energy on teaching processes which will be used very little (*see* Moore and Williams for figures on frequency of use of some calculations).

Table 1

Red	Orange	Yellow	Green	Blue
5 + 9	135 + 100	139 + 28	592 + 276	3964 + 7123 + 4918 + 5960
13 − 8	85 − 20	33 − 26	592 − 276	
4 × 7	5 × 30	17 × 3	931 × 8	931 × 768
35 ÷ 5	90 ÷ 3	72 ÷ 4	693 ÷ 7	8391 ÷ 57

I have put some typical calculations in each band, but have no wish to make very precise distinctions. In general terms the descriptions of the bands are these:

Red band   This is the only one clearly defined and it contains number bonds up to 10 + 10 and 10 X 10 and their inverses. It is highly desirable to have all these facts available for instant recall.

Orange band   These are roughly addition, subtraction, multiplication and division with a number with a single non-zero digit and for which everything is fairly straightforward. They can all be done by a one-step mental process, given thorough knowledge of results in the red band. It is to these calculations that one most frequently sees standard written algorithms inappropriately applied.

Yellow band   This covers the range of calculations for which mental methods are entirely appropriate. The average person in the street, given a practical, motivating context, would do these in his head. So can average 11 year olds, given encouragement. It is for calculations in this band that one so often sees the disjunction between a child's space of written numbers and his space of spoken numbers.

Green band   These could be done mentally but on the whole few people would want to, or need to.

Blue band   In a practical situation it would be absurd to use a mental process for these. If a calculator were available, it would be equally absurd to use a written method.

Proposal

I think that the reasons for teaching the standard written algorithms are out of date, and that it is time we all took notice of this. I believe there is a place for mental algorithms, for the use of calculators, and for ad hoc, non-standard written methods. I think a large amount of time is at present wasted on attempts to teach and to learn the standard algorithms, and that the most common results are frustration, unhappiness and a deteriorating attitude to mathematics.

I therefore propose, for consideration and criticism, an alternative approach to the teaching of elementary arithmetic. Very roughly, children should go through three stages, progressing according to their ability.

Stage 1 The acquisition of mental techniques for calculations in the red, orange, and yellow bands.
Stage 2 The use of calculators for green and blue calculations.
Stage 3 The development of some casual written methods.

I must stress that I am referring to only one aspect of children's mathematics. Calculations are only a part of number work, and number only a part of mathematics.

I want to elaborate a little on these three stages (particularly the first) but clearly I cannot do more than give an outline. I make no reference to children's ages, since the age at which they can begin to understand a given aspect of number work is so variable.

Stage 1

I imagine there is little controversy in the suggestion that red and orange band calculations should be done in the head. Nevertheless it is important to remember that children do take quite a time to appreciate facts like $47 + 10 = 57$ and $13 \times 10 = 130$. This is a measure of the subtlety and power of our place-value system. It is also an indication of the nature of children's problem: if they are not certain of facts like these, they should not be rushed to calculations like $47 + 18$ or 13×12.

Two sorts of understanding have to be fostered at this stage. First the understanding of numbers and the place-value system. One tool which I think is invaluable for this is the number line. This version is commonly met in infants classes:

1 2 3 4 5 6 7 8 9 10 11 12 13 14 15 16 17 18 19 20

but for bigger number the place-value structure needs to be emphasised:

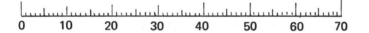

Further extensions to hundreds, thousands, fractional numbers and negative numbers are also invaluable. Use of these number lines can help to give children a personal, *overall* picture of the numbers (and how they relate to each other) which I think is often missing. Mathematicians seem commonly to possess an iconic number line permanently available in their heads, and we might attempt to give children a similar icon.

The other part of understanding is of the meaning and nature of the four operations: of multiplication as repeated addition, of division both as repeated subtraction and as the opposite of multiplication, of subtraction both as 'take away' and, perhaps more importantly, 'and how many [more]'. This point seems to be particularly important. Both large and small subtractions make more sense in terms of complementary addition: how does one work out $15 - 8$, $311 - 275$?

Given understanding of and facility with calculations in the red and orange bands, and some personal picture of the number system, children should have little difficulty in developing methods for dealing with yellow band problems. The usual mental algorithms seem to be based on serial enumeration, as in $47 + 34$: 47, 57, 67, 77, 81; or on successive approximation, as in 17×4: $20 \times 4 = 80$, 76, 72, 68; or on some icon such as a number line: $110 - 88$:

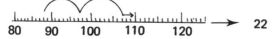   22

183

It is perfectly possible for these methods to be recorded, and doing so may help children to be aware of their mental operations. If free format recording is allowed, children are less likely to develop the all too common inhibition about expressing their own mathematical thoughts. As they become confident, they will abbreviate what they write. The aim is an internalised process which is understood, rather than an externalised one which may not be.

Stage 2

Understanding of larger numbers is a necessary preliminary to using them in green and blue band calculations. Given this, and the understanding of mental methods for the previous bands, children will be able and likely to make sensible use of calculators for more difficult problems. Their personal understanding of number should make it unlikely that they will ask 'Is it an add, Miss?' and press the wrong button. They will be able to use orange band calculations to check the machine's answer for reasonableness.

They will get pleasure from observing that their answers to simpler problems agree with those on the calculator. There will be no disjunction between their 'spoken' space and their 'calculator' space. The calculator will make sense.

Stage 3

Money calculations are rather anomalous in that it is sometimes necessary to work to 4 or 5 significant figures, an accuracy which seldom makes sense in other areas. But money calculations are those most frequently used by the person in the street, so it would be sensible to provide most people with means to add or subtract numbers like 54.75 and 32.80 when they have no calculator available. Non-standard written methods for dealing with these can be adapted by children and teachers from mental algorithms used for more manageable numbers. For instance, addition can easily and sensibly proceed from the left:

$$
\begin{array}{r}
54\ .75 \\
32\ .80 \\
\hline
8\cancel{6}7.55 \\
\end{array}
$$

Subtraction by complementary addition can be recorded in a variety of ways, e.g.

$$
\begin{array}{ll}
32.80 & \\
42.80 & 10 \\
52.80 & 20 \\
54.80 & 22 \\
54.75 & 21.95 \\
\end{array}
$$

A person who has to do a lot of such calculations will soon develop methods of a brevity suited to his needs. Here is a non-standard method for long multiplication:

$$
\begin{array}{r|rr}
 & 20 & 3 \\
\hline
10 & 200 & 30 \\
8 & 160 & 24 \\
\hline
 & & 414 \\
\end{array}
$$

h shows how much diagrams can help. The important thing is a process which is
igible (to the user), rather than one which is standardised or quickest.

eat opportunity

advent of calculators has provided us with a great opportunity. We are freed from
necessity to provide every citizen with methods for dealing with calculations of
finite complexity. So we can abandon the standard written algorithms, of general
cability and limited intelligibility, in favour of methods more suited to the minds
purposes of the users. Up to now I don't think this point has been sufficiently
eciated. In his stimulating, and otherwise excellent article, Michael Girling writes:
most refined methods of long division, for instance . . . need not be taught.'
teach any 'refined' methods? They would only be needed by people who do
of calculations, and for such people a calculator is a better aid than a pencil and
r.

difficulty in advocating a programme such as this is the common confusion of
ept with algorithm. The argument starts from the quite acceptable premise
children should learn how to calculate and arrives at the conclusion that they
ld be taught the standard algorithms. Calculators can then be seen as a great
y in schools. The emphasis must be shifted to the other end of the argument.
dren should be helped to acquire sensible methods for calculating, and for the
rity of calculations met in everyday use these will be mental methods. Teaching
tal techniques will not lead to children doing less calculations in school: probably
will do more. More importantly children will acquire a better understanding than
n the repeated application of standard algorithms they do not comprehend. With
tal methods occupying their proper place as the principal means for doing simple
ulations, the position of calculators is clear. They are the sensible tool for difficult
ulations, the ideal complement to mental arithmetic.

ferences

iams, J. D., 'Arithmetic and the Difficulties of Calculative Thinking',
Educational Research, vol. 5, no. 3, 1962–3.
es, D. A., 'An investigation of the Differences Between Boys and Girls During the
Formative Years in the Methods Used to Solve Mathematical Problems', unpublished
M.phil. thesis, University of London. For an abbreviated account, *see Mathematics
n School,* vol. 4, no. 3, pp. 29–31, May 1975.
ris, M., 'Personal Factors in the Learning and Teaching of Mathematics in the
Primary School', unpublished M.A. dissertation, University of Southampton.
ore, N. and Williams, A., *Mathematics for Life,* Teachers Book, General Introduction.
wn, M. and Kuchemann, D., 'Is it an add, Miss?' *Mathematics in School,* vol. 5,
no. 5, November 1976.
ling, M., 'Towards a Definition of Basic Numeracy', *Mathematics Teaching,* no. 81.

17 Coping with word problems: observations of V. D. Petrova's class

Jeremy Kilpatrick (ed.)

Source: Kilpatrick J. et al. (eds), Soviet Studies in the Psychology of Learning and Teaching Mathematics, vol. 2, University of Chicago Press, Chicago, Illinois, 1975.

The pupils of V. D. Petrova (172nd School, fourth grade) attracted my attention. They showed (in individual experiments) an excellent ability to solve problems without assistance. The model for independent solution of problems that were quite complex for fourth grade was a pupil in this class, Valya K. [. . .]

Her solution was detailed and well substantiated. Valya's style of problem breakdown was characteristic of both good pupils and average pupils in this class. When difficulty arose, V. D. Petrova's pupils returned to the text of the problem, reread it, and looked through the solution they had done. They corrected most of the errors they made by themselves. They were able, in case of failure, to change the method of solution they were using or to replace it by a new one. They could outline a different plan of solution for a single problem. All of this shows a high level of development of the analytic–synthetic activity for the given grade. It should be noted that V. D. Petrova's pupils did not lower their level of achievement, as so often happens. Of the 36 pupils (all were passed) in the first quarter of the fifth grade, 11 received excellent marks in all their subjects, 18 pupils had 4s and 5s; and 7 had 4s and 3s. The mathematics instructor in the middle school mentioned the ability of V. D. Petrova's pupils to analyse the text of problems that were new for them.

Undoubtedly, the ability of these pupils to solve problems is determined by their entire system of working. However, it is also certain that their success in solving problems largely depends on the correct means of analysis that they used. These proper methods of working on problems and analyses of them are frequently instilled from the very beginning of instruction.

I observed V. D. Petrova systematically while she was teaching problem-solving during 1952–3 in the first grade. [. . . I shall describe . . .] the method she used in teaching first-grade pupils the methods of analysis and synthesis in solving problems.

Emphasis on reading the problem

The work on the analysis of a problem begins with reading it properly, with intona-

186

tional expression, and in this process the first primary separation of the text occurs, as well as the isolation of the unknown and the individual data. V. D. Petrova devotes much attention to this — she teaches her pupils how to read problems.

From the beginning the teacher continually emphasises that each word in the problem, regardless of how small it is, has its importance. If one changes 'tiny little words' — 'in' and 'on' — the entire sense of the problem is changed. These small but very important words must be emphasised by intonation. V. D. Petrova makes the pupils vary their intonation when they see punctuation marks (pauses), to aid in breaking down the problem into its component parts. She requires special expressive emphasis of the problem's question. All of these demands are mastered by the pupils, and they begin to demand it of themselves and of their classmates. A pupil read a problem:

> ' "Ten aspen . . . logs were put into a stove and—"
> She put in a pause which destroyed the logic, and the teacher immediately called her attention to this: "Where is the comma?" she asked.
> "After the word 'stove'," answered the girl.
> "Then a voice pause should be there also," the teacher reminded her and demanded another reading with the correct intonation.
> The girl read: "Ten aspen logs were put into a stove, and six fewer birch logs were put in than aspen. How many logs were put into the stove in all?"
> The teacher asked the class what other mistakes this girl had made in reading.
> The pupils noticed:
> "She read the word 'than' poorly."
> "She did not emphasise the word 'fewer'."
> "She did not emphasise the number . . ." '

The problem was read again, in an attempt to meet all of the teacher's demands. The monotony of this repeated reading did not deaden the girls' attention, because they were on the alert to notice if the reader made any mistakes and were to correct any inaccuracies.

The teacher emphasised that the solution itself largely depends on a correct reading of the problem: 'Valya, here, read the problem poorly and cannot explain its solution; and Katya was mistaken because she missed this important little word "than" when she read the problem at home,' she explained. The pupils developed a genuine respect for this stage of the work on a problem. Gradually they formed a sound habit of reading the text of a problem with the correct intonation, and the teacher devoted less and less attention to this stage.

Emphasis on a breakdown of the text of a problem

Although the individual data and the unknown are isolated while reading the problem, the teacher did not limit her class to this. In the initial period of teaching the separation of the text of the problem into individual data and the unknown, she singled this out as one stage in the work on problems. Having read the problem, the pupils were to enumerate each of the data and isolate the unknown in particular. Here is how this breakdown of the above problem was done by one of the pupils, Katya S.:

"It is known," she says, "that they put 10 aspen logs into the stove. It is also known that six fewer birch logs were put in than the number of aspen logs, but it is unknown how many logs were put into the stove in all." '

Here the text of the problem has been repeated in a slightly different form, and one datum was distinguished from another very precisely — this is one thing that must be taught. The investigation of the peculiarities of problem solving by young pupils has shown that, if they are only able to reproduce the text of a problem verbatim, they sometimes separate it into its components incorrectly, isolating partial complexes whose operations lead to mistakes (this type of mistake was described above).

At the end of the second quarter all the pupils in this class, even the weak ones, could break down the problem in this manner, and in the future the teacher became more and more inclined to skip this stage, returning to it only in more difficult cases.

Having separated the text of the problem, the pupils started a *more detailed analysis of each datum and the unknown.*

'What kind of logs were put in the stove?' the teacher asked.

'Birch and aspen.'

'How many aspen logs were put in?'

'Ten.'

'Read again what it says about the birch logs.'

'Six *fewer* birch logs were put in than aspen logs.'

'Fewer than what?'

'Than aspen logs.'

'And how many aspen logs?'

'Ten.'

'What is asked in the problem?'

'How many logs in all were put in.'

'In all — this is, consequently, what kind of logs?'

'Aspen and birch.'

After this type of breakdown the way to solve the problem will become clear.

If unfamiliar words are found in a problem, the teacher reveals their meaning in detail, so that the pupils can imagine very clearly the articles referred to in the problem.

Once, the number of pine trees that were sawed up into boards was mentioned in a problem. In repeating the problem, one girl used the word 'logs' in place of 'boards.' The teacher then explained the difference between the concepts. She cut up a stick into a 'board' and a 'log' and discussed the uses of boards and logs.

With this type of work, the problem evoked a more vivid, clear concept in the students and became part of life for them. Thus the solution was simplified for them, and they could verify their results more realistically. [. . .]

Emphasis on differentiation of concepts

The teacher always dwelt particularly on similar concepts which should be differentiated from one another. The confusion of concepts sometimes hinders the conscious solution of the problem (for example, a problem about 5-kopek pieces and 3-kopek pieces in the workbook).

The analysis of concepts that express a quantitative relationship between objects (*fewer than . . . so many times bigger than*, etc.) was guided by a great deal of systematic work by the teacher on these concepts. (I do not have the opportunity to explain this in more detail here.)

The teacher elaborates proper concepts about quantitative relationships between objects by visual material. In the analysis of problems she observes whether the pupils understand the meanings of all these 'small, but important, words,' so that they can imagine clearly the relationships described by the problem, and she turns to visual aids when difficulties arise.

Emphasis on substantiation

In solving problems, V. D. Petrova demands a substantiation of the method of solving of a problem from the text. She demands that the pupils point out the part of the text that determines the operation performed by the pupil. Thus, in solving the above problem about the aspen and the birch logs, the pupils asked, 'How many birch logs were brought?' To answer it they proposed subtracting six logs from 10 logs. The teacher requested rereading the part of the problem that stated that subtraction should be carried out ('six logs fewer'). Through this type of work the pupils became accustomed to conducting the solution on the basis of an analysis of the text, thus controlling their choice of operation.

The analysis is subordinate not only to the data contained in the problem but also to the intermediate data obtained during the solution. In doing the appropriate arithmetical operation, the pupils indicate precisely what kind of data they obtained and connect these data with those contained in the problem.

'Now we know,' a pupil said, in solving the problem about the logs, 'that they put 4 birch logs into the stove. We also know, that they put in 10 aspen logs . . . Now we can find out. . . .' He continued with the statement and resolution of the next question.

Emphasis on the question of a problem

V. D. Petrova devoted much attention to 'work on the question of a problem,' on the unknown. The pupils isolated and separated the unknown data. The teacher emphasised that determining the value of the unknown and answering the question of the problem are the goals of the solution and that there should be no superfluous operations – all operations should serve the one basic goal of determining the unknown.

When they found the value of the unknown, the girls explained: 'We have solved the problem because we have answered its question. In the question the following is asked: How many logs in all were put into the stove? We found out that 14 logs were put into the stove.'

189

'Katya here,' said the teacher, 'solved this problem in one operation: She subtracted 6 logs from 10 logs. Did she complete the problem?'

'No, Katya did not read the question of the problem. She didn't answer it,' the children explained.

This kind of work established the purpose of looking for the unknown in the solution and prevents superfluous syntheses.

V. D. Petrova teaches the pupils to ask themselves questions for different unknown data ('What can we find out if we know . . .') to select data for the question ('What must we know in order to determine . . .'). Sometimes she asks if they can immediately, with one operation, find the answer to the problem's question, and has them explain why this is impossible. Thus, she includes elements of the method of analysis, but still does not teach the pupils to conduct the 'classical' analysis of problems on their own.

She also teaches them different formulations of questions referring to a single operation. If one reads: 'A boy had 20 notebooks and gave half of them to his sister,' the following questions could be posed.

1 How many books did he have left?
2 To what is half the books equal?
3 How many notebooks did he give his sister?

The answer to these questions, as the pupils explain, is found in one operation: $20 \div 2$. This type of work makes the pupils' thought more flexible; the transition from one system of connections to another will not be so difficult for them. [. . .]

Emphasis on analysis of errors

V. D. Petrova also trains the pupils to analyse their mistakes, showing that the basic source of the mistake is a superficial analysis of the text. For example, they had the problem:

> 'Twenty birch trees were planted in a park, then 10 more poplars than birches, and as many linden trees as poplars and birches put together were planted. How many linden trees were planted?'

Valya S. found how many lindens were planted by adding 20 and 10.

The teacher, in reviewing the solution, asked the girls to indicate where Valya had gone wrong, and what part of the problem she had ignored ('10 more poplars than birches').

Nina K. solved a problem about nickels. To answer a question about the number of pennies in a nickel, she wrote the operation thus:

$$3 N \times 5 p$$

The teacher again demanded that the pupils show why Nina was wrong, what rule she had forgotten. The teacher requires independence in her pupils' problem solving and does not consider homework done unless the girl shows the sheet of scratch paper on which she solved the problem. The teacher told the girls how this pupil solved the problem, and then they all singled out the errors she made and told why the problem was not solved.

The pupils were gradually trained in controlling the operations they used and in correcting their mistakes; this training, as we saw, is reflected in their ability to solve problems.

Emphasis on developing language powers

A person thinks with words. 'Naked thoughts, free from linguistic material, free from linguistic "natural material," do not exist,' says J. V. Stalin. Developing the pupils' speech also involves developing logical thought and increasing the level of their analytic–synthetic activity.

V. D. Petrova worked very hard to develop the speech powers of her pupils. She broadened their active vocabulary, including words to signify abstract concepts (weight, quantity, etc.). She constantly required detailed, precise answers, without extra words, to her questions. By the first half of the year her first-graders could, without the teacher's helping questions, transmit the content of a problem and explain how to solve it.

An individual experiment

At the end of the year an individual experiment with 15 pupils was conducted (5 having 5s, 5 having 4s, and 5 having 3s in arithmetic). The following problem was given for independent solution:

> 'Forty metres of satin were brought into a store. Half the material was sold on the first day, and 7 metres less was sold on the second day than on the first. How many metres of satin were sold on the second day?'

Of the 15 pupils, only one required some help from the experimenter; the rest solved the problem all by themselves, giving a detailed explanation of the course of solution. As an example of such a solution and the explanation of this problem, I introduce the record of Zhenya S. (she had a '4' in arithmetic). After repeating the text of the problem, Zhenya began its breakdown:

> 'We know that 40 metres of material were brought into the store, and we know that half of the material was sold on the first day, but it is unknown how many metres were sold on the second day. This we shall have to find out. In order to find out how many metres were sold on the first day, we must divide: 40 m ÷ 2 = 20 m. Twenty m of material were sold on the first day.
>
> Now we know that 20 metres were sold in one day, and that 7 m less were sold on the second day, but it is unknown how many metres were sold on the second day.
>
> In order to find out how many metres of material were sold on the second day, we must subtract. 20 m − 7 m = 13 m. Thirteen metres of material were sold on the second day.'

Such a detailed, well-founded solution was very typical of the pupils in V. D. Petrova's class.

The initial knowledge of functional relationships between data was given by V. D. Petrova in first grade during the solution of simple problems. Later, in grades 3 and 4, she broadened the scope of the connections to be learned and achieved a sound mastery of them. She worked hard to decrease the time spent in translating the concrete data of the problem into more abstract mathematical concepts.

Thus, in solving quite a complex problem involving finding the difference in gasoline consumption of two different automobiles, the fourth-grade pupils indicated that they must explain which of the automobiles consumed more gasoline and by what amount.

'What shall we do?' asked the teacher.

'We should compare the amount of gasoline used by the automobiles. In order to do this, we must subtract the amount of gasoline consumed by one automobile from the amount of gasoline consumed by the other, and thus find the difference between them.'

'The difference of what?' The teacher demanded precision.

'We shall find the difference in gasoline consumption,' a girl answered.

Thus, the entire course of the solution was traced in an abstract formulation.

Emphasis on alternative solution

V. D. Petrova ordinarily considers and evaluates, from the point of view of their productiveness, various possible solutions of a single problem and the solution of problems without using numbers or numerical formulas.

These means of training instill in pupils the ability to plan different courses of solution of a problem and the ability to choose the most rational of them. This was very clearly shown [. . .] by fourth-grade pupils in the 172nd School. The girls planned two or three possible ways to solve a problem and indicated the best one. All of this shows a high level of analytic—synthetic activity.

Her success in her work was determined, as I have already indicated, by her entire approach, not just in arithmetic lessons. The ability to think logically, to reason, to express thoughts precisely and accurately, all of this she taught the pupils in all the lessons. The methods used by this teacher are described in the methodological literature. The definite, strictly-thought-out system of using them was valuable in her work, and as a result, this method was mastered not only by the best pupils, but by the weaker ones as well, and these became means of creative thinking for them. As was indicated above, the fourth-grade pupils of V. D. Petrova, made very few errors in analysis when they solved a difficult problem on their own, and when difficulties arose they turned to a repeated analysis of the text, analysed their reasoning and mistakes. All of this shows the productiveness of the system described here.

18 Learning their tables: a suggested reorientation

Alistair McIntosh

Source: Mathematics Teaching, vol. 56, pp. 2–5 Autumn 1971.

Introduction

In spite of the advent of modern mathematics in all its many-headed, misunderstood, mindblocking glory, in the middle of any discussion about primary mathematics comes the *cri de coeur*, 'and what about learning their tables?' Hackles rise amongst the traditionalists; eyebrows rise amongst the moderns. The primary teacher cries from the bowels of his Nuffield-fed being: 'Understanding is all: rote-learning is an abomination.' 'Rubbish!' mutters the secondary teacher from the ordered chasm of his brain, 'they don't realise the pressures we face' – and another attempt at primary-secondary liaison falters and dies. 'Well, we tried,' says the primary teacher, 'but they don't understand.' 'Well, we understand', says the secondary teacher, 'but they are trying – very!'

Some assumptions

I want to make some suggestions which I hope may clear the air, suggestions based on a number of assumptions which I believe would be generally accepted. The assumptions are these:

1 Both points of view contain a degree of truth, but they are in both cases presented in too extreme a form. Thus on the one hand we can be tolerably certain, both from the results of research and from our own individual observation of children in our classrooms, that children do better what they understand, enjoy it more, and can build more upon it. On the other hand the bonds between numbers, whether addition/subtraction bonds or multiplication/division bonds are essential bricks *on* which to build, and essential tools *with* which to build. For example there is no doubt that number patterns provide a rich, fertile field of exploration in the junior and lower secondary school; but if these patterns depend solely on addition and subtraction they are very restricted; if they are to include patterns involving multiplication and division, then some immediate recognition of certain 'table' facts is necessary.

For example, here is a series of numbers:

$$0, 2, 6, 12, 20, 30, 42 \ldots$$

What is the pattern? Most people I have asked see this in terms of successive additions of 2, 4, 6, 8, 10 . . . What is the 8th number? Easy, add 14, it is 56. What is the 10th number? Easy, add 16, then 18 . . . 90. What is the 100th number? Wait a minute, I'm not going to add all those up.

Can you see the pattern in some other way? Think about 42, or 56 or 90. *If we know the multiplication facts*, we may re-see the pattern as:

$$0 \times 1, 1 \times 2, 2 \times 3, 3 \times 4, 4 \times 5, 5 \times 6 \ldots$$

Then the 100th number is easy.

2 These table-facts are *only* bricks or tools – they are not an end in themselves. They are useless except in so far as they are used.

3 It is the facts themselves ($3 \times 4 = 12$, $12 \div 4 = 3$, the factors of 12 are 1, 2, 3, 4, 6, 12) which are important; the table form ($3 \times 1 = 3, 3 \times 2 = 6, 3 \times 3 = 9 \ldots$) is quite unimportant. We do want children to know these facts, and the inter-connections between them; we will not mind if they are not learned in table form.

4 The table form of learning these facts in many ways obscures the inter-connections; at the least, it is not helpful in highlighting these connections. For example, consider the following statements:

$3 \times 4 = 12$
$4 \times 3 = 12$
$3 \times 4 = 4 \times 3$
3 is a factor of 12
4 is a factor of 12
12 is a multiple of 3
12 is a multiple of 4
$12 \div 4 = 3$
$12 \div 3 = 4$
$12_{\text{base }10} = 110_{\text{base }3} = 30_{\text{base }4}$

All these statements are very closely connected, and all are important: but the table form highlights only the first two statements and ignores or obscures all the rest.

Other disadvantages of concentration on the table form are:

(a) It obscures the relationship
between multiples of 2, 4 and 8
between multiples of 3, 6 and 9
and between multiples of 5 and 10.

(b) 63 and 64 are, after all, next to each other on the number line, yet they appear in quite different tables. The connection between 8×8 and 7×9, as one instance of the general case $x^2 - 1 = (x + 1)(x - 1)$ comes, I find, to most teachers as a complete surprise; and yet the tables conceal many instances of this general form: 3 and 4, 8 and 9, 15 and 16, 24 and 25, 35 and 36, 48 and 49, etc.

(c) Commutativity is not made explicit: for example 4 X 7 and 7 X 4 appear in quite different tables. Of course one points out the connection, but one shouldn't have to.

(d) 24 appears in many different tables. In general the table form concentrates on multiplication and multiples, and is unhelpful about division and factors; and yet the set of factors of a number is at least as important as the set of multiples of a number. I have recently asked ten separate groups of primary teachers to write down (i) the multiples of 3 as far as 24 and (ii) the factors of 24. In every case part (ii) took twice as long, caused twice the number of worried looks, and was incorrectly done by most.

(e) The table form makes the 10 times table look easy: it is, of course, easy to memorise this particular set of facts; but it completely obscures the point that these facts are one of the corner stones of *place value* rather than of simple multiplication. Keeping only to base ten, it does not seem to me that 'three tens make thirty' and 'ten threes make thirty' are equally obvious. The first *is* simple: the second is not at all so obvious.

(f) The multiples of 11 and 12 are simply not worth the trouble involved. The 11 times table is useless, and the 12 times table is better seen as a question of long multiplication, particularly as metrication and decimalisation will make these facts less commonly used.

5 Children learn better by starting with a small collection of things which they understand and then, when these are familiar, by building on these facts and extending them, using similar methods. For example larger numbers should be seen as extensions of smaller numbers which behave in a similar way, just as negative numbers and rationals are an extension of the natural numbers. The table form, however, keeps leap-frogging up the number line, and then leaping back to square one in a manner calculated to bemuse the clearest young mind.

6 Children of primary age need visual or tactual pegs on which to hang abstractions. Thus numbers in particular, being totally abstract, need some visual or tactual representation to make them accessible to young children.

7 The reasons why a teacher may wish children to know the multiplication/ division bonds between numbers may well be different from the reasons which may impel *children* to want to know them. The teacher's reasons may be more remote and long-term; children will need more immediate satisfactions, and these satisfactions will be more successful if they are intrinsic to the field of study than rewards/marks/punishments, which are extrinsic, which say in effect, 'I can't think of a reason why you should want to know those facts, so I'll make you learn them regardless'. Such an attitude is at best an admission of failure; at worst it is an insult to the child's ability and desire to learn.

8 A personal belief, but one I know is shared by others: the numbers from 1 to 100 are a much under-used source of excitement for children. The introduction of place value opens up the possibility (or the threat) of using much larger numbers; it often tends to obscure the over-riding importance of familiarity with the smaller numbers. It is, for example, on an investigation of patterns and connections between these numbers that the generalisations of the algebra

numbers will be properly based. Too often the generalisations precede the investigations; too often the investigations are never undertaken.

For example, the series 0, 2, 6, 12, 20, 30, 42 . . . may be seen by some as

0×1 and by others as	$0^2 + 0$
1×2	$1^2 + 1$
2×3	$2^2 + 2$
3×4	$3^2 + 3$
4×5	$4^2 + 4$
$\vdots$	$\vdots$

Clearly these sets of expressions are equivalent, and we can *go on* to write this equivalence more neatly as $n \times (n + 1) = n^2 + n$.

That is the right order of events:

(a) play with numbers
(b) find some patterns
(c) generalise by algebra.

Some proposals

Now to some concrete proposals, first about restructuring the order in which these facts should be met by children, then about methods.

My proposal about the order in which children should meet these facts is very simple: instead of separating the facts into ten subsets — the ten tables — I suggest that they should be built up in three stages:

Stage 1 — Acquaintance with numbers up to 20 (*roughly* the infant stage).
Stage 2 — Acquaintance with numbers up to 50 (*roughly* the lower junior stage).
Stage 3 — Acquaintance with numbers up to 100 (*roughly* the upper junior stage).

Thus all the following are examples of Stage 1 facts, and all are equally important:

$3 \times 5 = 15$
$12 \div 4 = 3$
$2 \times 3 = 3 \times 2$
multiples of 4 are 4, 8, 12, 16, 20
factors of 18 are 1, 2, 3, 6, 9, 18
13 is a prime number

The general intention would be that children should initially become friendly with the numbers up to 20; this familiarity would then be extended to the numbers up to 50, and finally to 100.

The two main advantages which I see in such a restructuring would be first, that each stage would build on the previous stage, extending and enlarging while including it, and second that at any stage teachers and children would have a coherent set of numbers within which most aspects of number work could be explored. At present children are more than likely to meet numbers like 27, 40, even 100 as numbers appearing in tables, *before* they meet them as numbers which they can use for addition and subtraction.

Methodology — the basic concept of the rectangle

How then could children explore these numbers, bearing in mind that they need concrete representations of them? My suggestions here are not radically new, but I do believe that they bring together a number of strands present in number work but not hitherto unified from the start.

An important starting point is that we are here primarily concerned with multiplication and division. So long as addition and subtraction are the main concern, the number line is a useful metaphor. Addition and subtraction can usefully be seen as moves to the right and left respectively along the number line. Moreover the number line (or more accurately the free vectors associated with addition and subtraction) can be made concrete in the form of wooden or plastic strips — as with Unifix, Cuisenaire, Colour-Factor or Stern materials.

However, when we come to multiplication and division, the use of the number line tells only half the story. The two operations *can* be seen as repeated addition and subtraction ('so many lots of 3' or 'how many threes in . . .'). But in fact we can see in any classroom that the usual representation of 4 X 3 is not

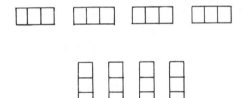

but

While up to this point the rods are seen as strips, only incidentally having width as well as length, children are suddenly assumed to accept that the width, being one unit, is also important, and the rectangle is introduced as the model.

I suggest that we make quite explicit the implication of this changeover, and see multiplication as a two-dimensional question — the making of rectangular arrays — as opposed to addition and subtraction whose analogy is the one-dimensional idea of length.

Whereas the addition and subtraction bonds will be seen in terms of *strips*, the multiplication and division bonds will be seen primarily in terms of *rectangles*. This idea is incorporated in the Dienes AEM material, but where this is used it is not introduced until the age of 9 or 10, and is then introduced in a rather perfunctory manner at a late stage in the child's development. It seems so fundamental and fruitful an idea that it should be introduced at a much earlier stage.

This, incidentally, would make much more sense of the Cartesian product, introduced to many teachers by the Nuffield 5—13 Mathematics Project in a way calculated to deter them from understanding it. For, in practical terms, the idea of the Cartesian product is the notion of the rectangle in which both measurements are equals, as opposed to the traditional view of multiplication as repeated addition on the number line where, for example, in 'three lots of four' the 'three' and the 'four' are two different sorts of numbers. Secondary teachers will no doubt be aware of the difficulties caused by the idea of multiplication as repeated addition when fractions are introduced.

Finally, here are a series of jottings about the rectangular array, which may suggest activities at various levels.

1 Man seems to like the rectangular array: milk bottled in a crate, windows in office blocks, floor tiles, banks of switches, pegboard, graph paper, calendars (I can see at a glance from my calendar for June that 30 is not divisible by 7).

2 Logic blocks:

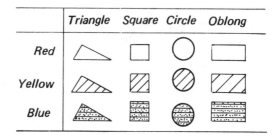

	Triangle	Square	Circle	Oblong
Red				
Yellow				
Blue				

Four shapes; *three* colours; *twelve* pieces.

3 Factors of 6:

  O O O O O O O O O O O O
           O O O O O O
                O O O
                    O
                    O

'Obviously' multiplication is commutative.

4 Prime numbers:

  O O and O O O and O O O O O

5 Square numbers:

  O and O O and O O O
     O O   O O O
          O O O

'Obviously' squares are rectangles – special rectangles.

6 Multiples of 3:

  O and O O and O O O
  O   O O O O O
  O   O O O O O

7 Consolidation

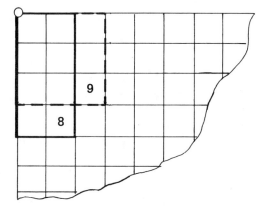

All the possible rectangles up to 6 by 6. Where are the multiples of 4? Where are the squares?

8 Consolidation again.

Take a piece of squared paper 10 by 10. Place a dot in the top left hand corner as shown. This will form the top left hand corner of a lot of rectangles which you can see on the squared paper. Two of these have been outlined on the diagram. Can you see why 8 and 9 have been written in two of the small squares? Write a number for the same reason in each of the small squares on your squared paper.

9 An extension to long multiplication: 27 × 13

27
<u>13</u>
<u>81</u> → rectangle 3 × 27
270 → rectangle 10 × 27

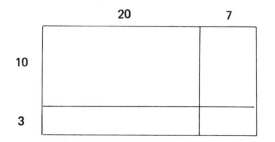

10 An extension to fractions.

● ● ○ represents ⅔ (the ratio of shaded to
the whole)

● ● ● ○ represents ¾ (the ratio of shaded
to the whole)

● ● ○ represents ⅔ × ¾, the result of which
● ● ○ is clearly $\frac{6}{12}$ (the ratio of shaded
● ● ○ to the whole).
○ ○ ○

Clearly ⅔ × ¾ is the same as $\dfrac{2 \times 3}{3 \times 4}$

(the comparison of two rectangles)

Conclusion

I hope these suggestions are seen to be both intelligible and practical, not as a radical change suggesting that the facts are unimportant or as a denial of what is useful in present practice, but as a sensible shift of emphasis which incorporates this important aspect of primary work in a wider and more mathematically coherent context. [...]

19 Taking time out

Daphne Kerslake

Source: Mathematics Teaching, vol. 73, pp. 8–10, December 1975.

<<<<<<<<<<<<<<<<<<<<<<<<<<<<<<<<<<<<<<<<<<<<<<<<<<<<<<<

Grandmother to 7 year old: 'I'll buy a watch for your birthday if you learn to tell the time by then.'
Teacher to student: 'The children should be able to tell the hours and half-hours, but they not very good at the quarter-hours yet.'
Teacher to 8 year old: 'What is the time?'
　'Twenty-five past ten.'
　'Twenty-five what? What is it twenty-five of?'
　'Twenty-five anything, I suppose.'
　Why is it that 'time' is so difficult to teach? It is the one aspect of mathematics that is still conventionally taught by rote, and one that causes many children considerable problems. How often do we see teachers manipulating the hands of a cardboard or wooden 'clock', saying 'What time is it now?'
　'Half past two.'
　'Good. Now what time is it?' as she moves the hands.
　'Quarter past ten.'
　'Right. Now you seem to understand.'
　Yet the clock on the wall of the classroom is suggesting that it is 11.30. Now we all like to think of teachers being in control of the situation, but to give the child the impression that his teacher can actually control the passage of time is surely going a bit far! Are we also making it difficult for a child to develop a concept of time, when we use these so-called 'clocks', and pages of clock faces stamped on a page, all recording different times simultaneously?
　It is important to realise that 'telling the time' is nothing more than a dial-reading exercise, and is not necessarily related to the concept of time itself. It is possible to read a dial without having any understanding of what the dial is measuring. Interpreting a clock face bears the same relation to time as using a metre rule does to the concept of length, although the clock as a measuring device is considerably more complex than a rule. It is worth considering clocks in the context of other dial-reading activities. It is not assumed, for example, by gas and electricity boards that people in general are capable of reading their

own meters. If one is out when the meter is to be read, a card is left behind, not asking one to read the dials, but to draw the position of the hands on a picture of the set of dials. It is rather like a child telling you that 'the big hand is on the seven and the small hand on the five.' In some cases, one is not asked to draw a picture of the dials, but to record the digits on either side of the hands. Yet, although the electricity and gas meters have several dials, numbered in alternate directions, they are in many ways much easier to read than clock dials. Each dial has only one hand, and has a set of digits 0—9 only. Compare this with the two hands of a clock, moving at different rates over a single scale with digits 1—12, which have to be interpreted differently, depending on the size of the hand. So a hand pointing at a seven may call for the response 'seven', or 'twenty-five to' or 'thirty-five past'. A hand pointing to a nine is sometimes to be interpreted as 'quarter-to' in addition to 'nine', 'forty-five', 'fifteen'. To add to the confusion, some watches have no digits at all marked on them, and the child will see clocks with Roman numerals, twenty-four hour clocks and digital clocks. With all this, 8 year olds are expected to be able to tell the time, while adults are not expected to read meters. Indeed, if the reading of meters is taught in school at all, then it is often done in secondary schools, perhaps in the third or fourth year, or as part of a general sixth form course! A good argument could be made for removing 'telling the time' from the primary school curriculum, and treating clocks as one of a set of dials, including speedometers, fuel guages and so on in the secondary school. But unfortunately this argument is not socially very acceptable, least of all to parents who like to be able to set time limits on children's movements, and to give them times to be home by, for example.

There is however a great deal that can be done by small children that will help to develop their *concept* of time. Time is a difficult experience to describe. The notion of it being continuous, extending infinitely into past and future, is a disturbing one, and the dictionary definitions of time as 'a limited stretch of continued existence' or 'the interval between two events' do not really make the idea much easier. Edmund Leach, addressing the Second International Congress on Mathematical Education in Exeter, suggested that time experience appears in six quite separable forms.

1 time as alternation,
2 time as sequence,
3 time as distance,
4 time as delimitation,
5 time as repetition,
6 time as ageing.

Some of these aspects can certainly provide practical activities that can be made use of in the classroom. Indeed the routine of a school day can lead to the idea of alternation — week followed by weekend followed by week, etc. — and of repetition, when the class has P.E. every Tuesday afternoon, for example. The passage of time as an ageing process can be seen in its effect on growing things kept in the classroom, weekly records on a graph of a growing plant, perhaps, or termly ones of the height of the children themselves. Activities involving timing events give the idea of delimitation, with each event having a beginning and an end. So, using arbitrary units of time, such as the time taken by water to flow from a can with a hole in its bottom, or the time it takes the can to sink when it is placed in water or the time it takes the sand to flow from one end of an eggtimer, we can time any events we choose, the time it takes to walk upstairs or downstairs, run along the corridor, walk backwards along it, count up to one hundred, or whatever. Thus we can emphasise the passage of time and the beginning and end of the activity defining an interval of time. We could use clockwork devices, and find the time they take to run down, or combine ideas of time and distance in finding how long it takes for a model car or train to travel a fixed distance. The related procedure of finding how far something travels in a fixed time, together with that of finding how long it takes to travel a fixed distance, will prepare the way for an understanding of speed. A graph of the time taken by children to travel a fixed distance is also interesting in that the child who 'wins' the 'race' has the shortest time, and therefore the smallest column on the graph, a counterexample to the common feeling that 'more is best'. Music, with its different lengths of notes and repeated rhythms, also gives valuable time experiences. The sound when a chime bar is struck will fade with time, a plucked string can be seen to vibrate for a time; some music is played fast, some slowly, and we may move quickly or slowly in response to it.

A young child entering school often has a very sketchy idea of time. Words like 'yesterday', 'last week,' 'tomorrow' (which is often used by teachers and parents as a delaying tactic, and is synonymous with 'never'!) are often not yet understood. Certainly the idea of 'last year' is likely to be very hazy. It is quite common to find a child asking half way through the morning if it is 'going-home time', or whether they have had dinner yet. It has to be explained that Saturdays and Sundays are not school days. Research suggests that it is reasonable to expect understanding of the child's own age, of morning and of afternoon by the age of six, and weeks, months and years by the age of eight, although we have all probably suffered from a grossly exaggerated view of our own age by a child, such as when we are asked if we can remember seeing Queen Elizabeth the First! We are also told that only about two thirds of all 8 year olds realise that it is the same day of the week in a nearby town. Yet in two or three years at school we expect children to be able to mark off the passage of time in hours, half-hours and quarter-hours. An hour, the first unit conventionally dealt with, is a difficult unit of time for a child, being too long for one span of attention, whereas the seconds that a stop-clock measures are much more realistic. A child can measure events in seconds and minutes much more easily; he can concentrate his attention for that period. Using hours first is a bit like expecting a child to measure in kilometres before any experience of metres or centimetres. Indeed, how well are we able to estimate the period of an hour? We all know of hours that seem to pass like minutes, and hours that seem to go on for days! This is very like the young child's view of 'five', as shown by Piaget, that spread out can seem to be more than five, and pushed together can seem less. Perhaps we are none of us at Piaget's stage of conservation as far as our concept of time is concerned.

The child's concept of time, then, is more likely to be developed by the 'timing' activities mentioned earlier, than by concentrating on 'telling the time', and likely to be harmed by wooden or cardboard 'clocks' and rows of clock faces stamped on exercise books' However, it is clearly important for a child to learn to tell the time in the conventional sense. Now, instead of measuring the passage of time, one is trying to pinpoint a particular moment of time. The clock, of course, since it has to measure something which stretches infinitely from the past to the future, is constructed so that when it arrives at the end of its scale, at 12 o'clock, it goes back to the beginning and starts again. And of course, by the time that it it 5 o'clock, the seconds have ticked by, and our reading is no longer accurate. At least when a child measures a length, he can takes his time over interpreting the ruler, and can check his measurement as many times as he likes. A child is more likely to learn to tell the time when he has a need to do so, and the first times to be important to him are the times of his favourite television programmes, the end of the school morning or afternoon, his bed-time, the time he gets up, and so on. These times may well seem to be more difficult, as they are more likely to be awkward times like 5.10, 6.40, 7.35, 12.30 and 3.45 than the hours that we tend to teach first, followed by half-hours then quarters. But children by no means always learn in the same nice tidy ways that we as adults think might be best for them. We no longer teach all about the number 1 first, then move to the number 2 and so on, and we certainly do not expect them to learn all the two letter words like 'at', 'as', 'on', 'of', 'to', 'by', 'an' before they learn to recognise three- and four-letter words. Children often learn in a random fashion, although we may prefer to present them with logical structures.

We fall back on encouraging learning by rote when the ideas we are trying to teach are too difficult for the learner. If we are prepared to spend more time on developing the concept of time and less on 'telling' it, we may make things easier for ourselves and the children.

20 Teaching algebra

David Hale

Source: specially written for this volume

<<<<<<<<<<<<<<<<<<<<<<<<<<<<<<<<<<<<<<<<<<<<<<<<<<<<<<

Introduction

Until fairly recent times only the abler child was expected to study algebra as part of his or her mathematical education and it is probably still true that the average man (or woman) in the street regards anyone who can 'do algebra' as rather unusual, perhaps slightly odd. When confronting the challenge of giving all pupils an opportunity to learn some algebra, we do well to remember that past generations of educators have regarded algebra for all as either an irrelevant slogan or too difficult a task to attempt. There is little doubt that, with hindsight, these views were unduly pessimistic and defeatist. But it can also reasonably be argued that algebra, perhaps more than any other area of mathematics, needs sensitive and imaginative treatment by the teacher if it is to have meaning and interest for all pupils.

If there is general agreement that one of the contemporary aims of mathematics teaching should be to provide most children with an understanding of, and a reasonable facility in, the application of algebraic methods, then there is also some obligation to ask to what extent we are succeeding in this aim; is the effort being made by teachers and pupils producing a reasonable pay-off? An objective reading of HMSO's report on secondary education (1979) and their report of 1980 would seem to suggest that for many 15 to 16 year olds, perhaps a majority, the outcome of their algebraic efforts is disappointing; they have little confidence in applying the algebraic procedures which have been practised regularly over the preceding three years or so.

There are several possible responses to this apparent lack of success:

1 abandon the aim of algebra for all,
2 practise the procedures (collecting like terms, removing brackets, etc.) even more assiduously than before,
3 plan the early stages of learning algebra in such a way that later developments are based on a sound basis of understanding and experience.

This article takes the view that the first response is unacceptable — a considerable educational gain would be lost — and that the second response has and is, being tried with little sign of benefit to the majority of pupils. It is the third option which may provide the most hopeful means of improving the quality of algebraic performance in the classroom. The article suggests what might be involved in developing a sound basis of understanding and experience in algebra.

How algebra begins in many classrooms today

Apart from a fortunate minority, adults tend to remember their first encounter with algebra at school as a sudden and traumatic experience which left a lasting and not always happy impression. In all probability the encounter was with the manipulation of algebraic symbols rather than with the notion of algebra as a generalised version of previous work in arithmetic. The result of such initiation was often counter-productive: many adults will say that they never did understand what was happening once letters, as well as numbers, started to appear on the blackboard.

Have recent generations of pupils had better algebraic experiences? Clearly there have been significant gains, not least in pupils' attitudes towards mathematics in general and algebra in particular. But the impression persists that pupils are introduced to algebra today in ways that have changed little over the years, and as a result may be as mystified as their parents were about the letters which suddenly appear on the blackboard and in the text book. The 11 year old pupil may still be solving simple linear equations by applying rules in an unthinking way and neglecting to check the reasonableness of answers.

Consider an equation as $2x - 3 = 9$ (or the form $2 \times \square - 3 = 9$). Some 11 year olds will interpret it as: 'I think of a number, double it and subtract three. The answer I get is nine'. This interpretation, followed by a trial-and-error method of solution might provide a surer basis for later work than the early introduction of rules for solution of the 'change side, change sign' variety.

On another occasion the children might be working through an exercise on the collection of like terms. They may be working on the expression

$$3a + 2b - 3a - 4b + 5b$$

and, remembering the advice 'you can't add apples and bananas'.

(It is interesting to note that this statement can be criticised on at least three counts — mathematically, pedagogically, and as a matter of common sense. How many pupils believe, as a result, that algebra is a strange game played with the initial letters of nouns?)

Or again, the exercise may be concerned with substitution but it is unlikely that the expressions involved will have any tangible meaning: at best the pupil demonstrates that he or she can follow an abstract procedure successfully.

They may be told that in a given sequence the nth term $= 4n + 4$ and asked to find the nth term when $n = 100$ by substitution. This formula *could* relate to the length of wood needed to surround a square picture whose side is n cm long *and* might conceivably be used by professional picture framers to price the frames they make for customers. Knowing this would provide a tangible reason for the existence and use of such a formula.

There is another more subtle and important sense in which children's introduction to algebra may be unsatisfactory. If algebra is seen by the pupil as a completely new topic, unrelated to any previous mathematical knowledge or experience he or she has acquired, then it will not be surprising if lack of confidence and understanding soon lead to disenchantment and frustration. This is precisely how many pupils appear to see the topic: with no roots and no context.

What can be done to give algebra a meaningful context

It is important to recognise that the roots of algebra lie in the arithmetic of primary and first schools. There is a crucial role for teachers in providing clear links with past work; this cannot be overemphasised. The examples in the previous section also suggest that the teaching of algebra calls for a resourceful and imaginative approach and it may be helpful to take these points a little further and try to indicate some teaching approaches which may particularly facilitate pupils' learning.

Number work which involves recognising, describing or extending patterns has considerable value as a precursor to formal algebra. For instance, the teacher who helps children to notice the patterns in number as they learn their elementary number bonds is, at the same time, laying the foundations of algebra which will then leave links with their early experience. Whilst emphasising that important foundations for algebra need to be laid before the pupil reaches the secondary stage, it is not being suggested here that an introduction to algebraic symbolism is necessarily appropriate — that will depend on the judgement of the primary school teacher.

Personal experience as well as research evidence indicates that we all need tangible assistance in moving towards the acquisition of abstract notions such as that of generalisation, a key concept of algebra. The teacher who devises appropriate class and group activities involving the use of concrete materials — cubes, matchsticks, squared paper, etc. — is giving pupils vital reference points for later work of a more abstract nature. Teachers can refer children to earlier apparatus-based activities which all embody the same mathematical concepts and help them to extract what is the same about all of them. The resulting abstraction involves children in generalising their experiences, thereby giving them a grasp of this fundamental algebraic idea. In the primary stages this will usually involve verbal statements, but the principle is precisely the same as the more sophisticated processes using letters and numbers developed later in the middle and secondary levels. It may not be sufficiently realised, though, that the use of such materials can profitably extend into the secondary school. As algebraic work progresses and the use of symbols increases the need to give an understandable context persists though this may now be done by reference to everyday situations in which formulae or expressions arise rather than the use of concrete objects themselves.

One such example is the not very well-known formula:

$$d = \frac{72}{r}$$

This gives the time, d years, in which prices will double given an annual inflation rate of r per cent. Thus if inflation runs at 12% per annum, prices will double about every 6 years.

If it is important for the teacher to devise appropriate activities using a range of ideas and materials, then his or her role as manager and director of the activities in the classroom is crucial. The task is complex and involves ensuring that there is sufficient time for class or group discussions. It is easy to underestimate how long pupils will need first to collect their thoughts into a sufficiently ordered form and then to express them in a coherent way; any attempt to rush this process will almost certainly be self-defeating. The value of pupils communicating orally their tentative generalisations in situations such as the following matchstick square example cannot be over stressed.

matchstick squares

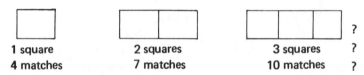

| 1 square | 2 squares | 3 squares | ? |
| 4 matches | 7 matches | 10 matches | ? |

Until a child has attempted to express in simple everyday language how the number of matchsticks is related to the number of squares, it is unlikely that the use of algebraic symbolism will serve a useful purpose, indeed it may inhibit future development by introducing a degree of abstraction for which the pupil is not ready.

In the type of activity just referred to, the nature and timing of the teacher's intervention is all important. On the one hand he or she will want pupils to make the verbal generalisation about numbers of matches and squares for themselves, on the other hand there will be some, perhaps the majority, who need various degrees of guidance if they are to be successful within a reasonable time. The professional skill involved in handling such a situation is of a high order: pupils who make the generalisation quickly will need further challenge and stimulus, others will require patient and positive encouragement if they are to reach their goal.

Concluding comments

The need for pupils to play an active part in learning algebra has long been recognised but not always practised.

> It should be borne in mind, however, that the pupil will benefit more from the invention and interpretation of formulae than from their application, since the latter process may easily be and remain merely mechanical.
>
> (Senior School Mathematics)

If pupils are to achieve a pay-off which is commensurate with the time and effort expended on algebra it could be claimed that two major conditions need to be fulfilled:

1 The early work should develop naturally from previous arithmetical experience and there should be ample time for discussion leading to the expression of generalisations in simple everyday language.

2 Subsequent work should not be obsessively concerned with symbol manipulation for its own sake; techniques should be learned and practised only in so far as they will be needed to solve problems which are seen to be interesting (as in the case of some recreational puzzles) or relevant ('real life' application for example).

The illustrations given in this article are intended to suggest how these conditions might be met in the classroom.

References

Aspects of Secondary Education in England, HMSO, 1979.
Mathematical development: Secondary Survey Report No. 1, HMSO, 1980.
Senior School Mathematics: Board of Education, HMSO, 1935.

21 A structural approach to primary school geometry

David Fielker

Source: Mathematics Teaching vol. 63, pp. 12–17, June 1973.

If one takes a cynical view of primary-school geometry today — and I have met many teachers who do — then one could very well dismiss it as a series of party tricks. One dabbles in curve-stitching, symmetry, tessellations and a few topological topics, all of which may be a lot of fun, and generally recognisable perhaps as geometry, but where does it all fit in?

Everybody does curve-stitching, from the age of five up to fifteen in fact, and they all seem to get the same out of it. The sole justification seems to be a demonstration that curves can be produced from straight lines. The rest is art or design.

Symmetry usually involves a look at butterflies and buildings, and at Christmas the windows of any primary school are decorated with symmetrical Christmas trees and snowflakes (the latter usually octagonal rather than hexagonal!) — which seems to be more Christmas decoration than mathematics.

Most primary pupils now study something we call 'shape'. This means that they can recognise a square, rectangle, triangle or circle, and perhaps a hexagon; it depends which logical blocks you use! But too many infant classrooms have a chart on the wall saying 'these are triangles' and showing lots of coloured triangles, all equilateral and all with a horizontal base, so that the children do not recognise a triangle which is a different shape or a different way up. And too many pupils use incorrectly the words 'rectangle' and 'oblong'.

These are details, it is true, but primary school geometry, free from a practical introduction to Euclid and from the numerical aspects of length, area and volume, seems to be nothing but detail, a patchy set of enjoyable experiences with no structure to hold them together other than the teacher's intuitive feeling that it is all part of mathematics.

We seem to have the topic of number sorted out. We realise the psychological and pedagogical implications of one-to-one correspondence and conservation, we know the difference between ordinal and cardinal number, and we recognise that there are concepts of natural number and place value, etc. We have some order in which to develop these ideas.

It may be more helpful to analyse number from a more mathematical point of view. We have, for instance, different *sets* of numbers, whole numbers, fractions, and later positive and negative integers, and within these we have subsets like even or odd numbers, square numbers and multiples of three. Then we do things with numbers, usually the 'four rules', addition, subtraction, multiplication and division. These are ways of taking two numbers and combining them to produce a third number, and these are called *operations*.

Less obvious is the emphasis we put on *relations* between numbers. We begin with relations like 'bigger than' and 'smaller than', which we apply to things other than numbers, and progress to more sophisticated relations like 'is double', 'is the square of', or 'is divisible by'.

If we isolate the *structure* of the number situation then we have the ideas on which all mathematical structures are based. We have *sets* (in this case sets of numbers); we have *operations* on these sets, i.e. ways of combining two members of a set to produce a third; and we have *relations* between members of a set. (If you want to get more abstract than this then you can have *sets of relations* and *operations* on these and . . .).

Now if we want to think in a structural way about geometry, let's take these three ideas. In geometry we have *sets* of things, and in fact we have more choice than we do in arithmetic. Let's explore *operations* on these sets, that is, ways of combining two geometric entities to produce a geometric entity, and *relations* between these entities. There will probably be a difference in emphasis, because usually in the primary school one is concerned with operations on numbers. (I am not sure if this is a good thing, and it might be an idea if we thought more about relations between numbers instead of worrying so much about the four rules.) Perhaps the emphasis in geometry is on relations, but we shall see; because thinking about the *whole* structure in any branch of mathematics usually opens up more possibilities.

Now what sort of geometric entities can we deal with?

Take a straight line.

This is not much on its own, so take another straight line.

We don't get much out of combining the two straight lines, so let's explore relations between them. (The pupils should tackle all these problems with shapes drawn on tracing paper or acetate sheet.) If I move one of them I can perceive a relation which changes, the *angle* between them. Can we think of angle as a relation between two straight lines? In fact, whichever way you teach the idea of angle it amounts to this. And there are some particular cases of this relation, like 'perpendicular'

or 'parallel'.

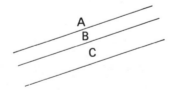

Yet how often are these two relations taught quite separately from the idea of angle? The structural approach is unifying — these are all relations between straight lines. Furthermore the relation 'perpendicular' can be freed from 'horizontal' and 'vertical'. (Are these relations, and where do they fit in?)

One consequence of thinking structurally is that we can borrow structural ideas from other branches of mathematics. We know that if 3 is bigger than 2, and 2 is bigger than 1, then 3 is bigger than 1; and we can solve those old 11+ riddles about Bill being older than Charlie and Charlie being older than Alfred. Consider three parallel lines, A, B and C

'A is parallel to B and B to C' the class of 11 year olds told me.

'Then A is parallel to C' I said, without thinking.

'No,' they said!

'Why not?'

'Because B is in the way!'

I can make a square

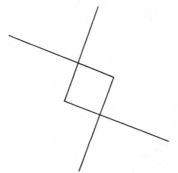

In fact, I can make a whole set of squares, and can specify the relation between the right angles to ensure this. I can make a set of rectangles,

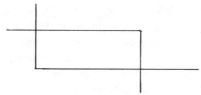

with similar considerations; or a set of kites;

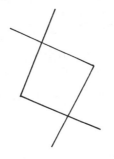

or a more general set of quadrilaterals (all with a particular property that will be more evident to the mathematician — but this need not concern us).

Take a set of parallel lines. (This now becomes a member of a set — a set of parallels.) Combine this with another set of parallel lines.

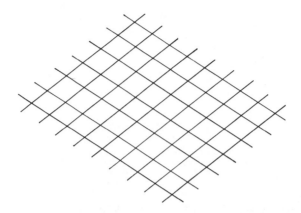

According to the relation between the two sets (if you can bear in mind which are sets and which sets are members — you see how complex the situation can be if you want it to!) the shapes that appear will be different rhombuses ('diamonds' is such an ambiguous word), and just as 'perpendicular' was a particular angle relation so the square is seen as a particular member of the set of rhombuses. In the same way, if the distances between one set of parallel lines are different from those of the other, a tessellation of parallelograms is produced and the rectangle is seen as a particular parallelogram. Note also how the relation between the two sets of lines tells you something about the angle properties of a parallelogram.

Now we can perhaps achieve something more fruitful with circles than some nomenclature and an idea about π. Consider possible relations between a circle and a straight line

and between two circles.

The idea of tangency becomes a simple one, and so does the idea of a common tangent.

Perhaps the ultimate problem for bright juniors is: how many distinct ways can you arrange three different circles?

Pupils can experiment with cardboard discs to find ways of arranging sets of circles so that they touch. What happens if you draw in some common tangents?

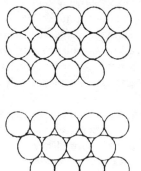

A related set of problems is due to Colin Banwell. Can you arrange sets of circles so that each touches 2 others; 3 others; 4 others; etc.? How many distinct arrangements are there each time?

We seem to have done quite a lot without saying very much about shape. Our geometrical entities have been straight lines or circles which are simpler than polygons, but polygons have been produced by combining them, that is operating on them.

Sets of shapes can be sorted into sets, remembering that younger children in particular may not choose the attributes that seem obvious to us (*see* 'Sets for Squares' in *Mathematical Teaching*, no. 61). But in their continual classification pupils will appreciate relations like reflection, rotation, congruence and similarity, and symmetry in particular will appear as a relation between a shape and itself.

Geometrical shapes, a set of wooden shapes produced by School Utilities, is particularly interesting for the opportunities it provides for operation on shapes. For instance, two right-angled triangles will combine to give a rectangle.

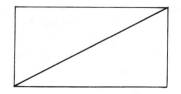

This raises problems like: what other shapes can be made from the two triangles? What shapes can be made from two isosceles right-angled triangles?

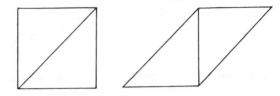

What other shapes will combine to give a rectangle, or a square?

This last question is rather like following sums (3 + 7 = ?, 4 + 6 = ?) with the question: what can you add together to make 10? The 'story of ten' becomes 'the story of the rectangle'. In other words, the operation of combination becomes the inverse one of dissection. As well as asking what shapes fitted together will make, we can ask what shapes taken apart will make. Both activities are embodied in the well-known tangram, for instance, another geometrical toy that we can now fit into the structure.

There is a connection here with simple fractions, which need not worry us too much, but it reminds me of Derick Last's stimulating film loop *Let's Take Half*, Rank, which suggests a variety of dissections of a square. Other ideas appeared in 'Dissections on a Geoboard' in *Mathematics Teaching*, no. 61.

Tessellations, too, can be seen as combinations of shapes, taken many at a time instead of just two, in the same way as 2 + 2 can be extended to 2 + 2 + 2 . . . Tessellation is the geometric analogue of multiplication!

We need not go quite as far as this. There are some interesting duplication (or replication) problems in which a shape becomes enlarged by being combined with itself or with other shapes.

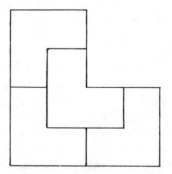

Both tangrams and polyominoes provide some well-known puzzles.

We can become too obsessed with the non-overlapping juxtaposition of shapes typified by polyominoes. Take some clear plastic polygons like Geometric Shapes (Taskmaster) and what pupil will not be tempted to put one square on top of the other?

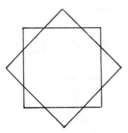

You can pat him on the head and say, 'That's very nice. Now get on with what I have asked you to do'! Or you can base a whole lesson on a discussion of what he has produced. (How many sides has it, 8 or 16? What will other polygons produce? When is the octagon regular?) One problem is to find out what else can be produced from the intersection of the two squares. By just using a right angle of each we can produce the quadrilaterals discussed earlier. Can you produce a pentagon, a hexagon or a heptagon? For each set of polygons, what is special about them?

All these examples do not provide a syllabus for primary school geometry. Structure is not a syllabus, although it may help you to put a syllabus together. And there is no reason why you should not continue to teach geometry in bits and pieces. The question 'Where does it all fit in?' is asked by teachers, not by pupils. The structure gives the teacher a mathematical frame of reference, and therefore some coherence *for the teacher* to the activities given to the pupils.

The pupils do not worry about the lack of coherence. As long as they are having fun with the activity and getting something out of it they will not mind what they do. They do not want a structure yet. They will understand structure later, when they are at the top of the secondary school, or perhaps not until they teach mathematics!

Perhaps even for the primary teacher the structure is not of first importance. What is important is what activities to give the pupils. The advantage of the structure is that when you begin to see where things fit in you also see where the gaps are. If you know where a particular activity fits into the structure you can then examine the structure for other activities, and for problems that the pupils can solve.

For one of the barren aspects of primary school geometry is that so much of it concerns the formation of concepts about space and the mere observation of geometrical entities in space. We look round the room and observe rectangles, or look at leaves and observe symmetry. In arithmetic we pose problems and encourage pupils to think about solutions (though that may be debatable). This is not so in geometry, which tends at primary level to be all observation and no problems. Structure provides the problems as well as the activities.

And it makes you feel better about the party tricks.

22 From edges to solids

Marie Kuper and Marion Walter

Source: Mathematics Teaching, vol. 74, March 1976.

Choose three numbers, for example, 3, 5, 8. Draw and cut out all possible rectangles using any of these numbers as the lengths of the sides.

Sometimes, when they begin, children will say that they cannot make a rectangle out of only three lengths or sides, so you need to explain that they are allowed to use a length more than once. Some children think that squares are not rectangles, and this confusion affords a good opportunity for discussion. Once the children get going, they soon find all six rectangles.

We have then provided each small group of children with about fifteen rectangles of each type. One does not need quite that many cut-outs but it is useful for the children to have more than they really need. Now ask each group to make all possible different boxes with these rectangles. Do not, at this point, explain what you mean by 'different'. You may want to ask the children to guess in advance how many different boxes there will be. Even adults do not always come 'close' in their guesses.

It is interesting to watch children (and adults!) make the boxes. Some do it by laying out the nets of the boxes and then sticking the pieces together. Others hold up the pieces in their final positions and stick them piece by piece. Combinations that do not work are often tried.

When the boxes have been made, you can ask them to check that no two boxes are the same shape.

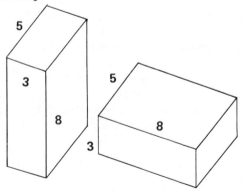

Children can then compare their collections and reassure themselves that they have all ten possibilities.

A challenging problem now is to order the boxes by eye according to volume. Try this yourself first! Let the children label and list the boxes in order of their guesses and only then let them calculate the volume of the boxes. When they have completed a table they may be surprised!

Table 1

	Box	Volume
A	3, 3, 3	27
B	3, 3, 5	45
C	3, . . .	. .
D	. . .	. .
E	. . .	. .
.	. . .	. .
.	. . .	. .
J	8, 8, 8	512

One may try other number triples as starting points. Arranging the boxes by eye may then be more (or less) difficult.

You can suggest a variety of games to give children a better 'feel' for the differently shaped boxes. Ask two or more children to play together. One child closes his eyes, while the other hides a box; then the first child tries to find which one was hidden. This is not so easy.

Another game is based on arranging the boxes in sets. One child groups the boxes into two or more sets, according to a rule of his own. The other child, or children, try to guess the rule the first one used. Among classifications that children have chosen in this game are:

1 those with square faces, those without,
2 those that are cubes, those that are non-cubes;
3 those with some 3 cm edges, those without any 3 cm edges. (They may say, 'Those that are flat and those that are not'.)

Of course, you could encourage them to find non-empty intersections if these are not suggested by the children.

It is not impossible for even young children to make the following table. They can find the necessary information by counting.

Table 2

No. of edge lengths	Possible no. of squares	Possible no. of rectangles (non-squares)	Total
1	1	0	1
2	2	1	3
3	3	3	6
4	4	6	10

They can examine the table for number patterns and perhaps even find the general rule. We shall discuss this activity more fully later.

If you arrange the boxes in order of increasing *volume,* will they also be in order of increasing *surface area*? What about the sums of the edge lengths? Are they in the same order? How is this related to the volume of the box?

Incidentally, even children who have not learned to calculate volume can compare volumes by filling the boxes with small beans (then counting or weighting them), or packing them tightly with unit cubes. While trying to fill a box with cubes a ten-year-old realised very quickly that she would not have to complete filling the box but needed only to do the following,

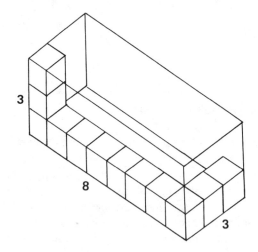

and she did the rest by multiplying.

If you provide one set of well-made boxes then the volumes can be found with sand or even water. Graph paper can be used to compare surface areas, by counting squares. Do not attempt to get the children to make well finished boxes at this stage. If they need a well-made set of boxes then give them a pre-pared set. It is important however, that the accuracy of building does not distract them while they are finding out how many boxes it is possible to make.

With older children we can generalise the above questions to any number of different lengths.

Given four lengths, such as 2, 3, 5 and 8, there are at least two ways in which a pupil can tackle the problem of how many rectangles and boxes there are. One way is to draw and build and then count. Comparison by the pupils will help to eliminate duplicates and find any missing ones. Another method is to find a systematic way to tabulate the rectangles and boxes. The problem can also be solved using combinatorial theory.

Let us first look at the specific case of only three lengths, such as 3, 5 and 8. For a rectangle of sides a and b we can first choose a as 3. Then b will be 3, 5 or 8 giving three different rectangles. Taking a as 5 we can get a new rectangle when b is 5 or 8. Finally, if a is 8, there is only the 8 by 8 square. In all we have

$$3 + 2 + 1 = 6$$

different rectangles. By similar arguments one can find the number of rectangles, given 4, 5, 6, . . ., n different edge lengths. Now the pupils are ready to find the number of different boxes for a given value of n by working with edges and enumerating all possibilities without duplicates.

Another method is to consider *rectangles* rather than *edges* and enumerate how many ways they can be put together.

Table 3

No. of edge lengths (column 1)	No. of rectangles (column 2)	No. of boxes (column 3)
1	1	1
2	3	4
3	6	10
4	10	20

We can see some number patterns in this table. For example, the number of rectangles increases regularly, i.e. the differences are in arithmetic progression. The first differences in column 3 are the same numbers as in column 2. This pattern helps us to generalise for the case when the number of different edge lengths is n. By examining the table, pupils can notice that for the general case the number of rectangles will be

$$\frac{n(n + 1)}{2}$$

The number of boxes with n different edge lengths is more difficult to calculate. The students can certainly notice that the nth entry in column 3 is the sum of all possible rectangles up to n, i.e., the sum of the numbers in column 2.

One can also compute the number of rectangles starting with n edges by first looking at the non-square rectangles. There are

$$\binom{n}{2} = \frac{n(n - 1)}{2}$$

rectangles of that type. To this we must add the number of squares, which is of course n, so for n different edge lengths, we can make

$$\frac{n(n - 1)}{2} + n = n\frac{(n + 1)}{2}$$

different rectangles.

To find the total number of boxes, we first compute the number of boxes with no square sides. This is

$$\binom{n}{3} = \frac{n(n - 1)(n - 2)}{1.2.3}$$

221

For the number of boxes with two square faces we are free to choose only two lengths, that is the length of the side of the square and the length of the third edge. For each choice of a and b we get two different boxes, namely $a \times a \times b$ and $a \times b \times b$.

Thus we must multiply $\left(\dfrac{n}{2}\right)$ by 2.

There are n solids all of whose faces are squares, i.e. the cubes. Obviously it is not possible to make boxes with four or with an odd number of square sides, so our count is complete. In all we have

$$\frac{n(n-1)(n-2)}{1.2.3} + \frac{2n(n-1)}{1.2} + n$$
$$= \frac{n(n+1)(n+2)}{6}$$

different boxes. This result is equal to

$$\sum_{1}^{n} \frac{m(m+1)}{2}$$

Notice that the number of boxes without square faces is

$$\frac{n(n-1)(n-2)}{6}$$

Investigation of this question could be an interesting exercise for younger children and they could find the result inductively.

After we had built a set of ten boxes using edge lengths 2, 3 and 5, we ourselves tried to arrange them in order of volume by eye. We found that several pairs of boxes were rather difficult to put in the correct order. Both children and adults found it an enjoyable and surprisingly challenging exercise.

We wanted to investigate this situation further and see if it was possible to find a way to predict the 'dangerous' boxes, for this and other sets of numbers. We decided to arrange the boxes in a systematic order and arbitrarily chose the order shown. We labelled them A to J and repeated the calculations for a second set of a, b, c, the edge lengths, labelling these boxes A′ to J′. The results for our two sets of values are shown below.

Table 4

Boxes	Edge lengths 3, 5, 8	Volume	Boxes	Edge lengths 2, 7, 11	Volume
A	3, 3, 3	27	A′	2, 2, 2	8
B	3, 3, 5	45	B′	2, 2, 7	28
C	3, 3, 8	72	C′	2, 2, 11	44
D	3, 5, 5	75	D′	2, 7, 7	98
E	3, 5, 8	120	E′	2, 7, 11	154
F	3, 8, 8	192	F′	2, 11, 11	242
G	5, 5, 5	125	G′	7, 7, 7	343
H	5, 5, 8	200	H′	7, 7, 11	539
I	5, 5, 8	320	I′	7, 11, 11	847
J	8, 8, 8	512	J′	11, 11, 11	1331

Notice that according to our systematic listing of the boxes the first set (A to J) were not arranged in order of ascending volume, while the second set (A' to J') were. The pairs of boxes E and G, C and D were difficult to arrange by eye and, as can be seen, were close together in volume, but not adjacent in our table. This led us to ask the question, what are the conditions on edge lengths $a \leqslant b \leqslant c$ so that for *our* particular ordering system, the boxes would be arranged in order of ascending volume?

Table 5

Boxes	Edge lengths a, b, c	Volume	Ratio of the volume of neighbouring boxes
A	a, a, a	a^3	
B	a, a, b	$a^2 b$	$\dfrac{a}{b}$
C	a, a, c	$a^2 c$	$\dfrac{b}{c}$
D	a, b, b	ab^2	$\dfrac{ac}{b^2}$
E	a, b, c	abc	$\dfrac{b}{c}$
F	a, c, c	ac^2	$\dfrac{b}{c}$
G	b, b, b	b^3	$\dfrac{ac^2}{b^3}$
H	b, b, c	$b^2 c$	$\dfrac{b}{c}$
I	b, c, c	bc^2	$\dfrac{b}{c}$
J	c, c, c	c^3	$\dfrac{b}{c}$

We wrote the volumes algebraically, and asked a young student, Gabriel Kuper, to investigate the conditions we required. He examined the table and by comparing adjacent volumes reduced the condition for increasing volumes to

$$\frac{a}{b} < \frac{b^2}{c^2} < 1$$

Notice that the number of triples 2, 7, 11 satisfy these conditions since

$$\frac{2}{7} < \frac{49}{121} < 1$$

In our first triples 3, 5, 8,

$$\frac{3}{5} > \frac{25}{64}$$

so the condition is violated and indeed the boxes were not in order of increasing volume.

There are many other questions to explore. How can we predict which boxes are 'dangerous', i.e. difficult to arrange in order by eye? When is V_C, the volume of box C, equal to V_D, the volume of box D? What about V_F and V_G? If $V_G = V_D$, then $a^2c = ab^2$ and for $V_F = V_G$, $abc = b^3$. So boxes C and D, (and also F and G) are equal in volume when $\frac{b}{a} = \frac{b}{c}$, i.e., when b is the geometric mean of a and c. If also $a + b = c$, then c is divided in the golden ratio. Note that in the case of lengths 3, 5 and 8 used in our examples, $a + b = c$ and $\frac{a}{b}$ is very close to $\frac{b}{c}$. When we choose our lengths from the Fibonacci series, we will always get these boxes close together in volume, and the closeness will improve as we go on in the series. Other problems which can be investigated are the conditions on the surface areas, and the sums of the edge lengths.

One could calculate the ratios of the volumes of neighbouring boxes arranged in a different order. Would it help for analysis to use $a, a + d_1, a + d_2$ with $d_1 \leqslant d_2$, instead of a, b and c as the lengths of the edges? Using this notation certainly provides much practice in multiplying and dividing algebraic expressions.

There are a variety of other topics which connect naturally with this problem.

1 Colouring problems. How many ways can one colour the open box and the closed box? What is the connection between these two results? Explore this problem for different numbers of colours (*see* Gardner, M., 'New Mathematical Diversions', *Scientific American* for further discussion of the colouring problem).
2 Problems relating to the surface area of the boxes.
3 Questions relating to the number of square and rectangular faces the boxes have for specific and general cases.
4 How does the condition on neighbouring volumes generalise to 4 or more edges?
5 What problems can you generate if you become aware of the fact that a, b, c may or may not be relatively prime?
6 How many different tetrehedra can one make using any of three different lengths? Four different lengths [. . .]
[This problem] is not as easy as it looks and the reader is invited to try it! You may want to make the assumption that it is possible to make triangles from all combinations.)

Having started with a concrete activity of building boxes, a mathematically rich activity for young children, we ended up with problems challenging even to high school students. Investigating a situation is one way to develop curriculum materials and we did just that while writing this material for the Israel Ministry of Education and Culture. Since books already exist about cubes and other solids we decided to investigate rectangular boxes that were not necessarily cubes.

References

Bassetti, F., Ruchlis, H. and Malament, D., *Maths Projects: Polyhedral Shapes* Book Lab, New York.

Mold, J., *Solid Models*, Cambridge University Press.

Fielker, D., *Cubes*, Cambridge University Press.

Walter, M., *Boxes, Squares and other Things: A Teacher's Guide for a Unit in Informal Geometry*, National Council of Teachers of Mathematics, Washington, D.C.

Walter, M. and Brown, S. T., 'What if not' and 'What if not: An Exploration and Second Illustration', *Mathematical Teaching*, nos *46 & 51*. We did not follow this technique here but it led us to the idea of using rectangles and tetrahedra.

Wenninger, M., *Polyhedra Models for the Classroom*, National Council of Teachers of Mathematics.

23 Problem-solving in the primary school

Christine Taylor

Source: Mathematics Teaching, vol. 70, pp. 8–13, March 1975.

The scope of problem-solving activities is as wide as one wishes to make it. 'Problems' have had many connotations in the past, developing from the large, complicated calculation type, which was supposed to develop the mind, through the 'practical' and 'realistic' phases, where problems involved 'everyday situations' such as areas of netball pitches, while the types of activities remained the same, to a wider interpretation of 'problems' since 1960. As well as verbal problems, they now involve a wide variety of environmental situations, may use simple materials or structural apparatus, and cover shape and measures as well as number.

In a study conducted in the autumn of 1973 at Nottingham College of Education, I was interested in how children's mathematical reasoning could be developed in problem-solving situations using simple materials. I found that this could best be studied by considering individual responses, and therefore I taught only a small group of 8 year olds in a variety of situations.

Inherent in each of the situations produced was more than one problem. The child's first task, therefore, was to find a problem and then, I hoped, produce a solution. This type of situation requires a certain degree of adaptability from both sides. The child needs to take an open, critical look at the situation. However, the problem on which the child focuses may not be known to the teacher, or may not have been the one that he wanted to be considered. Does the teacher then redirect the child, or let him consider the problem at hand? I felt that as I had presented a relatively open situation, the child should tackle the problem that he had found.

This approach provided some interesting work. In the 'polyominoes' situation, children were asked to make given polyominoes from unit squares. I was particularly interested in how they classified polyominoes as 'the same'. In discussing 'sameness' the children produced many different problems which were followed up. For example, in trying to describe some of the polyominoes, the children focused on the number of sides of a shape. They pointed out that for any polyomino the minimum number of sides was four (by putting the squares

226

in a straight line). The maximum number of sides of a given polyomino and the different number of sides possible were considered, but Gary was particularly interested in the effect of adding one square to a tetromino.

Gary: When you add a square you lose a side.
Me: But how many sides do you add?
Gary: Three. But not always. If you put it in some places, it just reduces the number of sides, like if you put one there.

It just fits in with the lines already there.

This aspect of the problem was extended when the children considered which pentominoes could make open boxes'.

Sara: They [the pentominoes] have to have a lot of sides ... If the squares are all together you can't fold them up.

Gary: Mine have all got lots of sides.

Although the children did not produce formal conclusions on numbers of sides of polyominoes, it can be seen that their reasoning is sophisticated for 8 year olds, and that the problems were worthy of pursuit. However, the difficulty in this approach is that the child may focus on a particular aspect of a situation which leads to trivial work, or else is beyond his present capacity. For example, at the beginning of the sessions on polyominoes, the children tended to join the squares by the points or by part-sides rather than by complete edges [. . .] This type of join meant that there was a large increase in the number of polyominoes produced. As I was interested in classifications, not the maximum number of shapes produced, I directed the children towards a conventional join after the following conversation.

Gary: I can't get them perfect. There are a lot aren't there? [trominoes]
Sara: Those aren't real shapes.
Gary: Well, the squares touch each other.
Me: What is your rule for joining squares, Sara?
Sara: I use a side.
Me: Would it make it easier if you joined all your squares by whole sides?
Gary. Yes.

227

Me: Well, we'll look at all the shapes made when we join squares by sides, not points. Is that all right, Gary?

Gary: Yes, I can get rid of these now. I'm not sure what to do with this.

It's not joined by a point, but by half of each line. I don't think it is, but I'm not sure.

There followed a lengthy verbal explanation, illustrated by moving unit squares. Had the definition of a polyomino remained open, the interesting activities that followed would not, I feel, have been produced.

Another situation used Cuisenaire rods. The children were asked to make trains, with no specific number of carriages, to fit exactly into a given station. For example, 'What trains are the same length as the yellow station (rod)?' I was interested in each child's classification of 'train' and in his strategy for making all the trains. Did he classify rods in different orders as the same train? Did he start with the next largest rod to the station and systematically work down? When presented with the situation, children tended to consider the number of trains for each station and the sequence obtained by considering successive stations. For example, one can make 3 different trains for a light green station; light green, 1 red and 1 white, 3 whites. The sequence for the first four stations is 1, 2, 3, 5.

As the children had not focused on the various trains involved in each station they did not obtain them all, and therefore the sequences produced showed no pattern. If a situation is too complex for a child to cope with, it seems that he will tend to act by trial and error rather than through logic. It seemed necessary, therefore, to impose restrictions on the situation.

As there is only a certain probability that a child will focus on a suitable problem, it would seem that the teacher may need to intervene and so needs to view himself as a director rather than as part of an audience. However, the teacher does not need to produce rigid situations for which there is only one approach. In problem-solving situations children should be developing their own strategies, to produce adaptability.

In my study I was particularly interested in any development of reasoning, as theorists, such as Piaget, do not really consider what may help a child into the next 'stage'. The children I worked with found it difficult to cope with open-ended situations. Their actions were punctuated with 'Is this what you do?', 'Is this right?', tending to think that there was only one problem and similarly only one approach and one correct answer. This limited view of mathematics meant that, initially, the children needed to be well directed and encouraged in their activities. However, the changes in their responses during the course of the study led me to the conclusion that the effect of 'teacher expectation' is even greater than I had imagined.

During the early stages the children tended to produce 'answers' to a problem, without explanations for the derivations. For example, in the Cuisenaire situation I asked: 'Have you got all the trains for that station?'

Sara: Yes.
Me: How do you know?
Sara: I just have.

In work with Indian cards, the children had to find out which attribute I was thinking of. Their first attempts suggested that they were inexperienced at, or incapable of, reasoning, and our conversations were of the following format.

Karl: I bet it's the name.
Colin: No, it's got to be the colour of feathers; it's got to be.

After this initial work, I was undecided as to my next step. Would further examples with intensive questioning produce a study of 'non-answers' or, even worse, dampen the children's inquisitiveness? There was only one way to find out! In my initial work I pressed hard for reasons, consistantly asking 'why?' After only a couple of sessions, their responses tended to anticipate this question, although their reasons were obviously limited by their abilities and experiences. On reflection it seems that the children were at a stage where reasons were unimportant to them. However, development came slowly through a series of partial insights until they came to realise the need to support any hypothesis made and to use counter examples.

For example, the Cuisenaire trains situation was the first one attempted. Gary checked his trains. When asked what he was doing he replied 'trying to get it right', referring to a sequence that he had produced. His counter-example was seen as unhelpful to him as it disrupted his pattern. In a later problem, on finding the number of different ways of getting up stairs, Gary said 'Oh, I might have found a rule.' Although he stated it, he added that we would 'have to wait and see' if it applied to the next step, as he could not think of a reason for it.

As well as looking for reasons and being tentative about hypotheses, Gary soon realised the value of counter examples, and the need for consistency.

Gary: This might go kafoo. It'll go wrong.
Sara: I think I've got a pattern. 1, 2, 3, 5, 7, 10, 14. It goes up two there, two there, three there, four there.
Gary: Another pattern that's gone kafoo. It's usually my patterns that do that!

Such rapid development was not unusual. I was interested to see how children developed their powers of logic when they were constantly confronted in the classroom by the need for reasons. The following extracts are intended to illustrate the type of results obtained from this approach.

In making 'square numbers' by building onto the sides of a square with unit squares, two children obtained the series $1 + 3 + 5 + 7 + \ldots$ Gary expected this pattern to continue, and tried to explain why.

Gary: You add one to every side.

Me: How? Can you explain?

Gary: I'll make some. By adding that one you also add one to the other side as well, and the same with the other square.

Gary referred to his square and pointed to the arrowed unit squares.

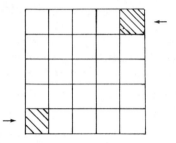

After further experience, he improved his rather limited explanations of why you only 'add on those two which join'.

Gary: The next square's one bigger; you widen it. So you have to add more.

Me: Good; but why have you got to add two more than the time before?

Gary: I've told you; to fill in the corners.

Me: Yes, but why are all the other squares that you add equal to the number before?

Gary: Well, it's a kind of optical illusion.

Me: Is it?

Gary: It looks as if it wouldn't be. If they're placed on top of each other you'll find that they're the same.

After a few manipulations Gary produced this.

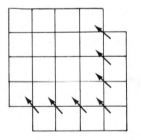

Gary: See, you push them up one from that corner onwards.

Me: So, you know that you have the same number there and then you add one to each end? (Help with verbal description).

Gary: Yes.

Me: Do you think that will always be so?

Gary: Yes.

Gary readily generalised and confidently used his rule. I felt that this was an adequate explanation at this stage. (No college student produced a better response!) It would seem that a teacher needs to weigh up the sophistication of proof against the highest level for a child at a given stage and the time which could be used for other pursuits.

On the other hand, Sara continued to build squares until she obtained $1 + 1 + 5 + \ldots + 19 + 21 + 23 + 25$. She could not see that a pattern existed, but could not accept that it would continue as she could not give an adequate explanation for it. This contrasted with her original behaviour, when she generalised as soon as possible. If I had wanted to use this series in context for further work, I would have to have produced a satisfactory explanation of it, at Sara's level. It would seem that once teachers have induced an enquiring attitude, they can no longer expect children to accept passively, without explanation, 'laws', 'rules' or 'tricks of the trade'.

Through discussions on the squares situation, Gary considered the total number of unit squares in a given square. Although he had not met square numbers before, he readily generalised that the total was equal to the square of the length of a side as it was 'the number of rows, times the number of columns, which is the same'. I hypothesised that this readiness was due to the general development of understanding through working with the situation. Gary was particularly interested in how many unit squares Sara had used.

Gary: It's fifteen by fifteen.
Me: Can you work that out?
Gary: No, I haven't gone higher than nine. (He referred to his tables.) I'm hopeless.
Me: Can you think of another way to do it?
Gary: Yes, the long way.
Me: What's that?
Gary: Count!
Me: Count them all! There must be an easier way. Could you split the big square up so that you could work out part of the square, then another part, instead of counting them all?
Gary: Well, I might have a way. Say it's 14 to start with. Divide by 2 and it's 7.
Me: Why?
Gary: Well, just half it. Now do seven fifteens.
Me: Can you do that?
Gary: No!
Me: Can you split it up again?
Gary: No, you keep losing a row. 15 to 14 you lose a row. 7 to 6 you lose another row. Then half of six is three. Three fifteens, that's a bit easier.

It would seem that Gary's manipulative experiences have helped him to discuss the problem abstractly. He added up three lots of 15.

$$
\begin{array}{r}
15 \\
15 \\
15 \\
\hline
45 \\
\hline
\end{array}
$$

Gary: 45. Oh yes, 45.
(He seemed to have lost the trend for a moment. I hint . . .)
Me: How many 3s are there in 15?
Gary: Oh, it will work out now! Four threes; no, five threes.
(He does a calculation).
Me: Can you say what you have done?
Gary: You get three fifteens, that makes forty-five. Then there's five forty-fives . . . two hundred and twenty-five!!

Although Gary apparently found out the relationship between the numbers by accident, he was able to adapt his method to further problems and enthusiastically calculated 14 X 14. He then considered 19 X 19.

Gary: Oh, 19 isn't an even split-up. Nothing makes 19.
Me: Is there another way you can split it up? (I was thinking of tens and units.)
Gary: You could do twenty and take some away, but I don't know how many to take away.

Gary knew that he had to take away two sides, but until he manually reduced a 20 X 20 to a 19 X 19, he forgot that a corner square needed to be taken away too. This meant that 39 squares were removed in all. Using his 'splitting' method, Gary calculated 20 X 20 and then subtracted 39.

A need to do a certain calculation led Gary to an introduction to long multiplication, which could have been followed up to lead to the traditional splitting into tens and units. I felt that my occasional intrusion, rather than an introduction to formal calculations, aided Gary's understanding and feel that his enthusiasm towards the calculations is particularly worth noting, considering that his initial comment on the subject was 'I'm hopeless'.

Thus I feel that attitude and expectation were strong influential factors in my results. It would seem that children can develop through the expectations presented by the teacher. Not only did the children in my own study develop their hypothesising and reasoning, but the encouragement to look for reasons seemed to produce a more logical, or systematic, approach to a situation. For example. when asked to make pentominoes, Sara added one square to each side of a tetromino and then compared the pentominoes to eliminate duplicates.

It is obvious, however, that expectation alone cannot account for the results. Other factors which seemed to affect problem-solving included the type of situation presented, the recording materials provided and whether the situation involved an element of competition.

As Piaget has stressed, children of this age find it difficult to work with abstract situations. Although I was able to obtain some success with the children in that area, I found that concrete situations motivated all children, whereas abstract ones created unexpected difficulties, as illustrated below. In one session, I presented a group of four children with squared paper, in anticipation of a consideration of routes on a grid. On reflection, an introduction using plain paper, or through a treasure island story, would have been more reasonable. However, on this occasion I jumped in at the deep end, explaining that each line was a road and that a town could be built at any cross-road, and faced the consequences!

The first problem arose when two children considered the road to run between two parallel lines, but that was only the beginning!

Me: Now, I want you to describe how you would get from one town to another town.
Colin: Posts, sign-posts.
Me: Pretend that someone knows where the towns are, but they don't know how to get from one town or the other, using the road that you have drawn. Is there any way that we can tell them?
Susan: You could post it.

'It' referred to the directions, and this led to further consideration of the practical problem of letting the person know, with an argument taking the forefront about the phone being more reliable than the post, as a letter can get lost.

Me: If I want to know how to get from the one town to the other, what would you do?
Colin: I ain't telling 'em. Let 'em find out for themselves!

Colin later had a change of heart and the children produced grid references without any further direction. However, a less abstract and more motivating introduction may have avoided such confrontations.

At the start of my study, I tended to ask the children to write everything down. It seems that teachers have a need for pieces of children's work to illustrate results! [. . .]

This insistence on recording led to irrelevant problems. For example, if one is interested in types of classification, skills such as symbolism need not be involved. In one situation a child could make triangles on a geoboard and could draw triangles on dotted or plain paper but she could not transfer one to the other. Although I was interested in her classification of 'the same triangle', I tried to insist that she made triangles on the geoboard and recorded them on paper, an unnecessary factor for this part of my study. While the child struggled with her problems of recording I could not study her classificatory skills.

As my ideas developed, recording was treated as an 'extra', something which could be used if required. I found that the children tended to be wary of symbolism. However, once needed, it was readily used and developed, beginning with a direct representation of the situation and progressing to more abstract symbols. Recording is not necessarily an aid to the development of reasoning in the preliminary stages, but at a certain stage it is useful and, at that point, a child often adopts it. For example, when Gary needed to sort out the confusion of triangles placed on top of one another on the geoboard, he decided that Sara's idea of representing triangles on dotted paper should be used. However, when making polyominoes, symbolism was a slower process.

Me: Would it help to draw them? Remember that I want you to find all the different shapes.
Gary: Yes.

However, Gary did not use the squares on the paper to draw the shapes. I had assumed a symbolic use for the paper when providing it, but Gary used it as he

233

would plain paper. I did not point out this difference, but Sara did. Gary did not seem to understand her and so ignored her. However later in the session he said, 'I'll use the squares on the paper. I'm getting confused. I'll use one square to one. I can see them more easily.' Gary also adopted this symbolism when building squares from unit squares. On spotting squared paper he commented, 'That's what I need. Now it's much easier.' It would seem that if symbolism is produced through the children's work, it is used meaningfully. I found that any imposed symbolism was difficult to use, without a great deal of practice in interpretation before commencing with the problem, without hindering reasoning.

Although I was interested in individual responses, I found group work particularly worthwhile. In the situations that the primary teacher wishes to present, the main advantage of the group situation seem to be that some individuals have more ideas than others and that any individual idea receives an evaluation which the individual working alone might not have given it. [. . .]

Groups are probably more effective when there is a complicated problem-solving situation, assuming that the children cooperate and coordinate their effort to minimise individual frustration. This depends upon the composition of the group. It would seem that a teacher needs to be observant of individual reactions to situations as the organisation of a group may affect motivation or anxiety. For example, I found that the lower ability children were helped to clarify their own thoughts by other children giving explanations in their own language. Alternatively, some situations produced a competitive element, with comments on classification of "the same" including "We're right, not them, ain't we?' and 'You must be thick', re-emphasising the 'only one right answer' attitude. Competition of the 'I've got more than you' sort had an obvious detrimental effect on one child; she began to tremble, bite her nails and worked well below normal 'capacity'.

In many situations, group work produced more conversation and participation, and 'better reasoning' seemed to take place. However, I could not judge whether this increased performance was due to the group situation alone or due to practice in the skills required for problem solving. It is probable, though, that better results were produced by diplomatic steering of arguments into discussions. It seems preferential to see children working together as a group to produce a solution, rather than competing against one another.

Thus it would seem that children's mathematical reasoning is affected by a variety of extraneous factors. However, I feel that if there is one factor which outweighs the others in effect, it is the expectation of the teacher. The developments in reasoning of the children in my study can best be explained through their reactions towards my attitude to problem-solving situations. At the end of one session a child looked me steadily in the eyes and declared 'You're mad on reasons.' To me, that is what mathematics is all about.

24 Teaching children to be mathematicians versus teaching about mathematics

Seymour Papert

Source: International Journal of Mathematics Education in Science and Technology vol. 3, pp. 249–262, (abridged) 1972.

≪≪≪

Summary

The important difference between the work of a child in an elementary mathematics class and that of a mathematician is not in the subject matter (old fashioned numbers versus groups or categories or whatever) but in the fact that the mathematician is creatively engaged in the pursuit of a personally meaningful project. In this respect a child's work in an art class is often close to that of a grown-up artist. The paper presents the results of some mathematical research guided by the goal of producing mathematical concepts and topics to close this gap. The prime example used here is 'turtle geometry', which is concerned with programming a moving point to generate geometric forms. By embodying the moving points as a 'cybernetic turtle' controlled by an actual computer, the constructive aspects of the theory come out sufficiently to capture the minds and imaginations of almost all the elementary school children with whom we have worked — including some at the lowest levels of previous mathematical performance.

Introduction

Being a mathematician is no more definable as 'knowing' a set of mathematical facts than being a poet is definable as knowing a set of linguistic facts. Some modern mathematical education reformers will give this statement a too easy assent with the comment: 'Yes, they must understand, not merely know'. But this misses the capital point that being a mathematician, again like being a poet, or a composer or an engineer, means *doing*, rather than knowing or understanding. This paper is an attempt to explore some ways in which one might be able to put children in a better position to *do* mathematics rather than merely to learn *about* it.

The plan of the essay is to develop some examples of new kinds of mathematical activity for children, and then to discuss the general issues alluded to in the preceding paragraph. Without the examples, abstract statements about 'doing', 'knowing' and 'understanding' mathematics cannot be expected to have more than a suggestive meaning. On the other hand the description of the examples will be easier to follow if the reader has a prior idea of their intention. And so the author will first sketch, very impressionistically, his position on some of the major issues. In doing so he will exploit the dialectical device employed in the previous paragraph to obtain a little more precision of statement by explicitly excluding the most likely misinterpretation.

It is generally assumed in our society that every child should, and can, have experience of creative work in language and plastic arts. It is equally generally assumed that very few people can work creatively in mathematics. The author believes that there has been an unwitting conspiracy of psychologists and mathematicians in maintaining this assumption. The psychologists contribute it out of genuine ignorance of what creative mathematical work might be like. The mathematicians, very often, do so out of elitism, in the form of a deep conviction that mathematical creativity is the privilege of a tiny minority.

Here again, if we want any clarity, it is necessary to ward off a too easy, superficial assent from mathematical education reformers who say, 'Yes, that's why we must use the method of discovery'. For when 'discovery' means discovery this is wonderful, but in reality 'discovery' usually means something akin to the following fantasy about a poetry class; the discovery method teacher has perfected a series of questions that lead the class to discover the line 'Mary had a little lamb'. The author's point is not that this would be good or bad but that no one would confuse it with creative work in poetry.

Is it possible for children to do creative mathematics (that is to say: to *do* mathematics) at all stages of their scholastic (and even adult!) lives? The author will argue that the answer is: yes, but a great deal of creative mathematical work by adult mathematicians is necessary to make it possible. The reason for the qualification is that the traditional branches of mathematics do not provide the most fertile ground for the easy, prolific growth of mathematical traits of mind. We may have to develop quite new branches of mathematics with the special property that they allow beginners more space to romp creatively, than does number theory or modernistic algebra. In the following pages will be found some specific examples which it would be pretentious to call 'new pedagogical oriented branches of mathematics' but which will suggest to cooperative readers what this phrase could mean.

Obstreperous readers will have no trouble finding objections. Mathematical elitists will say: 'How dare you bring these trivia to disturb our contemplation of the true mathematical structures'. Practical people will say: 'Romping? Romping? Who needs it? What about practical skills in arithmetic?'

The snob and the anti-snob are expressing the same objection in different words. Let me paraphrase it. 'Traditional schools have found mathematics hard to teach to so-called average children. Someone brings along a new set of activities, which seem to be fun and easy to learn. He declares them to be mathematics, but this does not turn them into solutions to any of the hard problems facing the world of mathematical education.'

236

This argument raises serious issues, from which the author will single out a question which he will ask in a number of different forms:

> In becoming a mathematician does one learn something other and more general than the specific content of particular mathematical topics? Is there such a thing as a 'mathematical way of thinking'? Can this be learned and taught? Once one has acquired it, does it then become quite easy to learn *particular* topics — like the ones that obsess our elitist and practical critics?

Psychologists sometimes react by saying, 'Oh, you mean the transfer problem'. But the author does not mean anything analogous to experiments on whether students who were taught algebra last year *automatically* learn geometry more easily than students who spent last year doing gymnastics. He is asking whether one can identify and teach (or foster the growth of) something *other* than algebra or geometry, which, once learned will make it easy to learn algebra and geometry. No doubt, this other thing (let us call it the MWOT) can only be taught by using particular topics as vehicles. But the 'transfer' experiment is profoundly changed if the question is whether one can *use* algebra as a *vehicle for deliberately teaching transferable general concepts and skills*. The conjecture underlying this essay is a very qualified affirmative answer to this question. Yes, one *can* use algebra as a vehicle for initiating students to the mathematical way of thinking. But, to do so effectively one should first identify as far as possible components of the general intellectual skills one is trying to teach; and when this is done it will appear that algebra (in any traditional sense) is not a particularly good vehicle.

The alternative choices of vehicle described below all involve using computers, but in a way that is very different from the usual suggestions of using them either as 'teaching machines' or as 'super slide-rules'. In our ideal of a school mathematical laboratory the computer is used as a means to control physical processes in order to achieve definite goals — for example as part of an auto-pilot system to fly model airplanes, or as the 'nervous system' of a model animal with balancing reflexes, walking ability, simple visual ability and so on. To achieve these goals, mathematical principles are needed; conversely, in this context, mathematical principles become sources of power, thereby acquiring meaning for large categories of students who fail to see any point or pleasure in bookish mathematics and who, under prevailing school conditions, simply drop out by labelling themselves 'not mathematically minded'.

The too easy acceptance of this takes the form: 'Yes, applications are motivating'. But 'motivation' fails to distinguish alienated work for a material or social reward from a true personal involvement. To develop this point the author needs to separate a number of aspects of the way the child relates to his work.

A simple, and important one, is the time scale. A child interested in flying model airplanes under computer control will work at this project over a long period. He will have time to try different approaches to sub-problems. He will have time to talk about it, to establish a common language with a collaborator or an instructor, to relate it to other interests and problems. This *project-oriented* approach contrasts with the *problem* approach of most mathematics teaching: a bad feature of the typical problem is that the child does not stay with it long enough to benefit much from success or from failure.

Along with time scale goes structure. A project is long enough to have recognisable phases — such as planning, choosing a strategy of attempting a very simple case first, finding the simple solution, *debugging* it and so on. And if the time scale is long enough and the structures clear enough, the child can develop a vocabulary for articulate discussion of the process of working towards his goals.

The author believes in articulate discussion (in monologue or dialogue) of how one solves problems, of why one fails that one, of what gaps or deformations exist in one's knowledge and of what could be done about it. The author will defend this belief against two quite distinct objections. One objection says: *'it is impossible to verbalise*; problems are solved by intuitive acts of insight and these cannot be articulated'. The other objection says: *'it is bad to verbalise*; remember the centipede who was paralysed when the toad asked which leg came after which'. [. . .]

A fundamental problem for the theory of mathematical education is to identify and name the concepts needed to enable the beginner to discuss his mathematical thinking in a clear articulate way. And when we know such concepts we may want to seek out (or invent!) areas of mathematical work which examplify these concepts particularly well. The next section of this paper will describe a new piece of mathematics with the property that it allows clear discussion and simple models of heuristics that are foggy and confusing for beginners when presented in the context of more traditional elementary mathematics.

Turtle geometry: a piece of learnable and lovable mathematics

The physical context for the following discussion is a quintuple consisting of a child, a teletype machine, a computer, a large flat surface and an apparatus called a *turtle*. A turtle is a cybernetic toy capable of moving forward or back in a particular direction (relative to itself) and of rotating about its central axis. It has a *pen,* which can be in two states called PENUP and PENDOWN. The turtle is made to act by typing commands whose effect is illustrated in figure 1.

At any time the turtle is at a particular *place* and facing in a particular *direction.* The place and direction together are the turtle's geometric *state.* Figure 1 shows the turtle in a field, used here only to give the reader a frame of reference.

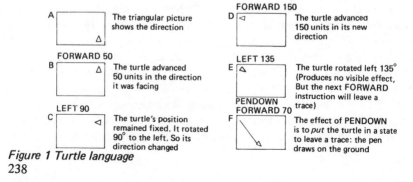

Figure 1 Turtle language

Direct Commands

The following commands will cause the turtle to draw figure 2.

```
TO PEACE
PENDOWN
FORWARD 100
RIGHT 60
FORWARD 100
BACK 100
LEFT 120
FORWARD 100
END
```

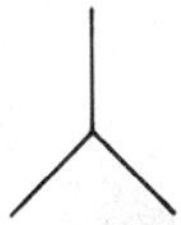

PEACE

Figure 2 A turtle procedure and the resulting diagram

Defining a procedure

The computer is assumed to accept the language LOGO (which we have developed expressly for the purpose of teaching children, not programming but mathematics). The LOGO idiom for asserting the fact that we are about to define a procedure is illustrated by the following example. We first decide on a *name* for the procedure. Suppose we choose 'PEACE'. Then we type:

TO PEACE
1 FORWARD 100
2 RIGHT 60   These are directions telling the computer how to
3 FORWARD 100 PEACE. The word 'TO' informs the computer that
4 BACK 100   the next word, 'PEACE', is being defined and that
5 LEFT 120   the numbered lines constitute its definition
6 FORWARD 100
END

The turtle does not move while we are typing this. The word 'TO' and the line numbers indicated that we were not telling it to go forward and so on; rather we were telling it *how* to execute the new command. When we have indicated by the word 'END' that our definition is complete the machine echoes back:

PEACE DEFINED

and now if we type

PENDOWN
PEACE

the turtle will carry out the commands and draw figure 2. Were we to omit the command 'PENDOWN' it would go through the motions of drawing it without leaving a visible trace.

The peace sign in figure 2 lacks a circle. How can we describe a circle in turtle language?

An idea that easily presents itself to mathematicians is: let the turtle take a tiny step forward, then turn a tiny amount and keep doing this. This might not quite produce a circle, but it is a good first plan, so let us begin to work on it. So

239

we define a procedure:

```
TO CIRCUS
1  FORWARD 5
2  RIGHT 2
3  CIRCUS
END
```

Notice two features

1 The procedure refers to itself in line 3. This looks circular (though not in the sense we require) but really is not. The effect is merely to set up a never-ending process by getting the computer into the tight spot *you* would be in if you were the kind of person who cannot fail to keep a promise and you had been tricked into saying, 'I promise to repeat the sentence I just said'.

2 We selected the numbers 5 and 7 because they seemed small, but without a firm idea of what would happen. However, an advantage of having a computer is that we can try our procedure to see what it does. If an undesirable effect follows we can always *debug* it; in this case, perhaps, by choosing different numbers.

[... It would of course be a little tedious to have to keep typing the complete procedure just because we wanted to change one or two numbers. It would be much more convenient to be able to include in our procedures more general instructions such as 'Take a step forward' 'Turn right through an angle' and then type in the step size and angle we required whenever we wanted the turtle to carry out the procedure. In this way we could experiment with different step and angle sizes just by typing in different pairs of numbers. The next example shows how we make procedures with such 'inputs'.]

The words on the title line preceded by ':' are names of the inputs, rather like the xs in school algebra.) In the fifth grade class we read *:NUMBER* as *dots NUMBER* or as *the thing of 'NUMBER'*, emphasising that what is being discussed is not the word 'NUMBER' but a thing of which this word is the name.

[The following procedure, POLY has two inputs, STEP and ANGLE. Otherwise it is the same as the CIRCUS procedure]

```
TO POLY :STEP :ANGLE
1  FORWARD :STEP
2  LEFT :ANGLE
3  POLY :STEP :ANGLE
END
```

This procedure generates a rather wonderful collection of pictures as we give it different inputs.

[... Suppose] we change the last line of POLY. We also change the title, though we do not need to do so.

Old procedure

```
TO POLY :STEP :ANGLE
1 FORWARD :STEP
2 LEFT :ANGLE
3 POLY :STEP :ANGLE
END
```

New procedure

```
TO POLYSPI :STEP :ANGLE
1 FORWARD :STEP
2 LEFT :ANGLE
3 POLYSPI :STEP+20 :ANGLE
END
```

The effect of POLYSPI is shown in figure 3. [Each step is 20 units longer than the previous one]

Figure 3 POLYSPI 5 90 or squiral

We have seen we can use POLY to draw a circle. Can we now use it to draw our PEACE sign? We could, but will do better to make a procedure, here called ARC whose effect will be to draw any circular segment given the diameter and the angle to be drawn as in figure 4. The procedure is as follows where in line 2 a special constant called 'PIE' is used and the asterisk sign is used for multiplication. (Do not assume that :PIE is what its name suggests.)

```
TO ARC :DIAM :SECTOR
1 IF :SECTOR-0 STOP
2 FORWARD : PIE :DIAM
3 RIGHT 1
4 ARC :DIAM :SECTOR-1
END
```

We can now make a procedure using the old procedure PEACE as a *sub-procedure*:

```
TO SUPERPEACE
1 ARC 200 360
2 RIGHT 90
3 PEACE
END
```

SUPERPEACE

Figure 4 A better peace sign using the old one as sub-procedure

Better yet we could rewrite PEACE to have inputs. For example:

241

```
TO PEACE :SIZE
1 FORWARD :SIZE
2 RIGHT 60
3 FORWARD :SIZE
4 BACK :SIZE
5 LEFT 120
6 FORWARD :SIZE
7 RIGHT 90
8 ARC 2 :SIZE 360
```

Then peace signs of different sizes can be made by the commands:

```
PEACE 100
PEACE 20
```

and so on.

[. . .]

Creativity? Mathematics?

In a class run by members of the MIT Artificial Intelligence Laboratory we have taught this kind of geometry to fifth graders, some of whom were in the lowest categories of performance in 'mathematics'. Their attitude towards mathematics as normally taught was well expressed by a fifth-grade girl who said firmly, 'There ain't nothing fun in maths!' She did not classify working with the computer as mathematics, and we saw no reason to disabuse her. There will be time for her to discover that what she is learning to do in an exciting and personal way will elucidate those strange rituals she meets in the mathematics class.

Typical activities in early stages of work with children of this age is exploring the behaviour of the procedure POLY by giving it different inputs. There is inevitable challenge — and competition — in producing beautiful or spectacular, or just different, effects. One gets ahead in the game by discovering a new phenomenon and by finding out what classes of angles will produce it.

The real excitement comes when one becomes courageous enough to change the procedure itself. For example making the change to POLYSPI occurs to some children and, in our class, led to a great deal of excitement around the truly spontaneous discovery of the figure now called a *squiral* (figure 3). (Note: By spontaneous the author means, amongst other things, to exclude the situation of the discovery teacher standing in front of the class soliciting pseudo-randomly generated suggestions. The squiral was found by this step — indeed once a few have done so it becomes derivative for the others. Nevertheless, we might encourage them to explore inputs to POLYSPI. There is room here for the discovery of more phenomena. For example, taking :ANGLE as 120 produces a neat triangular spiral. But 123 produces a different phenomena (as shown in figure 5).

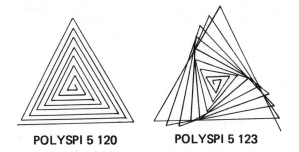

POLYSPI 5 120   POLYSPI 5 123

Figure 5 Exploring some spiral effects

What else produces similar effects? (*see* figure 6)

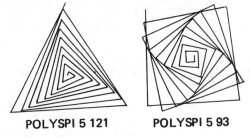

POLYSPI 5 121   POLYSPI 5 93

Figure 6 Understanding figure 5 better by exploring two related effects

The possibilities for original minor discoveries are great. One girl became excited for the first time about mathematics by realizing how easy it was to make a program for figure 7 by:

1 observing herself draw a similar figure,
2 *naming* the elements of her figure — 'BIG' and 'SMALL' — so that she could talk about them and so describe what she was doing,
3 describing it in LOGO.

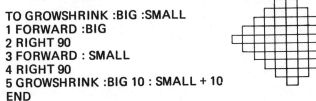

```
TO GROWSHRINK :BIG :SMALL
1 FORWARD :BIG
2 RIGHT 90
3 FORWARD : SMALL
4 RIGHT 90
5 GROWSHRINK :BIG 10 : SMALL + 10
END
```

Figure 7 Another direction of generalisation of POLY. This figure shows the intention of the child who wrote the procedure GROWSHRINK

The possibilities are endless. These are small discoveries. But perhaps one is already closer to mathematics in doing this than in learning new formal manipulations, transforming bases, intersecting sets and drifting through misty lessons on the difference between fractions, rationals and equivalence classes of pairs of

243

integers. Perhaps learning to make small discoveries puts one more surely on a path to making big ones than does faultlessly learning any number of sound algebraic concepts.

What are the primitive concepts of mathematics?

[. . .]

It is sometimes said that in teaching mathematics we should emphasise the process of mathematisation. The author says: 'Excellent!' But on condition that the child should have the experience of mathematising for himself. Otherwise the word 'mathematising' is just one more scholastic term. The thrust of the explorations which have been described is to allow the child to have living experiences of mathematising as an introduction to mathematics. We have seen how he mathematises [. . .] a squiral, his own behaviour in drawing a GROWSHRINK, [. . .] and so on. When mathematising familiar processes is a fluent, natural and enjoyable activity, then is the time to talk about mathematising mathematical structures, as in a good pure course on modern algebra.

But what are the ingredients of the process of mathematising? Is it possible to formulate and teach knowledge about how one is to tackle, for example, the problem of setting up a mathematical representation of an object such as the hearts and flowers we discussed earlier?

Our answer is very definitely affirmative, especially in the context of the kind of work described above. Consider, for example, how we would teach children to go about problems like drawing a heart. First step we say: if you cannot solve the problem as it stands, try simplifying it; if you cannot find a complete solution, find a partial one. No doubt everyone gives similar advice. The difference is that in this context the advice is concrete enough to be followed by children who seem quite impervious to the usual mathematics.

A simplification of the heart problem is to settle, as a first approximation, on a triangle; which we then consider to be a very primitive heart.

```
TO TRI
1 FORWARD 100
2 RIGHT 120
3 FORWARD 100
4 RIGHT 120
5 FORWARD 100
END
```

Now that we have this construction firmly in hand we can allow ourselves to modify it so as to make it a better heart. The obvious plan is to replace the horizontal line by a structure line. So we write a procedure to make this. First choose it a name, say 'TOP', then write:

```
TO TOP :SIZE
1 ARC :SIZE/2 180
2 RIGHT 180
3 ARC :SIZE/2 180
END
```

TOP

Replacing line 1 in TO TRI by TOP we get:

```
TO TRI
1 TOP 100
2 RIGHT 120
etc.
```

HEART WITH BUG

The effect is as shown! Is this a failure? We might have so classified it (and ourselves!) if we did not have another heuristic concept: BUGS and DEBUGGING. Our procedure did not fail. It has a perfectly intelligible *bug*. To find the bug we follow the procedure through in a very FORMAL way. (Formal is another concept we try to teach.) We soon find that the trouble is in line 2. Also we can see why. Replacing line 1 by TOP did what we wanted, but it also produced a SIDE-EFFECT. (Another important concept.) It left the turtle facing in a different direction. Correcting it is a mere matter of changing line 2 to RIGHT 30. And then we can go on to make the fully curved heart. Unless we decide that a straight-sided one is good for our purposes (*see* figure 8).

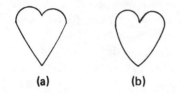

(a)   (b)

Figure 8 (a) Straight-sided heart; (b) Curved heart

Our image of teaching mathematics concentrates on teaching concepts and terminology to enable children to be articulate about the process of developing a mathematical analysis. Part of doing so is studying good models (such as the heart anecdote) and getting a lot of practice in describing one's own attempts at following the pattern of the model in other problems. It seems quite paradoxical that in developing mathematical curricula, whole conferences of superb mathematicians are devoted to discussing the appropriate language for expressing the *formal* part of mathematics, while the individual teacher or writer of textbooks is left to decide how (and even *whether*) to deal with heuristic concepts.

In summary, we have advanced three central theses:

1 The non-formal mathematical primitives are neglected in most discussions of mathematical curricula.
2 That the choice of content material, especially for the early years, should be made primarily as a function of its suitability for developing heuristic concepts.
3 Computational mathematics, in the sense illustrated by turtle geometry, has strong advantages in this respect over 'classical' topics.

SECTION 5　Organising the classroom

<<<<<<<<<<<<<<<<<<<<<<<<<<<<<<<<<<<<<<<<<<<<<<<<<<<<<

Introduction

The four chapters in this final section are all written by practising teachers, all of whom have worked closely with the *Developing Mathematical Thinking* course team. Each article describes the different experiences that these teachers have had in trying to develop mathematical thinking in their pupils by using the do, talk and record approach (DTR) described at the beginning of this book.

One of them, Bob Vertes, writing in a secondary school context, summarises the philosophy underlying this approach particularly well. 'Children have to be prepared to

1　think for themselves – form their own opinions, follow their own logic,
2　not be afraid to communicate their thinking for fear it may be wrong;
3　accept that wrong answers can also be helpful;
4　listen to their peers for comments in their own words (. . . . . .)
5　question their peers' ideas (or any unsupported statements of mine) asking for justification, example, or proof.'

This philosophy permeates everything that these four articles have to say.

The DTR approach is essentially a means of applying these principles to the mathematics classroom. It is often the case that they are applied elsewhere, and recognised as highly desirable, but mathematics is seen as somehow different. You will notice that the first of the chapters, written by Janette Warden, draws most of its examples from other areas of curriculum. She describes a way of working with children that will be familiar to many teachers – her strategy for organising topic work for National Children's Book Week, or for setting up debates, will ring many a bell. She herself had not found it easy to extend this into the children's mathematics. How does one get children to think for themselves about how numbers combine and to argue amicably with each other about their conclusions? And how does one get them to investigate geometric patterns and explain what they have found out to each other, while still being receptive to constructive comment? Yet if only one could, the benefits would be incalculable. If you want to understand something really well there is nothing like having to explain your thinking to someone else. If the listeners then question what is being said, and continue to do so until they understand too, then both explainer and listeners derive great benefit from the activity.

These articles describe many situations where the teacher felt that this really had happened. For example Deryn Harvey and Carole Senior include an account

246

of a group of children grappling with division. At the point described they were working on $72 \div 6$, a problem which they understood as finding out how many objects each of 6 people could have if 72 of the objects were shared equally between them. The children had collected 72 counters. Previous experience of dealing the counters out, like so many cards, had led them to accelerate the process somewhat, and this particular group were dealing them out three at a time instead of singly. All of the group understood this process: they had *done* it and *talked about* what they were doing until they were all convinced. They had *recorded* their actions in their own individual ways. But then one child, Stephen, proclaimed that he had a much quicker way. He maintained that you could give them 10 each, that there would be 12 left over, and that this would mean that each person could have 2 more. He convinced the rest of his group, and eventually the whole class, that you could solve such problems in this simple way. That Stephen was expected to explain his method to the satisfaction of his peers benefited all of them.

The 64 000 dollar question, though, is how one can actually make this kind of interchange happen without the classroom degenerating into complete chaos. In addition, how does one find the time to ensure that every child participates? All these teachers lay great stress on the need to train children if this approach is to be effective, and all describe, in their different ways, how they set about such training. The secret lies in the five points quoted earlier. When children try to think for themselves, and then discuss their thinking with each other, they can do a great deal of teaching for themselves to everybody's benefit: the teacher then does have the time to give help where it is really needed. The self-discipline associated with such relatively independent working is considerable, and children need time and help with this. That it can be done is evidenced by the following chapters, and that it is professionally rewarding is clear from the enthusiasm these teachers convey.

The first two chapters are both to do with primary-school children. One was written by Jeannette Warden, who was using these methods more or less on her own. By way of a contrast, the second comes from two teachers working in a school where DTR is standard practice. The second two chapters relate to older children in a comprehensive school, the first of these being written by the head of the mathematics department, Bob Vertes, and the second by a member of that department, Sandy Carter.

25 Making space for doing and talking with groups in a primary classroom

Janette Warden

Source: specially written for this volume

$\lll\lll\lll\lll\lll\lll\lll\lll\lll\lll\lll\lll\lll\lll\lll\lll\lll\lll\lll$

Introduction

I believe that by training children to think for themselves; to show initiative; to gain confidence; to be helpful and show tolerance towards others and to be self-assessing I am making them self-disciplined which in turn will enable them to reach their full potential in the learning situation. In order for these traits to develop it was necessary for me first to create a certain atmosphere in the classroom.

In this article I will show that creating this atmosphere involved making various disciplines to the children very clear from the moment they came in, and, then becoming more flexible as self-discipline developed; at which point it was possible to hand over to them. I shall show that these fundamental disciplines created for me the time to talk and listen.

I shall begin by describing how I made these disciplines clear during the 'settling in' period. It involved four areas:

1 discussion skills,
2 self-control,
3 ability to think for oneself,
4 self assessment.

I would like to look first of all at discussion skills.

Discussion skills

Through these I am trying to train children to use language to enable them to develop and organise their thinking. The majority of children I have taught have been ready and willing to talk, and I have found myself saying, on a number of occasions, 'You have too much to say'. It is not, therefore, just talking, but knowing when to talk and when to listen.

I start this training the moment I first meet a new class. Invariably I find that one of the first things that happens is that one child speaks to another while I

248

am speaking to the class. I either ask the child to repeat what I have just said, in order to point out that they should have been listening, or, I simply state that nobody talks while I am talking. I am in effect introducing the idea of really *listening* to someone who is talking. Very early on in this 'settling in' period I leave time for the children to ask questions or to add their views on what has already been said. I ask them things like: 'What do you feel about what has just been said? Would you like to add anything?' During this period I emphasise that we all listen to the child who is speaking.

I then follow with the teacher talking — instructing or suggesting and the children listening. The next stage is when I let the children talk while I listen. It is this stage I often find difficult. Recently I asked a new class what they thought about a particular topic that had been suggested and was confronted with a mass of blank faces accompanying a very long silence. It appeared that the children had never been asked for their views before and were completely at a loss as to know what I required of them. I needed a lot of patience.

I found I had to say things like; 'Well, what sort of things would you be interested in yourselves? What would you like to see happening? What would you do to make this project a success?' I also had to give them time to marshal their thoughts and there was silence for a while before they eventually got going. Within two or three weeks this class was able to cope much more readily with discussions like this at group level.

I have also had to deal with the opposite reaction with another class. Here it seemed as though everyone wanted to say something. I had to stop them and explain that if everyone called out at once we would not be able to hear each other property. We all agreed that the best way was for those who wanted to say something to put their hands up. In those early stages the children did not *listen* to each other, but merely waited for their turn to speak. After a while I began to intervene by following up something a child had said with questions like 'Do you think *Jean* has a good idea? Do you agree with what *Peter* has just said?' followed always by a 'Why?'

The final stage usually comes much later with children talking and listening to each other, either with the teacher present, or, in group planning without the teacher. I shall give examples of these later on.

Before the children will give each other their full attention when engaged in group discussion I find that I have to get across that every member of the class is entitled to my full attention when they are reading to me; being helped by me; or simply talking to me. On a number of occasions, with a new class, whilst, say, hearing a child read another child has come to ask a question, or, for help, and interrupts, I stop and tell the child not to interrupt but to wait. Afterwards I explain that it is not easy to listen to two people at the same time, and, that if we are listening properly we want to give our full attention to what is being said to us.

During these 'settling in' days, whilst I am still working with the class as a group or with individual children, in order to help the children gain confidence in their own judgements and ideas I constantly ask questions such as 'Well what do you think?' or 'Can you explain to me how you did this?' Later on when group work is more established I still ask these questions. They really help them to start thinking for themselves, often for the first time! I would now like to look at how this develops.

The class of 9 to 10 year olds already referred to as being completely at a loss initially were particularly responsive to my methods and quite early on in the autumn term I asked for their help with the organisation of National Children's Book Week. The first question I asked was 'How can we make it successful?' This was the most difficult part and produced some very long silences. The children finally decided to concentrate on three main areas. At this level of discussion, that is, with a whole class, I always get the children to sit either in a circle or move to the front of the classroom so that we can look at who is talking and hear each other. The children decided that they would like to work in groups and the following is an extract of the conversation between myself and the class.

Me	:	How can we organise it?
Children	:	Everyone can choose their own interest.
Me	:	How shall we do that?
Children	:	Children are asked to put up their hands when you call out each one.
		(This was done)
Me	:	Where will each group work?
		(At this point some of the children started counting in order to see where groups fitted into the existing arrangement of classroom furniture. I like to arrange the furniture so that I have room for group discussions or for practical sessions. Arrangements are changed according to the needs of the children.)
Children	:	We could work out by numbers.
		(This was done.)
Children	:	I think we should have leaders.
Me	:	What for?
Children	:	To look after work for the group.
		Help members of the group with what they have to do.
		To have meetings with you.

We then moved from class planning to group planning. This meant, of course, that I was not on hand to discuss with every group. In fact a great deal of my time was spent in 'listening in'.

One group had decided to plan a competition, giving each year group a subject. As the children worked I found that they were asking themselves questions like 'How are the entries going to be judged?' A list was drawn up which included points such as handwriting, spelling, and so on. (I provided the word criteria). This was most interesting for when the entries arrived I found that a lot had been discarded on the grounds that 'they weren't any good'. Here I intervened and pointed out that they had agreed upon criteria which they were now ignoring. They then agreed that each entry should be judged individually. It is not possible here to give further detailed examples of class and group planning but reflecting on my actions it showed me how important it is to know when to ask questions and what questions to ask thereby giving the children a 'lead' but not providing an answer or solution.

When working in groups which are occupied with different activities I ask each group to show their results in some way, and, to write a report which they can read to the rest of the class. Incidentally, this also means that I can bring the basic skills of reading and writing into my maths and science lessons. One area covered with this particular class was different types of sugar. Over a period of a week various types of sugar were collected together. At the beginning of one morning the children were placed in groups. (I worked with groups of mixed ability). Each group was given a task written on a sheet of paper, such as 'compare the various types of sugar using a microscope', or 'how quickly does each type of sugar dissolve? Do some dissolve more quickly than others?' There were six groups altogether. They were asked to have ready, by the end of the morning the results of their experiments in the form of charts, graphs, etc. and a report. After lunch each group gave their report at the end of which the children were encouraged to ask questions or to make any other comments. Discussion skills of listening and talking were vital here. The children had come a long way with developing them and the sessions went well.

This was designed to provoke the children into discussing how they could measure such things as the rate of dissolving.

I shall give one more example which showed me that specific discussion skills had been developed and were being used by the children. It concerns a series of debates held, with a class of 9 to 10 year olds in the summer term of the second year with me. As so often happens, something occurred which we felt we would like to discuss. I suggested that we had a debate, and gave a general outline as to how these operated. A title and a date for the debate was fixed. These were written up on a large sheet of paper and put up on the wall. Underneath was a sheet for volunteers to write up their names for chairman and speakers for and against. The children elected a chairman, I then had a 'teach-in' for these children explaining the procedure and they were given about a fortnight to prepare their speeches. During the lunch hour before the debate, which was always held first thing in the afternoon, the main participants arranged the furniture of the room. From the beginning I always sat in the audience and did not speak until the debate was thrown open. Here I tried to set an example of *listening* so that I could ask thought-provoking questions. I found that the children quickly accepted the fact that I was one of the audience, and, that I had opinions of my own which did not necessarily agree with theirs. I always voted last and they soon gave up trying to discover which way I was going to vote. These kinds of actions all contributed to the children learning to think for themselves. In maths classes I do the same thing by *listening* in to their group discussions. To begin with as I joined a group they would all stop and wait for me to 'cast my vote!' I had to say 'Don't stop. I've not come to tell you what to do, I've come to listen and ask questions,' but they soon got the idea.

In developing discussion skills I find it very important to become a member of the audience or group. The children seem to find it much easier to discuss what they are doing, or, to make suggestions in this more relaxed atmosphere . . . one in which people can 'never find me' because I am usually sharing a child's chair and joining in with the work of a group, either listening, or teaching.

I have found that a great deal of time is required to create this atmosphere and build up children's confidence to work in this way. I have also found that work of this nature not only requires discussion skills, but skills of another kind which I shall now consider under self-control.

Self-control

I believe that the children must have self-control as part of their self discipline. There is nothing worse than being constantly interrupted by children or a group that is playing around. I think there are two main points to consider, first the children's behaviour and their attitude to their work, and, second their attitude towards others.

I consider that the children have reached self-control when I can leave the classroom, or, a visitor can enter the classroom to talk to me, and the good working atmosphere does not change. If there was chaos whenever my back was turned then there would be little point in trying to work in the way I do for I would never be free to work or discuss with children. Occasionally the good working atmosphere is disturbed and I then tell the children that I do not want to be a policeman, but a teacher here to help them. This may not give the police the best image, but the children get the message.

The other point that remains under this heading of self-control is the children's attitude towards others. Working at this helps to create the right working atmosphere. I want the children to help others, show tolerance and give credit where it is due. 'Helping others' is a means of saving time and teaching effort. It cuts down the number of times I have to repeat myself, which is vital if I want to talk to a child or group and really tune-in to what they are doing and saying. When a child, who has been absent, has missed something new which I have taught, I usually ask another child in the group to 'help-out' by doing the teaching. Far from getting a child to do any job, I believe that the child who is doing the teaching or explaining is being given a chance to clarify his own thinking on the subject by having to show someone else. I always check up though, usually through discussion, to find out whether the main points have come across. I often find that the child who has been away responds very readily to this method and this may be because it makes them feel less conspicuous. It leaves me, of course, free to continue working with the rest of the class or with other groups whether discussing or teaching.

Another way I use 'helping others' is when a child comes and says 'I'm stuck

Miss.' I usually say 'Have you asked your next-door neighbour or someone else in your group?' I find that this either solves the problem, that is, someone else can help, or else it reveals a larger problem. Larger in the sense that more than one child is stuck and I can then help a group together rather than a series of individual children. In both cases I have saved time, and, in the first one or more of the children will have been clarifying their thinking through their use of language.

I also find that this 'helping others' atmosphere is very useful when a new child enters the class in the middle of a term just when everyone has settled down. A new child has so much to cope with and the more helpers there are the better.

I think tolerance and understanding the needs of others rather than simply putting up with them, is part of helping others. It is certainly an important part of learning to work and live together. I am thinking mainly about the tolerance needed when working with other people who may have different ideas from our own, or simply need more time. I have found that children can be very impatient with each other and are very quick to ridicule an idea which is not their own. I think this is where the listening skills are important and I have to take the lead. I find that I usually say 'Well, we have listened to your idea now we will listen to what *Mary* has to say and then decide together what we think about it.' In creating a tolerant atmosphere like this I have to be careful about my own reactions to the children's suggestions. Phrases such as 'you stupid boy' or 'what a stupid thing to say' cannot be part of my vocabulary. I come down very hard on children who use words like these.

Although we are concerned here with training children to work independently, I think a good sign of whether we are on the right lines is when the very poor readers in the class are not afraid or, as with my last class, cannot wait to volunteer, to read out loud in front of the class. I always feel that when this happens the children are gaining confidence and they are not afraid that someone will laugh at them. In my experience I have found that children will laugh readily at the poor readers, or those who make mistakes. This is something I jump on immediately it happens, with a very firm rebuke, and the children soon learn that it is not acceptable.

This attitude leads on to the giving 'credit where it is due'. I have found that once the children have gained confidence I can discuss with them their strengths and weaknesses first on their own and later within the groups. They are then more able to recognise when they or someone else has achieved a piece of work above their usual standard. We all like praise for a job well done, and we have all seen what a difference it can make to a child. However, I think the praise is even more important to the child when it is coming not just from me, but from the peer group as well. I often turn to the group and ask 'What do you feel about the way John read that?'

Ability to think for oneself

In the type of classroom I try to create it is essential that children learn to think for themselves. This is the third of the four areas I mentioned at the beginning of this article. Unless they do this I am going to be bogged down with questions like 'What shall I do now? Where shall I put this?' and be unable to carry out my main role which is to teach and guide through listening and talking.

A large part of this thinking for oneself will be to do with organisation. Where school policy either encourages or insists upon methods which aim to get children to do the thinking, guidelines regarding organisation will be necessary. So what kind of organisation am I talking about? I think one part is concerned with the physical organisation. The room has to be a working unit within which the children can have the freedom of movement they require, in order to carry out the type of activities which I have been describing. Initially I had to create this working unit, but found that, as the children gained more self-discipline, they sorted out for themselves where their group would be based. Eventually they moved furniture temporarily to fit a need and put it back when they had finished without bothering me except to ask permission to do it. This was considered a basic courtesy and of course warned us about what was happening.

Another aspect of organisation is the storage and use of materials and equipment. I teach the children to be responsible for getting out and putting away their own equipment. I make sure that it is accesible to them and that it has a home. I find that the use and collection of materials such as paper, crayons, and so on by the children needs careful training to begin with, but my aim is that the children should be able to collect what they need when they need it. This again leaves me free to get on with the job of talking and listening and it is certainly worth the initial time and trouble of training the children.

As I have already said, I am initially responsible for the organisation of the classroom, but I believe that by encouraging the children to make suggestions for 'a better place to sort the crayons' or 'where we can display the models?' I am continually helping them to think for themselves.

I think a further aspect of organisation concerns helping the children to answer questions like 'What shall I do next?' or 'I've finished what shall I do now?' for themselves. Again in the initial stages I am very much in control of the situation.

During my 'settling in' period I always write up either on the board or on a sheet of kitchen paper what the children can do when they have finished their work. I also use this procedure for a 'free-choice' session. I find that it gets the children used to reading instructions and gives them the idea of self-checking. I have always had workcards of various types available, but I have found that not all children want to do these. As time goes on, the children need these directions less and less and they organise themselves in various ways. At the end of one lesson, among other things, I had two children working at the sink on a set of cards about capacity; two working on a crossword puzzle; four doing their sewing, and many others finishing off various pieces of work. I think that these times, when children can choose for themselves, are very important. Choosing wisely in situations like this is, I believe, helping them to gain confidence in trying out ideas of their own, and when working with others they are using language which in turn is developing their thinking skills.

I do not think it is necessary for me, to go into further examples of the children learning to think for themselves. The examples I have given already show that children can be actively engaged in doing just that. A bonus is all the extra time it gives *me* to work with them in small groups.

Self-assessment

The final part of what I consider to be involved self-discipline is self-assessment. In some ways I have already looked at this when I talked about children becoming more aware of their own strengths and weaknesses. Very young children are often asked to 'talk about' their pictures while the teacher listens or asks questions. I like to carry this much further and ask the children what they think about their own work. In mathematics, questions such as 'Is that right?' followed by 'How do you know?' or 'How can you find out?' are very important. Even more important is getting them to reflect on the way in which they got their answers. I often suggest 'Let's go back and explain how you got this answer to be sure that you are happy with it.' I do this with right as well as wrong answers. Asking children to explain how they arrived at an answer is, I find, a useful method of discovering whether they really understand what they are doing. It also gives them the opportunity of putting their thoughts into words. Gradually the children gain confidence in language skills and I can have proper constructive discussions. They begin to develop a sense of honesty about their work and in the long run I find that I can use this to make more time for me by getting the children to correct some of their own work. In developing mathematical thinking through the use of language I am concerned not with 'right answers', but how the children got the answers. It follows, therefore, that a correct or incorrect answer is relatively unimportant and I can see no reason why, when the children are operating at the practice stage, they should not mark their own work.

I have now dealt with the four parts that I consider to be a part of the self-discipline of children and what I do to train them to become self-disciplined. I have also indicated how the investment of time and effort doing this eventually pays handsome dividends in creating more time for me to work with children in small groups and even on an invididual basis. Now I must talk about something which affects all of this and that is flexibility regarding organisation and learning.

Flexibility of organisation and learning

I have found that the more self-disciplined the children become, the more flexible I have to become. I should like to give some examples of what I mean.

I have already discussed the organisation of furniture in the classroom and said that I like the children to become involved in this. At the end of their first year, a class I had had for two years asked if they could plan the classroom for the following autumn term. Their ideas were very different from mine and I did not find it easy to 'hand over', but in fact we ended up with an unusual, but satisfactory working unit.

The same class took over after a television programme. I had carefully planned follow-up work for the programme which had been on road accidents. The children wanted to talk about the accidents in school and some of the dangerous things people did — like climbing drain pipes. We ended up working on a mathematical survey about the number of accidents in school; holding a 'prevent an accident week'; and issuing every child in the school with a leaflet, written by four of the boys, on 'how to prevent accidents in school'. The whole activity was far more exciting than anything I had planned. I realised that I had set standards in the 'settling in' period from which children had gained enough self-discipline to perceive their own learning interests. I was confident by this time that they could contribute towards their own learning experience.

I think being flexible is knowing when to let go and how to let go. The more I work in this way the easier I find it to judge when the children are ready. It has to be said, however, that the flexibility must work in both ways as I shall now show.

The class I worked with on National Children's Book Week had only been operating at group level for about half a term. On one afternoon, when the noise level had been getting higher than I normally tolerate, there was an outburst of angry shouts from one group. Without any hesitation I pulled the whole situation back under my control with 'That's it, that's enough. Pack everything away and sit down.' This was done in silence which gave us all time to calm down. A quarter of an hour later we talked about what had happened and why it had happened. The reasons we gave each other are not relevant here, but what is important is that the children had been trying out their own self-discipline which had broken down. I had to be ready to go right back to the beginning, by putting myself in complete control. From here I had to put the pieces back together again and restore the children's confidence by assuring them that they 'could do it'.

Classroom policy

So far I have explained how I try to organise my classroom to make time for me to work with individual children or groups of children. This is not something that can be achieved overnight, so I think it is very important to have a consistent policy across all classes in a school. Without such a policy it takes a long time to establish the groundwork and when you have established it, unless you can take the children through to the end of their primary-school days, they will experience many problems in the future.

The class which I had so carefully trained for two years, where the respect was mutual, where we talked openly about the things that concerned us, were suddenly with another teacher whose policy was different to mine. I felt that two years work had been wasted and I think that they felt that what they had to offer was not needed or wanted any more. Had there been a policy, the next teacher would have been able to build on the existing strengths.

Despite this I have continued to work in the way I have described and have found that the 'follow-on' problems only seem to occur when you have had the children for more than a year. The 'settling in' problems however, never lessen and eventually lead to the teacher's frustration. I am sure that they would lessen with a policy and again you could then build on strengths which are already there. I have no doubt that this exciting way of teaching enables children to reach their full potential and provides the teacher with the greatest satisfaction.

26 Training middle-school children to do, talk and record

Deryn Harvey and Carole Senior

Source: specially written for this volume

≪≪

This chapter is constructed in question and answer format and is based on the discussions we had with members of the *Developing Mathematical Thinking* course team.

How did you both become interested in looking closely at your teaching methods and become involved with the Open University?

To answer this we really have to look back over the last five years' history of the school in which we're both teaching. The process of formulating a maths policy, in our present school began long before Carole and I appeared on the scene. We're just one part of an ongoing series of mathematical developments. Delving into the annals of the school we found that staff and head alike felt that there was a need to look into the teaching of maths in the 8 to 12 years age range middle school in which they found themselves.

With the aid of outside bodies the staff directed much of their energy into maths discussions, maths courses and practical workshops for the staff as a whole. The parents didn't escape either. With the full support of the head parents' meetings and workshops were held to help explain the developing maths policy of the school.

Some of the staff, who are still with us and won't mind at all my saying this, were strongly against the concept of do, talk and record. Perhaps this short example sums up the past and now present attitude towards maths. These teachers are an essential part of the first-year team, a team whose teaching is now geared wholly to setting up the pre-conditions for do, talk and record to work for the children's time at our school.

> 'Fran: At first I had reservations. I thought, at the time, that this method might have advantages for the less able children but felt that for more able children too long spent on practical aspects of maths, without relating it back to maths they were used to doing, and methods they might meet in the high schools, might confuse them. I now feel that this system helps them more for any approach they might meet later. The main "plus", though, is how much the children themselves enjoy it.'

'Margaret: At first I was very sceptical, now I'm completely won over. One child in my class last year, Stephen, claimed he had "done hundreds tens and units" already. During the course of a practical lesson in my classroom on this subject, his face lit up and he said "Oh! I never realised that one ten was equal to ten units" in a blinding flash of revelation. I have never complained about this method of maths teaching again.'

As a result of this process of looking at themselves, a 'manual' was produced by the staff for the staff in the first-year team. The three first-year classes work to this scheme. Newcomers to the team have help in the form of an experienced teacher for two out of four hours per week.

Of invaluable use has been the extra pair of hands provided throughout the school by a more than supportive head teacher. First year teach mixed ability with help for each class for half of the week. I help the second-year classes twice a week. The third and fourth year are set for maths, when the two classes are set into three groups.

One of the outside agents referred to was Nick James, then advisory teacher for maths in the London Borough of Ealing. He, it was who first suggested the do, talk and record model as a basis for action in our classrooms, producing papers to develop the idea (*see* James 1976 and 1977). He subsequently became involved with the Open University, joining a course team (EM 235, *Developing Mathematical Thinking* of which this book is a part). This course discusses do, talk and record, showing how it can help develop mathematical thinking in children. Secondly, I had worked alongside a head, keenly aware of do, talk and record as a teaching method at a previous school where I had responsibility for maths. So I had for some years been aware of my own changing attitude towards maths, an attitude I hasten to add which could only be improved (an unfavourable legacy from my own school days). Carole would like it put on record that maths was anything but her favourite subject at school too.

My arrival at the school two years ago coincided with the maturing of the first-year scheme, and I was aware immediately of the questioning attitude of the staff about their approach to maths, constantly aware that they should never rest on decisions made five years ago. Aware that the maths curriculum should be ongoing in its development, I was delighted to come into a school where much of the hard work of converting to do, talk and record had been done.

This was the atmosphere into which Carole came a year ago. Carole's teaching in her previous school was also along the do, talk and record principle. However she was doing 'what came naturally'! She hadn't actually stopped and given it the formal title of do, talk and record. The Open University team opened her eyes to the educational term they had given to her style of teaching. Carole took over, mid-year, from a second-year teacher, who had set up over the previous four terms a maths class well trained in the concept of do, talk and record. Carole's first maths class was a sea of children getting out apparatus, folders, work cards and carefully explaining to their new teacher how they did maths! Carole's second class hasn't had such an easy transition to a different teacher. But more of that later.

In the light of the changes and development in our school the Open University thought we might be able to provide some help in some of the video programmes associated with this course. Both Carole and I were involved with our own pupils, in the subsequent filming. This question and answer session is an offshoot from the many informal lunchtime discussions we both had with the Open University team while they were filming at our school.

The answers to the questions which follow are our own thoughts and experiences on our teaching of maths.

What do you have to do to get the children working independently and with confidence?

First and foremost the children need confidence. A child who runs to the teacher every few minutes is probably insecure in what they're doing. To operate do, talk and record, is hopeless if you're forever tied up with children seeking reassurance.

To begin with the 'How did you do that?' question usually elicits a defensive, 'What's wrong, what's wrong?' response from the child. Part of the training is to get children used to us questioning like this and them replying without fear of being wrong. I'm always aware of the need to attune my ears for a response different from the preconceived one I might have been expecting. This is very important.

Recently I had a fine example of my *not* listening properly to some of my fourth years. I was mingling with the fourth-year class and for a few minutes had had no opportunity to discuss their work with any group. Coming upon Kakel and Steven and feeling a very strong urge to say something (!) I thought they looked likely customers. They were involved in measuring the number of containers needed to fill a certain vessel. Steven using a meat-paste jar would count, taking turns with Kakel who was using a yoghurt pot. The counting sequence went something like this:

S : 86, 87, 88.
K : 92.
S : 93, 94, 95, 96.
K : 100, 104 and so on.

Jumping straight in with 'What on earth are you doing counting like that, you're counting all wrong . . . and what's more your containers aren't even the same size?' Questions these might have been, but my tone was definitely one of 'How can you be so stupid?' Fortunately past training and confidence building won the day. Very calmly, the boys put me in my place and explained what must by now be apparent to you. The yoghurt pot held four times the amount of water that the meat pot did. This explained why Kakel added four onto the count. I had interrupted them at a crucial stage in their project. However they were recording as they went so not too much damage was done. I had to learn not to make mistakes like that.

Confidence building also means doing away with pages upon pages of crosses and ticks – an aspect dealt with later. There is one practical point about working independently. If on any day, I find I've not prepared the room properly, if the scissors are missing or we're short of paper, the children cannot work independently. I know I'll have that all too familiar queue of wails, 'where's this, where's that?' guaranteed to irritate my none too placid nature! This seems so obvious, yet it's crucial for instilling independence in the children, freeing one from so many administrative organisational tasks which interfere with my listening and talking to children.

Won't this mean a lot more work for me?

First the bad news. Initially yes! We've both found it difficult to start do, talk and record, with a class used for the past year or so to working quietly at their desks. So you have to have your class ready to work on their own, without constant attention from you. I can't be all over the room at once, so training is essential. We say 'training', making it sound rather like Barbara Woodhouse and her dogs! Ethos is what we mean. It's very important we've found.

Carole has found it hard work this year getting her class to respond to her practical/discussion filled lessons, and has found the do, talk and record on a class level rather than in groups a good way to get the class talking and listening in the early days. Gradually the class-based activities and class discussions have given way to group and individual work. However, we both think that doing and talking with individuals and groups cannot wholly replace doing, talking and recording with the whole class. Both class and group discussions have their place.

Initially it's more work in the lesson time too (but the time goes very quickly!). You are always looking for an opening to talk or listen to children. You're always treading carefully, but at the same time having to be aware of what is going on all over the room. You cannot say, 'now children let us work in silence' and so defeat the object of the lesson. But having talking children and a mingling teacher is hard work. In the early days we found noise a great problem – but more of that one later.

Now the good news. Banished is that awful repetitive marking. Of course we need to see their work but hopefully we are working alongside them and seeing the fruits of their labours as we go along. The 'marking' is more interesting as it's words and figures. The child explains whilst we contribute and amend. Recently this struck me very forcibly. My fourth years were working on capacity and volume. Many of their observations would be impossible to mark in the isolation of the staffroom. For instance they had to estimate the capacity of vessels before they actually measured them. Then, having measured them they had to graph the results. They were so pleased when they saw their estimates and actual measurements beginning to coincide that, like the results of a game, they needed to come and tell me. I then asked them if they thought they were getting a feel for the units employed. Could they think of a reason why their graphs looked the way they did? These were all facets that couldn't be looked at in the 'record and then I'll mark it' situation.

Once the system is set up for a topic or group of topics it is self-perpetuating. It goes on daily with little need for preparation on your part. For example, to enable the group working on measuring mass, length and capacity to work well, I had to collect together necessary materials and work out assignments. This took time but once done it needed no evening work for quite a while leaving me free to concentrate on some other aspect of the curriculum. I also have had that particular maths class for one and a half years so the initial training period is well passed. I thoroughly enjoy that class now!

What was it like creating a classroom atmosphere to start with?

We have already dealt more with the physical work involved with the do, talk and record method of teaching, but there is also the mental strain of creating the right ethos. Of course, once built up this ethos is a total thing, pervading the whole of classroom life, – but it isn't easy.

The class I am teaching now is full of very independent personalities, all eager to have their say, but not that eager to listen to each other. This, therefore, had to be one of the first priorities – training them to listen to each other, and to me, and valuing each other's contributions. I have had to stamp on sniggering and verbal criticism of each other's contributions, otherwise the tentative, less confident children clam up and won't attempt a contribution in a class or group discussion. I am very hard on a child interfering with another childs' work in any lesson. I also try to encourage them to work independently of me and, as mentioned elsewhere, only turn to me for help when they are really stuck, and have tried everything they can think of.

As I said it isn't easy. I get fed up with stressing the same attitudes over and over again. I try to reason with the class when things go wrong, and we discuss the rules that we have and the reasons why we have them – eliciting these reasons from them rather than giving them to them as can 'I say, therefore you will do' formula, although there are obviously times when I wonder whether the reasoning is a waste of time and an 'I say, you do' attitude wouldn't be quicker and easier. I am trying to give them an attitude for the future though, one that is independent and thought out by themselves. For the same reasons I don't want them thinking of me as the fount of all knowledge. I try to expose my weaknesses to them – both to show that I don't know everything there is to know, no one can, and that I am a human being with feelings, emotions and 'off days' too.

What level of noise do I tolerate?

Noise can be one of the greatest bugbears to the success of children doing, talking and recording their way through maths. We both remember being probationers and being over anxious about noise levels, always worried the head might look through the door and see the children talking or even worse, playing. We also recall not having a chance to get down to any teaching as we were constantly stopping to admonish the class for being noisy.

To work the do, talk and record method you have got to accept from the outset that there will be noise. I've yet to see successful do, talk and record done in silence! Once you accept there will be noise you have to decide on a reasonable level. In our classrooms we can distinguish two types of noise which we and the children refer to as 'silly noise' and 'busy noise'.

We are all aiming for 'busy noise'. Instead of merely telling the children to be quiet we find that by eliciting reasons from the children themselves we get far more cooperation. They know from an early stage that we do, talk and *listen*. They know that to talk and listen you can't have shouting. If ever we need to stop to remind everyone in the room of this, the conversation will always go something like this:

Me : All stop for a moment and listen please. Why have we stopped?
Pupil : Because it's too noisy.
Me : So why did I stop you?
Pupil : Because you can't think and you can't hear what Jillian is saying.
Me : As you continue could you make sure that you can hear what your friends are saying? Carry on.

It may sound like some kind of catechism I know, but variations on this conversation always reduce the noise level. We both try not to raise our voices when speaking to individuals or the whole class. I try to make my voice serve as an example to the children. If I shout at them then I can't really complain if the children have loud voices and shout at me too.

Finally, Carole has found that other areas of the curriculum can help here. She has a strong tradition of drama with her classes and she feels that the very necessary discipline of the drama and physical education lesson overlaps and helps in maths. The use of 'freeze' as a command in drama and physical education is Carole's method of arresting the children's attention when things get out of hand in the early days. So why not she thought, use it in maths too? It worked and gave her the opportunity to reason with the children about the noise level in the class.

How do I measure their learning and progress?

We can't tell anyone how best to monitor the progress of their own children. Should this question really read 'If I can't see pages of right and wrong sums, how do I know what the children have assimilated?' So you are as worried as the children are about pages of work and marks? In our classes, mark books do contain marks as there are tables tests, number-bond questions and quick mental arithmetic practice, especially in my streamed classes. However, the marks are punctuated with comments and notes on the results of the *practical* oral tests I like to give them. I am at present adapting and devising some of these. The tests are taken in groups of up to four. The children use apparatus wherever necessary and are asked to explain verbally what they are doing. Until recently, setting pupils in the upper school for maths has been based on the results of written tests. This year we have done this based on the practical tests I have described.

We have had fewer changes between the ability gaps than usual and the staff involved feel that the children have been set more accurately than in the past. One example illustrates for me the value of such tests when children have been used to working with do, talk and record methods. At the start of the second year, one of the practical tests we were giving involved place value. Gary had had to work very hard all his first year in a do, talk and record way to grasp this concept and he had eventually reached the recording stage. Jeremy on the other hand was a boy of average ability who had joined us after the first year and missed out on the excellent grounding I think they get in the first year. He had a great deal of difficulty with the place-value test and apparently had never grasped the concept at all. By contrast, Gary, a poor reader with low motivation, fared well and demonstrated that he knew what he was doing. Jeremy is now in a very small remedial maths group regaining the practical do, talk, and record groundwork which he needs before he can go on.

We are now working on a fuller range of tests. This way a child could be tested orally on a variety of concepts and the testing can be done during lesson time in an informal, non-threatening way. Another way of keeping a check on progress is the reporting back sessions which we feel are integral to successful maths teaching. At first the children may be hesitant, but once they are confident of expressing themselves and giving their opinions in public, the reporting back sessions are valuable to both pupils and teacher.

Finally progress and attainment cannot always be broken down into quantified terms. We seem to be carrying around a fair amount in our heads. I believe it is called professional judgement! Without our own opinions and assessments in our heads we would all be lost.

This sounds fine for fourth years, but what about first and second years?

We would not say it was difficult to do, talk, and record with first years. After all this is the way they have been working in the first school. In nursery and reception classes the accepted way of teaching is do, talk and record, as the children's recording facilities are limited at the infant stage. In our first year (8 year olds) they are not so far removed from the practical work and accompanying chat of the first school. So what's new!?

I find with younger children, though, that my approach to the lesson is different from the teaching of maths in the upper school. These lessons are more formally structured. I have a recognisable beginning, middle and end. When I go in I talk with the whole class making sure everybody knows what to do, and stressing where they will find any necessary equipment. Then we have the working session, when they need constant direction and encouragement towards a balanced output between doing, talking and recording. Then there is the pulling together for the end of the lesson, where the class and I discuss individual work if necessary. Much of this time is used reiterating and rewarding behaviour important to the running of do, talk and record: things like training them to listen, praising them for getting on in their groups and working things out together and only coming to me when they are really stuck.

By the time the children reach the third and fourth year, there is less need for such a highly structured format. My third- and fourth-year classes come straight in and start work, often without any word from me. This is of invaluable help to me as I can waste no time getting in to listen to individuals or groups, helping where necessary. Also, being the deputy head, I often have matters to attend to.

Sometimes we stop in the middle of a lesson for reminders on sorting out of common problems, but I try to leave class discussion until the end of the day when the children have launched straight into their work. What I am saying is that it is possible to use this method with first years, but I do find that initially a highly structured approach to an apparently informal teaching method is necessary to maintain temper and sanity.

One final note here. It has been helpful to us in our school in having the resources to put in a second teacher with the younger classes. To successfully run our first-year programme as previously mentioned, the head drafts in a second teacher for half the maths time in any week. It really is of enormous help to have that assistance whilst doing the early training that seems so vital to enabling do, talk and record work. This does not however mean that it is impossible to operate this way if such help is not forthcoming. It just takes a whole lot longer.

Surely if I repeatedly have to tell children what I want them to do it defeats the object of my do, talk and record lessons?

Having to tell children what to do can fall into two categories: 1 the actual mathematical task you are setting and 2 where to find the apparatus or whatever is required by the children. For example:

Category 1 My children had had a class discussion lesson on making solid shapes out of sugar paper. During the next lesson they had tried to make their own solid shapes with little or no prompting from me – experimentation was what was required not success – failure didn't matter at all. Lesson 3 went like this at the beginning:

Me: Right, what were we all doing last lesson?
Class: Trying to make solid shapes, Miss.
Me: Did anyone succeed? Can you tell us about it, what you did, how you did it?

Discussion followed from various children about what they did, how they did it, what they did wrong, what they found out. After much discussion, category 1 comes in.

Me: Right now, from what you have learned from each other and your own experiments, I want you to try again and see what you can do this time.

Then on to category 2.

Me: I've put more sugar paper out on the table at the back of the room. You know where the scissors and glue are. Off you go.

I am then quite hard on children who haven't listened and pestered me with requests like 'where's the paper/glue/scissors, Miss?'. I point out that it wastes my time to have to say things over and over again. This is what I mean by training them to 'listen'.

In both areas the telling is only an important element of the lesson while the children are being 'trained' to work in this way. It is very possible that the ethos and organisation in classrooms is such that very little 'training' like this is required.

With regard to the practical apparatus, providing we've seen to it that the things required are to hand, and the children know where they are, they can be encouraged to help themselves in a responsible way, without having to refer to us all the time. They must also be trained, though, to replace durables and tidy up after themselves at the end of a lesson.

Surely children need the reassurance of a 'page of ticks?'

A page of ticks means satisfaction for the child and often I suspect for the teacher. Conversely a page of crosses can destroy confidence. A page with constructive criticism or written praise by the teacher provides satisfaction also. The child may possibly be reassured by ticks, but surely their own conversation with the teacher will also provide satisfaction, especially when the teacher is pointing out how much of an explanation is perfect. In conversation, the children often see their mistakes for themselves and this doubles their reward. Not only did the teacher react with encouragement to the 'right' bits, but they also needed nobody to point out the 'wrong' bits. They got all the way there by their *own* thinking. We feel that this way the page of ticks is traded for a more lasting satisfaction.

Edith Biggs, H.M. Staff Inspector (retired) first made me realise the importance of never saying 'That's wrong'. I've learned a lot from Miss Biggs, because I've never been afraid I was making a fool of myself. Whatever response I gave in our many discussions she never made me feel I'd said something absurd or wrong, just that an awful lot of it was right. She then gave either me the time to check my statements and spot the gaps in my thinking for myself or showed me something else that caused me to rethink my ideas later.

Let me tell you about Steven. I am sure he will remember how to do long division longer than those only taught tricks and given ticks. The class (second years) had been working for some time with bottle tops and counters to work out division problems. They had reached the stage of recording and I was aiming for the time when the children could abandon the apparatus and the '1 for you, 1 for him' approach. They had been asked to do this division:

$$6\overline{)72}$$

The children had been putting the total number of counters into a box and then sharing them into the required sets. Most were at the stage of trying to cut down their work by giving out more than 1 at a time. Steven's group were giving them out in threes.

$_o{}^o{}_o$	3	3	3	3	3	3 →	I have taken 18 from the box
$_o{}^o{}_o$	3	3	3	3	3	3 →	I have taken 36 from the box
$_o{}^o{}_o$	3	3	3	3	3	3 →	I have taken 54 from the the box
$_o{}^o{}_o$	3	3	3	3	3	3 →	I have taken 72 from the box
	12	12	12	12	12	12	

So 72 shared between 6 is 12 each. Steven however found this far too long. 'Miss', he called out, 'you don't need all those tops and those long lines of writing. It's easier this way!' $6\overline{)72}$ 'I don't need to give out small numbers, that's long. You can give them 10 each straight away. That uses 60 up. Then you've got 12 left, so that's 2 more. So they get 12 each altogether.'

After this he went straight onto $12\overline{)150}$ and numbers divided by 13, 14, 15 using the same principle. That way (the one I was aiming for) became known as Steven's method from then on and eventually we all adopted it.

Similarly David 'discovered' the formula for area of a triangle. The 'Eureka' principle made sure those two children never forgot their methods. Neither did they need to bother with a page of ticks! That everyone else adopted their 'method' was reassurance enough. We call this the 'big tick' and find one 'big tick' equals lots of smaller ones. We don't have big crosses, at least not regarding answers. Only when it comes to behaviour, then sometimes a reprimand is seen as a very big cross. They always seem to be given for things like interrupting, not listening and laughing at someone else's effort to explain — all ethos-creating issues.

What do I do when lots of children want my help at once?

This can happen at any time, with my method of maths teaching. Text-book dominated lessons can just as easily give the teacher queues of children round the desk waiting for an answer to questions like 'what do we do here Miss?' 'I don't understand what they mean here, Miss?'

As we are building the child's responsibility for its own work, it should eventually cut down the number of questions, both about the work and the organisation that children bother us with. We do see that this gets better as the children get older and more used to working in this way. It is possible to develop a child's initiative, so that he/she will automatically try certain steps before running to the teacher for help. Practice in looking things up, trying things out for themselves, asking each other, doing their own thinking, bears fruit not only in maths but in all other areas of the curriculum. One can also use the 'infectious diseases' idea, where children explain things to, and help out, other children.

Angela (fourth year) had just completed a graph showing her estimation of the capacity of certain vessels as opposed to the actual capacity. I wasn't able to spend the time necessary at that particular moment so I suggested she showed it to Karen who was also waiting. Then both of them were to come back later with Karen's opinion of Angela's results together with any criticism and alterations necessary to the graph. This way I was free to continue with Wayne and in fact found time to go to the two girls myself.

Sometimes I find the queue inevitably somewhat longer than I'd like. Some of my standard queue reducers are as follows:

1 Is there anybody who knows I can deal with them quickly — let me see you first. This disposes with those going to the dentist, those who've lost their pencil and those who feel sick!

2 Have you had your worked checked by someone else first?

3 If it's book-based practice work they often need reminding that it should be marked from answers kept around the room before showing me.

4 If it's a problem several in the queue need sorting out I deal with that in a group.

5 Desperation! when most of the class wants me I do the same as every other teacher would and sit them all down or stop them *in situ* and address the whole class. This gives me a necessary breathing space because I can't stand the pressure of virtually the whole class waiting in a queue.

As well as giving you space to talk to other children, it also shows that children's own ideas are to be respected, not just the teacher's or a textbook's. It also teaches children to listen to each other. It is training again. In time, children only seek any help when they really need it — valuable training for independence in later life.

If I'm the only person in my school using these methods won't it ultimately be a waste of time and effort?

I think anything which helps build a child's confidence and independence is worth doing. I feel I see the benefits even on a short-term basis, even if at times the going seems hard. This doesn't just apply to maths, but to all areas of the curriculum as the methods involved in working this way generate a general ethos which permeates the classroom. In fact its rather a chicken—egg, egg—chicken situation, one needs a certain ethos in which to teach maths in this way but the ethos creates the situation in which the maths can be taught in this way.

There is a possibility that you might influence your colleagues to work this way too? If they see that this method works for you, that you enjoy working in this way, and that the children enjoy it and benefit in a variety of ways, then that's the best possible recommendation. Even if you have little success in influencing your colleagues it is still worth it for the benefit it brings to the children and the enjoyment you can get from it yourself. Just be prepared for the hard but rewarding work involved in setting up the general classroom ethos. This setting up period will take at least the first half of the first term, if not longer.

In our school we are lucky. The support and encouragement of the head enabled us all to change over to a do, talk and record way of working and now, as I said in the introduction, we have formulated a school policy in maths and we all work to the same goals of getting the children to think for themselves. We all expect similar levels of responsibility, initiative, and independence and we train them right from the start to develop these qualities. Such training shows them that we value these attributes in their behaviour.

Will the parents understand and appreciate this approach to the teaching of maths?

This is what our headmaster had to say when this question was posed.

> 'We had outside advice from the Education Authority over several terms. The advisory teacher in maths worked once a week with the teachers, who were sceptical to start with. Now they are convinced of the value of teaching in a do, talk and record way.
>
> At the end of the first year a parents evening was held. Children and parents came in and worked together. It was made as informal as possible (with tea and cakes). All went well and this led to the rewriting of our approach to maths in the school. Parents seemed to accept what was being done, although there were some who didn't want to be involved, being quite happy to let the school get on with it.'

Regular parent evenings like this have meant that parents do understand what we are doing now.

What do the children get out of this?

We feel our children are now able to work independently when necessary. They develop initiative. If I'm talking to a group or individual they know not to interrupt and, rather than wait about for help they will often try to help themselves. If a child waits by me for some period of time I know it's probably because it's my help he needs. Even then making an aside from the group discussion I can encourage the child to perhaps first seek help from a friend. Here I find it's essential to point out that the children do need to know where all materials are kept and what they may or may not take.

How else do the children benefit? They are gaining in ability and confidence in expressing themselves, an important across the curriculum point. They have learnt how to talk to each other and most importantly to listen to each other as well as to the teacher. After five years of do, talk and record in our school we can certainly see the fruits of our labours. The third and fourth years have a sound base on which to build the topic centred work of the upper school. But we did have some hard, concerted training to do in those early terms.

Finally, do the kids enjoy it?

I will let the children answer this one for themselves.

> Debra: I like making things with my fingers it helps me understand. I make shapes at home. I use my brain.
>
> Jayne: I like making things as well. In a book you might not understand what they tell you, if you do it yourself you remember.

	In the first school we used colour factor to help us do our maths.
Sharon:	I liked doing symmetry and making shapes. You didn't tell us exactly how to make the shapes, we had to try and make them ourselves. Symmetry, I didn't understand, I found a lot out with that.
Mark:	I don't like working from books, I don't like maths that much. Some books are hard to understand. I like the different sort of maths, when you find things out.
Stephen:	I like Mrs Harvey's maths because of the work that she gives us. When we did solid shapes she got me to come out to the board and see if I could design a plan for a Toblerone box. First of all I tried to make a square box, it didn't work when I was gluing it.
Deborah: (4th yr)	I like maths. It's not really maths though is it?
Karen: (4th yr)	It's good to do the things yourself. I didn't really know about kilograms and litres and measuring before. Now I can imagine it myself.
Wayne: (4th yr)	I like the mess you can make and no one shouts, well as long as you clear it up.

References

James, C. N., 'Mathematics from Middle Schools to High Schools, Part 1. An approach to Mathematical Understanding and Development for Middle Schools.' *Ealing Education Service*, Ealing Teachers' Centre Publication, 1976.

James, C. N., 'A series of Concept Development Papers:

1 Place Value
2 Addition in Hundreds, Tens, and Units
3 Subtraction (Comparison and Take away)
4 Multiplication
5 Division.'

Ealing Education Service, Ealing Teachers' Centre Publication, 1977.

The Open University, *EM 235 Developing Mathematical Thinking,* The Open University Press, 1982.

27 Doing, talking and recording with a whole class in a comprehensive school

Bob Vertes

Source: specially written for this volume

<<<<<<<<<<<<<<<<<<<<<<<<<<<<<<<<<<<<<<<<<<<<<<<<<<<<<<<

Introduction

To set the scene: I am the head of a mathematics department in a 1100 pupil mixed comprehensive, with some 10 years' teaching experience behind me. Early on in my teaching career I found myself able to try various techniques to overcome the hurdle of lack of confidence in their ability, that many pupils put in the path of their mathematical learning. I found it necessary to train pupils to have certain attitudes and expectations within lessons, and quite a large change in approach was called for, from them as from me, before the most conducive atmosphere was created in the classroom.

Essentially I try to get the classroom run in what I imagine (without experience of it) is a 'research team' atmosphere. They need to accept me as the one responsible for directing the activities, coordinating them, and evaluating them in the final instance — but they also need to accept some views of their own role not generally given pupils in the classroom. The following ten points are a nearly complete summary of those.

They have to be prepared to:

1 Think for themselves — form their own opinions, follow their own logic.
2 Not be afraid to communicate their thinking for fear it may be wrong.
3 Accept that wrong answers can also be helpful.
4 Listen to their peers, for comments in their own words (which may well be as useful as mine, and perhaps be all the clearer for being phrased in less formal language).
5 Question their peers' ideas (or any unsupported statements of mine) asking for justification, example, or proof.
6 Accept that as well as the 'simple' problem to which we are bending our minds, there may be side issues, or issues to lead us further, perhaps to generalised results.
7 Accept that some correct facts which seem to relate to the situation are not, in fact, useful, that is, that on occasion there is a surfeit of information from

which we have to sieve the essentials to combine together to achieve a desired end result.

8 Accept that some problems are open ended, that is, the methods adopted for solution are what matter, and not the answers.

9 Accept that more than one method of solution may exist for a problem, and that often these are equally valid.

10 Come to realise that once they understand something it is much easier to recall it when necessary, especially in comparison to a rote formula. The difficulty here is, once you have reached a convincing result, to write reasons and result in the formal language that is used in textbooks, examination papers, and by 'mathematicians', and even to use symbolic language, standard notation, to abbreviate this recording of process and results.

Introducing the class to the behaviour pattern observed

When I get a new class to teach, or when a new pupil arrives in my classroom, I try to have a little chat to them about what my approach and expectations of them are. I emphasise that when I am talking I expect them to listen to me, but I contrast this by explaining that I shall want to hear them talking, thinking out loud; that their fellow pupils will also be listening to them, and questioning and further that they must listen to their friends' comments, evaluate them and question if they have any doubts. The only really effective way that this message gets across is, in my experience, to start with an 'investigation'. (I will write more of that later) — but it is that approach that I generally use to introduce a new topic or extension of material covered sometime previously. After a topic has been introduced, during 'practice session' lessons, the pupils are still using certain novel approaches: they will have been given the green light to talk among themselves, in groups of 2 or 3 (so long as it is on relevant matter); to try each question themselves, but compare answers, and, more important, method with the others in their 'team'; and (only) then to indicate if temporarily beaten by a question.

The investigation method

A new second-year (12 year olds) class who have met coordinates before but not equations of lines (though they had solved simple equations) were due to be taught how to give a set of points an equation. They were given a grid, points (1, 3) and (4, 3). I suggested they drew up a table with 2 rows, marked x and y, and about 5 columns.

x	1	4		
y	3	3		

They were then told to find some other coordinates on the line through the two points. (2, 3) (3, 3) arrive quickly, but they learnt not to stay between the two given points necessarily, so we get, say, (6, 3).

x	1	4	2	3	6
y	3	3	3	3	3

As I took responses from the class, occasionally picking someone who does not have their hand up, I was careful to praise any correct statement — but when I received an answer I often waited, or asked 'Agreed?' so that if, for example, someone says (3, 2) instead of (2, 3) I hope for a correcting response. This trains them to listen to each other, and to increase their role as controlling their learning, diminishing mine as the sole judge of accuracy. There are times when it is just as well — I make mistakes too! It is my policy, though, to try to 'let down gently' in case of error — so I will in the above instance say to the pupil, 'Fine, right point, but you got the x and y in the wrong order', and often issue a reminder to the whole class to beware of this error. This reduces the 'guilt' of the pupils, and, I hope, lets them see that their error has not angered or distressed me, but in fact has been valuable as a caution to the class.

The pattern in the above table is easily and quickly identified, but the stages are often as follows:

Pupil 1:   They're all three.
Teacher: What are?
Pupil 1:   The numbers.
Teacher: All of them?
Pupil 1:   The ones on the bottom line.
Teacher: What are the bottom line numbers?
Pupil 2: y numbers.
Teacher: So can you give me a rule? A statement that is true?
Pupil 2:   The y numbers are all 3.
Teacher: Always 3? (pause). Look at your graphs!
Pupil 2:   Yes
(I then write this statement on the board: 'the y number is always 3')
Teacher: Can anyone put this as an equation? A statement with an equals sign in it?
Pupil 3: $y = 3$
Teacher: Fine. Any problems anyone?

Of further use in developing my approach is a later stage in the same topic when a table has been reached like that below.

x	1	2	3	4	5
y	3	4	5	6	7

A pupil asked a very pertinent question for which she was fulsomely praised, as it gave the class some thinking to do, but made the later stages easier.

Pupil: Does it matter which x numbers we use?

This is an important question. It links up the fact that the result is not just specific to the 2 points' numbers which we started with, but can be generalised. More than this, it has taught them a technique which can be applied to other questions. It led to one girl putting the x numbers in order 1, 2, 3, 4, 5. Once I spot somebody recognising that patterns are going to make life easier, I will praise, and draw the attention of the class, to this fact. I frequently tell them that the mathematics we learn is full of patterns and if only they can learn to use them, or spot them when in use, their work becomes easier.

Solutions from the second 'box' referred to are listed, and equations 'drawn from them'. For example:

Words	Equation
x add 2 is y	$y = x + 2$
x is 2 less than y	$x = y - 2$
y is 2 more than x	
There's a difference of 2 between x and y.	
y take x gives 2	$y - x = 2$

All the above will be clearly on the board. I accept all new solutions, we even have a quick vote on the most popular (the vote is then derided as not being important *really*). An importance of taking all offers is in particular to build confidence, which is what often holds back their progress; but also vital, in my opinion, is their appreciation that the process of seeking out patterns for themselves is what doing maths is all about. It is thinking mathematically. The fact that this pattern is describable in words or symbols in a number of different, but correct ways, is stressed by me, so that they begin to have faith in their own logic, in their capacity to come up with the (or *a*) right answer; and in their ability to 'pull out' a right answer from the data available.

Investigations

I do, as I have said, make a regular habit of emphasising whenever opportunity arises, that mathematics is full of patterns such as shapes (common polygons, tessellations, angle properties, symmetry, loci) and numbers (sequences, graphs, pythagoras theorem). Many rules are visible occurring in different branches of the subject. As an example, what I refer to as the 'domino rule' occurs:

1 in multiplying (cancelling fractions $\frac{2}{3} \times \frac{3}{5} = \frac{2}{5}$

2 in matrix multiplication $\begin{pmatrix} \cdot & \cdot & \cdot \\ \cdot & \cdot & \cdot \end{pmatrix} \begin{pmatrix} \cdot \\ \cdot \\ \cdot \end{pmatrix} = \begin{pmatrix} \cdot \\ \cdot \end{pmatrix}$

2 by 3 3 by 1 2 by 1
(must
match)

3 in 'chain rule' differentiation: $\dfrac{dv}{du} \times \dfrac{du}{dm} = \dfrac{dv}{dm}$

4 in vectors (relative velocity) $_A V_B = {_A}V_E + {_E}V_B$

and there are probably other instances: where the middle two items must match, and the first and last give the 2 components of the answer.

The sorts of investigation with which I often start work with a new group, to get them to see that they can be 'doing maths' without necessarily being able to compartmentalise it in a subject or topic heading (like decimals, or fractions, or algebra) are for example:

The handshake problem

30 people in the class go to a party and everyone shakes hands once with everybody else. How many handshakes were there altogether?

The anti *magic square*

Put the numbers 1−9 in the grid so that in each of the eight directions you get a *different* total. (Another variation on the rather often used magic square).

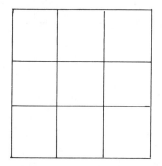

I won't spoil your fun by giving you the answers, but suffice it to say neither is as easy as it looks, though each is easy enough at first glance for most pupils to be interested in willing to try it. I first incur the displeasure of some of the class by telling them to work in a small group; I do *not* allow wild guesses unsupported by evidence, preferring first to take any offers of how we could approach the problem logically. The first one is straightforward *if* one first takes *smaller* classes, that is small parties, then spots the pattern, puts it into a formula, and (ideally) generalises, taking the specific case 30 after generalising. The *real* problem is of course not '30' but *N* people at a party, and by the end of that investigation most classes will, if my original 10 points were followed, have a good idea of what is required of them. Since they can see the results, they usually quickly acquiesce into that method of working.

Although the result of my 'favourite' investigation is a little awkward to obtain using rigorous mathematical method, certainly too advanced for 15 year olds, the point it makes is usually well taken:

The circle areas problem

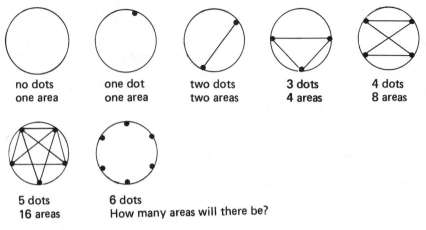

| no dots | one dot | two dots | 3 dots | 4 dots |
| one area | one area | two areas | 4 areas | 8 areas |

5 dots
16 areas

6 dots
How many areas will there be?

The answer is *not* 32, and for 7 dots, all connected up, the answer is not 64. This usually stumps most of those pupils who rush to plump for the 'obvious' answer. By drawing, the correct answer can generally be obtained, but one or two sections which are very small, or made up by 3 lines interactions virtually coincident, are very easily overlooked.

Continuing sequences

It is worth mentioning, I feel, that the 'method of differences', which I use on occasions when a technique for continuing sequences is required, can be a simple, useful tool in investigations. It relies on looking at differences between successive terms, and looking at successive lines of those until a line of *constant* differences are obtained, from where we can build up to find the real term, then the rest, and so on. For example:

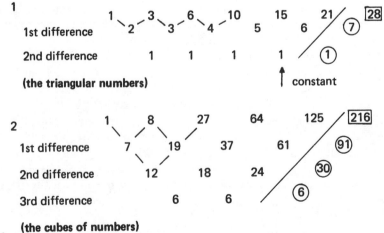

276

3 The above example

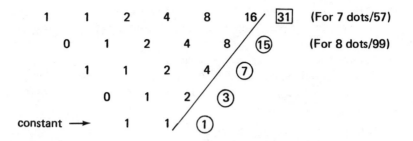

A nice example of one which illustrates two routes to the same result is to look at the problem of finding how many diagonals there are in an N-sided polygon.

The sequence obtained by separate drawings of triangles, squares or pentagons, yields

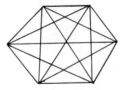

$$\text{numbers of} \atop \text{diagonals} \quad N = \begin{pmatrix} 1 & 2 \\ 0 & 0 \end{pmatrix} \begin{matrix} 3 & 4 & 5 & 6 & 7 \\ 0 & 2 & 5 & 9 & 14 \end{matrix}$$

$$\underset{\substack{\text{no shape} \\ \text{can be drawn}}}{\uparrow}$$

For example: $N = 6$, number of diagonals $= 9$

Looking arithmetically/algebraically at the sequence may or may not get you to a general formula, though I find most pupils can continue the sequence.

As an exercise in logic, directed questions can get most pupils to a formula as follows. I would first ask for them to check that they had drawn 3 or 4 diagrams. Then ask if a polygon has N sides, how many vertices (corners) has it? Followed by 'To how many corners can you *not* draw a diagonal? It has, in my experience, quickly become agreed by a class that it is 3, provided those participating are asked to justify their answers (2 is the first answer given usually), the 3 being the vertex chosen and the 2 either side of it. It then becomes clear that there were $N - 3$ diagonals from any one of the points — hence $N(N - 3)$ from the N points. The last step, to realise that you have to divide by 2 to get the right answers, usually follows if you remember to *check* back and see if the answer obtained here corresponds to that obtained by 'experiment'.

The *main* reasons why I find this investigative method, and investigations generally, extremely useful are because:

1 they use, develop and make interesting the techniques of pattern spotting;
2 they practise logical thinking;
3 since often there is more than a single method of approach to a problem, or different ways of working the results, they emphasise that different approaches can be equally vital;
4 they teach mathematical processes and reasoning while appearing often to be arithmetic based (i.e. using numbers) which are the symbols the pupils feel most confident using;
5 they can practise *together*, involving friends or family. (Every few weeks I try to set an investigation or puzzle for homework. It's an excellent way of trying to get my message across to parents, many of whom feel maths is just pages full of sums.

The joy of discovery, the ease of recall of items discovered is not just a bonus effect but a major reason for adopting this approach. I often remind a class how many things they remember ever so easily simply because they discovered it for themselves, or because they're really interested, such as names of pop stars and records or football results, while they forget so much that they get regularly tested on, and would expect to recall more and more easily. It is why I don't always tell them the 'answer' for quite a while after I set an investigation, preferring to increase the number of hints, or to suggest some self-directing questions they could use, if they are getting bogged down. What is amusing is how often they can recall not just the method but the answer to investigations done a year or more ago!

Stuck!

There are two expressions which are used too often by pupils in order (often) to get out of thinking or working. 'I'm stuck' or 'I don't get it' called out or stated after a brief consideration of a question is not easily tolerated in my lessons – or rather not when I consider it is simply a 'get out' from work. In themselves the expressions are acceptable, but I need to train the pupils I teach to use them only when it signifies a certain (not the *initial*) stage in a process of working towards a result.

The obvious disaffection that being 'stuck' or 'not getting it' creates can be avoided, or at least diminished by training pupils soon after you first meet them, to listen carefully to questions you ask them when they say they are 'stuck'. They should then learn to ask themselves these type of questions even if you're not available. I tend to refer to them as self-directing questions. They will, if you learn to pose and answer them, lead you through, round or beyond thinking hurdles.

Early on with a new class, when I'm covering a topic like geometry (which often worries the average or weak pupil), I try to devote a lesson or two to working through a whole set of examples on the board. Either I initially go through a worked example, thinking out loud and confirming my thoughts next to the 'official' working on the board, then getting more and more pupils involved in the solution process of later questions; or, more frequently now that I'm reasonably confident in the process, straight away getting contributions from pupils. Either way, the self-directing questions tend to arise quickly, if in batches, as follows:

1 What does the question tell you? What information is given? Would a diagram help? Would a table, or a list, be helpful to display the information?
2 What do we need to find (or prove)? Is it anything I can get from the information directly (or from the diagram or table)? Can I use symbols to shortcut the work?

These stages require an enquiring, open mind, and also some patience. Some pupils will 'get there' quickly, but for real success, I always allow a bit of 'thinking time' and wait for hands to go up — *especially* early on in any lesson. I may pick on the shy ones, to encourage them to contribute. I am also quite nasty to those that shout out. I like to emphasise we're not in a race, or I'll get one or two of those that I think don't understand the impatient one's comment (even if correct) to 'grill him' to see if he can explain why his answer's right. If he can, he gets away with a mild rebuke, with a bit of praise, but if he can't it's a useful demonstration that he must think out why as well as what, the answer is, as he gave it. At this early stage, as later, I *record* all contributions so all can see current 'state of play', and *reward* contributions (verbally) so all feel able and willing to say something.

These two stages over, if the pupil(s) say 'stuck', I now consider it a legitimate state. Prior to this the 'thinker' has opted out of really investigating whether he has the ability to answer the question. He has made a snap judgment, one to give him an easy way out. The question now appropriate is such as:
3 Is there anything that is true, and looks relevant, that can be written down? Own words or symbols, preferably with a reason, but 'hunches' are allowed, (even if occasionally wrong). If there is no progress to a general result, can a few simpler examples or special cases lead us to any further results (or even conjectures) perhaps by looking at a pattern? Has a question like this been done before? Has the textbook got any examples like this?

I accept that not all pupils will consistently be able to continue this process, so it's at this stage I get them to compare notes with a neighbour, and see if their focal ideas can get them a stage further. I try to encourage them to question any step the other pupil has made without reasons, and to ensure they are convinced by any reasons given. Failing this, they need to challenge, in a friendly way, the other pupil(s) with whom they are working. If they can get used to doing this, then rather than competition between them (an unnecessary burden on the thinking process, as in many school activities, in my opinion) they will learn co-operation. I find that as they learn to respect their peers' abilities and comments, so they gain in self respect, and self confidence, recognising that their own opinions are sought and included.

I have a little bit of extra 'inter-personal training' to do to achieve this all round increase in self respect and respect for others. Obviously discussion skills play a part in the work, and some collusion between discursive subject teachers play a part in the work, and some collusion between discursive subject teachers (e.g. English, History) and myself often helps to get them to practise giving an opinion and respect another's opinion or comments. I am quick to clamp down on any ridiculing of 'wrong' answers. There is nothing so inhibiting as being publicly shamed, and I want to eliminate that form of 'I'm stuck' which says really, either 'there you are, I've failed again' or 'I'm scared to say, because I might make a fool of myself'. When I start teaching about circles, I ask a simple question, 'How do I draw a circle?' Some wit usually says 'use a compass' and there is an inevitable titter around the room. I use this situation to point out

1   'compass' *v* 'compasses'
2   it *is* a perfectly correct answer, whether we mean drawing round a compass or using compasses.
3   there may be other methods which can be used without having either of these pieces of equipment, such as ruler and pencil, the 'envelope' method.

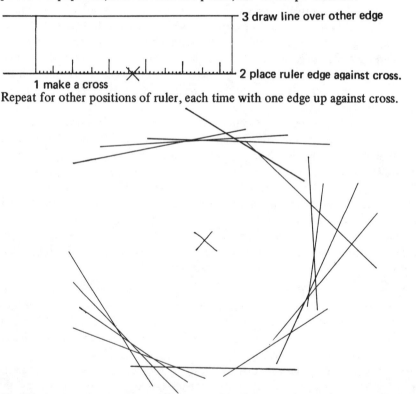

3 draw line over other edge

2 place ruler edge against cross.

1 make a cross

Repeat for other positions of ruler, each time with one edge up against cross.

The lines are each tangents to a circle, centred on the cross, so the straight lines enclose or 'envelop' a circle. A small problem can arise, namely that a few pupils will copy rather than write their own ideas down, when set to work in class. I try to apportion the blame between copier and copied, and ask who's done the thinking? Share by all means but try to contribute equally, and don't copy unless you really understand what is going on.

Mark schemes

Very early in my taking over a new class, they will be told that arithmetic is the least important of the skills I need of them, that answers need not always be correct (indeed that I may well make some errors on occasion), but that the way they get to the answers and the way they set out the reasons for their answers are much more important.

One way I use to get this message across, that is, that *process* not *product* is what really matters, is by adopting a marking scheme for their class, home and test work, which emphasises their working especially at the start of a question. This is so that they get used to reasoning, sorting out whether they know the right process, rather than to hasty answers or guesswork. Intuitive ability is fine, but few people can rely on it for a sufficiently high success rate to avoid the need for learning to give step by step accounts of working, answers and reasons. As I've said earlier, I work through a number of examples to illustrate the steps I feel necessary in solving a problem, not so much teaching as getting the class to listen and watch as I illustrate how I personally approach, evaluate, tackle, lay-out and solve the question. Even when I begin to involve them in problem solving as *I* record their comments I am careful to lay it out as I hope they will learn to by illustrations of mark schemes for such work. The scheme shows where marks are allotted for working or reasons (that is, 'method marks'), and (if and when examples can be found from their work) where I prefer someone's attempt with the wrong answer but the right process, to someone else's who may have the right answer but either hasn't shown working, or has made an error, or even two cancelling each other.

Checking

The last of the techniques I try to emphasise (if this section seems to be an afterthought, it is the same attitude that the pupils display to it at first) is that they should try to check their work. To compare theory with reality, to see if a result is sensible, compatible with the information, of the right magnitude, fitting the equation and so on. This largely removes the occasionally irritating chorus of 'Sir, is this right?' diminishes the 'hands up' and the queues at the desk, and more importantly, from the point of view that the pupils' benefit is more important than the teacher's, it gets the pupils to realise that their efforts can be checked by themselves. They also realise that conjectures *can* be tested, that guesses can be investigated as being right or intuitive. Checking compensates only slightly for the weighting of marks in favour of process, rather than 'product'.

Conclusion

The most delightfully rewarding part of teaching for me has always been seeing the joy on the face of a pupil who has 'discovered' some fact. It may be understanding a simple idea, or the final result of a complex calculation, but the sheer satisfaction is tremendous. It is only so if the pupil has been enabled or encouraged to reach the conclusion himself, and has not in response to a query simply been *told*.

I believe there's an internationally used proverb:

'Give a man a fish, and you feed him for a day
Teach the man to fish, and you feed him for a lifetime.'

I adopt this philosophy, and adapt the proverb:

Tell a pupil the answer, and you satisfy him for the moment
Teach him how to find the answer, and you provide for him for a lifetime.

28 Doing, talking and recording in remedial and other situations in a comprehensive school

Sandy Carter

Source: specially written for this volume

⋘⋘⋘⋘⋘⋘⋘⋘⋘⋘⋘⋘⋘⋘⋘⋘⋘⋘⋘⋘⋘⋘⋘⋘⋘⋘⋘⋘⋘⋘⋘

In this article I intend to refer to two classes that I am teaching this year. The first is a small group of first years who are in fact remedial (many of them have quite severe emotional problems as well as learning difficulties). The second is a fifth year CSE group, many of whom are quite capable and may go on to study O-level in the lower sixth.

When considering the first year remedial group it is as well to remember that the majority of those pupils have lost a lot of confidence in themselves generally and more specifically in their ability to cope mathematically. A great deal of my time is there fore spent re-building this 'lost confidenct' as well as attempting to put into operation any remedial help that is required.

On arrival at our school these pupils are usually assessed, as accurately as possible, so that where necessary, individual programmes can be devised to cope with certain pupil's specific problems. In order to do this assessment I rely on diagnostic tests and 'pupil talk'. By 'pupil talk' I mean open discussion between the pupils themselves as well as me. I find that through open discussion I can learn a great deal about each pupil; their confused thought processes, lack of knowledge and to what extent their confidence is actually lacking. Talk enables us all to learn from each other and it can help to build up the trust and rapport, that is in my opinion very essential. It is always my intention at this stage to also show to the pupils that although I am very firm in my approach to teaching I am also patient and willing to give to each of them as much time as I can. I think that time is the most important thing that we can offer these children. Very often they are in the state that they are in due to the fact that time in teaching is at a premium everywhere. None of us have enough of this valuable commodity.

As we are all aware, pupils need to be able to listen in order to gain anything from talk, but many remedial pupils are unable to listen properly. This inability to listen is probably linked to their lack of concentration. Like most areas where there is a deficiency certain training can help overcome these problems. I attempt to train those pupils by adopting various techniques that I have

283

discovered work for me. An example of this is that during a period of discussion it becomes a great deal easier for us all to participate and listen if we sit in a group close to each other as opposed to being spread out around the room. I tell the pupils that they must listen to what people have to say so that they can grasp the points in discussion first time. I personally have no intention of making statements to the group more than once; mind you this is my general teaching philosophy anyway. I know that if the pupils see that I am prepared to keep repeating myself they will be lazy when it comes to listening. If I give a mental arithmetic test, the pupils know that I am prepared to say the question twice and the answer only once.

I have discovered through experience again that I can train children to respond to certain verbal signals. By this is meant that I use just one word for example, my favourite word seems to be 'right' and I can use this in so many different ways by altering the intonation. When I say 'right!' sharply, usually meaning that I am ready to proceed and need their full attention, the pupils respond accordingly. If I say the same word softly the inference is that as far as I am concerned all is well, and that I am pleased. Children learn to react to my voice in this manner and I find I am able to use one word to transmit a whole range of meaning that could in some instances be 'wordy', repetitive and 'heavy going' for both me and the pupils. I am sure that verbosity encourages pupils to switch off as opposed to listening. To sum up I suppose one could say that pupils will listen if they consider that what is being said to them is important, relevant and meaningful.

Whilst training children to listen, my 'hidden intentions' are to also prepare children to talk confidently and with greater understanding. It is important that they have these qualities when talking so that their audience has the necessary desire to listen. When these children talk I do not expect them to use the high powered jargon that this subject can demand. On the contrary, I am more than happy for these children to adopt a language of their own as long as we are all on the same wavelength.

The use of apparatus can act as a good medium for this, because the pupils' talk can develop from their actions. Recently, after struggling with some pupils, trying to develop a greater understanding of the division concept, I resorted to coloured counters. We pretended that we had fifteen sweets to be divided between the three of us. One particular pupil who had been sharing the sweets later announced that the symbol ÷ meant 'shared between'. I encouraged this by saying something like 'Well done Angela; yes that is a very good description of precisely what you did and an excellent new name for division.' The same situation occurred with multiplication whereby the phrase 'lots of' was used and understood by many pupils.

An experience I recently encountered with one of these pupils is probably worth relating at this point. A little girl, who has obvious difficulties in understanding anything relating to maths, frowned very deeply every time I began to speak. I could almost read in her face 'This is maths, and I don't understand maths, so I'm not going to understand this.'

My initial chat with Caroline was completely fruitless. She continually repeated, 'I don't understand, I don't know what you mean.' According to her
maths book she was able to cope with both addition and subtraction by using
an algorithm and most of her work was correct. I decided to use the abacus with
Caroline – hoping to get her to talk to me whilst we explored the possibilities
of the abacus together. Caroline was unable to talk freely unless I intervened
prompting, questioning, encouraging and eventually I abandoned talking in
terms of maths. We spent time talking just generally and Caroline became much
more relaxed. We then looked at her exercise book and discussed her success
rate for here was proof that she was capable of good, correct work – I praised
her accordingly. I moved Caroline back to the abacus and now she was much
more relaxed and as she began to talk her own natural language was used. As
she spoke she looked for my reaction. As I listened and nodded, praised, reassured, Caroline certainly began to gain more confidence and a good rapport
developed between us. The barrier began to break down – it was good. Praise
such as 'Good girl', 'Well done' 'That's nice', 'Oh I like that', always seem to
go down well with this type of child. I wanted Caroline to see that there is no
wrong but that there are varying degrees of right. If she and I were communicating with each other and there was mutual understanding, then we had success.
Caroline has improved tremendously in both ability and understanding. She
still looks puzzled but only occasionally!

In order to have time to spend with children like this, I have to organise
the rest of the group for a twenty minute maths games session. This may involve clock bingo, probability using dice or a banking game. I ask the pupils
not to disturb me and to solve any problems they may have through group
discussion. I do make sure that they have understood how to play the games
before hand. This usually works well, I find.

I use games a great deal in order to make mathematics fun and interesting.
One class game I frequently use is called 'buggy'. I read about it in a journal
and decided to give it a try as a part of my 'confidence building' programme.
'Bugs' are repeated errors that children make and the game involves putting
onto the blackboard a series of these and for each one that the pupils can
correct they receive a house point.

Here are some typical 'buggies'

1)	207	2)	406	3)	476
	+ 194		− 138		+ 195
	3911		332		1211

As the pupils become less inhibited and gain more confidence they begin to
'openly' identify with the 'bugs' and become prepared to talk about them. I
have had incidences when a pupil realises he has a 'bug' that has not been
mentioned and he will be quite happy to get up and show the class. This type
of lesson I would liken to group therapy, particularly as there is the opportunity
for pupils to disclose the fact that their difficulties are experienced by others
and many pupils do use this opportunity. I have actually heard a pupil say

'Yes, I did that like Simon except that I was worse because I did it when I was adding as well'. I really believe that once pupils begin to recognise errors like this they are beginning to think mathematically and also they are really getting inside the subject.

Another game that has proved both successful and enjoyable is called the 'Number Storywriting' game. The pupils think of a sum and write it out on a piece of paper for example:

$$\begin{array}{r} 298 \\ -197 \\ \hline 101 \end{array}$$

They fold the piece of paper and put it in a 'hat'. Each pupil then choses a sum from the hat and attempts to write a story about the sum that he has chosen. The pupils in turn write their stories on the blackboard with the sum and if the sum and the story match then they win a house point for their team. If they don't match then the other team attempt to re-write the story and gain a house point bonus. A very interesting example of this 'mis-matching' was when one of the pupils called John picked out the following sum $301 - 187 = 114$. As his story he wrote: 'There were 301 soldiers and then 187 more soldiers came along. Now 187 soldiers got shot, how many were there left.'

His colleagues recognised his mistake and were very keen to help him. Pupils such as John do not appear to feel embarrassment, resentment or shame. The atmosphere that is created in the classroom is such that we are all tolerant of each other's errors including mine. Once again there is no wrong as such. I prefer to suggest that if we are all looking for understanding then a story may be written or spoken in an alternative way.

I find that audio visual aids can be a very valuable part of a lesson particularly if I am aiming to achieve a certain 'quality' of talk. I regularly use a tape recorder which the children seem to enjoy. Taping, talking then playing back and attempting to improve upon the first performance is really what we do together. Pupils like to see if they can become better even to the point of competing against themselves. To promote discussion we usually choose a topic, such as a balance. A pupil may attempt to describe to the group the attributes they have found or discovered about it — its versatility. When the tape is played back I quite often find myself saying 'look that bit's good, can you hear for yourself that's what you did'. At this point the remainder of the pupils may take over by saying 'Oh yes I left out such and such' or 'I could have said . . . then it would have sounded better I think.' As the teacher and the adult in the situation I usually take the opportunity to say 'Great. You can see that there is nothing wrong with your thinking there are just a few gaps but with a little help you soon spot them for yourself.'

The fifth year became my responsibility at the beginning of their 4th year and I had not taught any of them before. In this situation I always like to ensure that they perform well in their exams at the end of the two-year period. I tell the pupils that I am prepared to and will work extremely hard as well as giving all my efforts to encourage and help them to succeed but I expect them to respond in the same way. Pupils need to be trained to work hard and to learn all about effort.

I have found that the only way that I can really train them in this respect is to make them really interested and keen so that they want to give the effort. For example, if I offer a particular problem area to be solved by the pupils, I will go along with them and help them all I can to the point where they can really begin to grapple. Once they have reached this point I then encourage them not to give up but to pursue their line of thinking in order to achieve the final result. This is where the effort comes in. I attempt to get this attitude going right at the beginning and I really work the pupils as hard as I can.

One problem I experienced at the beginning was that many pupils had a poor attitude to homework. I began to give very low grades when homework was not handed in, D, for example. This worked for a while, but was never one hundred per cent successful so I hit upon the idea of involving the parents. I started a scheme whereby the parents had to sign the homework – this signature was not only to confirm that the work had been completed at home but also that it was considered to be satisfactory as far as the parents were concerned. This I found to be a personal safeguard too. Faced with an irate parent querying homework (as happens on occasions) I could very easily put the ball in their court. This system has worked very well; as the exams draw near the onus is now squarely on them.

This group as you can imagine are fairly bright, and I suppose, with this in mind I was quite amazed when I received their first piece of written work for marking. Nearly all of these pupils only put the answers down in their exercise books; this concerned me a great deal. I needed to know why these pupils were so concerned to omit any calculations and where they did their thinking. By talking to these pupils it became obvious that the answers were the only important part. 'After all you only need to know if the answer is right or wrong' was the response. The general opinion was that 'you don't show your workings out 'cos it makes the book messy.' I now had to stress the importance of showing all their thinking in their books and give them the reasons why this is so necessary.

One of the main reasons I give is the simple fact that I cannot see into their heads to see what in fact is going on. I cannot always spend the time that I would like to, talking to them to see how they are progressing and whether confusions are developing that need sorting out early on, and so they must communicate all this to me on paper. Certain problems that they will encounter are going to be long and require logical reasoning and so to get into the habit of proceeding through their work methodically is a good thing. I also inform them that I check their work thoroughly when I mark it and I like to see all their thought processes at work just as the examiner will ultimately. All the time that they are working I encourage them to confer with a colleague. I say to the pupils 'Go through the sum with James, see where you agree and where you differ.' This encourages them to record their work fairly accurately. I also expect them to use each other's knowledge and only if they are experiencing real difficulties do I help out. I do quite often, however, intervene and ask 'an answer-only oriented pupil', 'How did you get that.' Of course they jump to the defensive and exclaim 'Why what's wrong?' My response to this is usually 'I didn't say anything was wrong but I am interested in your thoughts.' When I do this I make a point of choosing correct answers initially so that I am not breaking any confidences.

It took a long time to get these pupils to change their ways. Some resented change while others had no idea exactly what I was expecting. I decided to spend some time showing them how to set out their work and I prepared model answer sheets for each exercise they attempted. I did this for about six lessons and although some of them were beginning to get the idea, some were still not quite sure how much detail to put down or 'where to put the odd little sum'. I used the overhead projector to illustrate to them how I personally work through a problem; how I set down any thoughts and how I attempt to reach a logical conclusion. The pupils enjoyed this and I think for many of them this was a better way of explaining my expectations. My doing, talking and recording showed them a real example. In order to promote this idea I decided on an incentive scheme. For each problem that the pupils worked through I devised an individual mark scheme. For example:

Problem: Find 20 per cent of £180

$$\frac{20}{100} \times \frac{180}{1} \qquad \text{(1 mark)}$$

$$\frac{2\cancel{0}}{1\cancel{0}\cancel{0}} \times \frac{18\cancel{0}}{1} \qquad \text{(cancelling 1 mark)}$$

Answer £36   (1 mark)

This is a simple example, but even if the pupils were able to gain a solution by using mental arithmetic I still asked them to show their thinking and awarded marks accordingly.

20 per cent of £1 means 20p in every £1   (1)
So 20 × 180 = 3600   (1)   = £36   (1).

I always award more marks for the calculating than for the answer. I do realise that this involves a lot of extra work on my part but I feel it is definitely worth doing.

This group have never been very self-confident and seemed to need constant reassurance from me which I found particularly demanding as well as taxing. Generally my methods of reassurance take the form of constant praising, questioning and hopefully developing a good rapport. I try to show the pupils that they are gaining a certain amount of success and that I approve by my gestures and comments which I hope are always constructive. I have noticed that if the pupils have a good working relationship with me then they tend to care about what I think; they want to please me because in turn they know I generally respond favourably and that usually makes them feel good and ready to tackle the next hurdle confidently.

Before these pupils gained any confidence of any description, they would never attempt a problem, they always turned to me and announced that they were 'stuck'; 26 pupils all being stuck at the same time is an impossible situation and I needed to do something to resolve it. Firstly I decided to make a conscious effort to use more open questions, to encourage the pupils to do some thinking. I read that this type of approach was considered to be a good way of promoting self-confidence and breaking down fears. There was definitely some improvement, but I think that the moment they began to take responsibility for their own learning produced the best results. In order to develop this I adopted phrases such as 'Be bold. Use your own thought processes. Go on, make a mistake and I will prove to you that you were on the right tracks and if you had continued you would have got the answer eventually.' 'Take responsibility for your own learning, share it with others, learn from them, you have such a lot to offer each other.'

Without a lot more directing, the pupils began to confer with one another and I encouraged this while still keeping tabs on the noise level. In the early stages this sometimes got out of hand. Then I would stop them and say — 'Look I can't hear what Carol is saying and she is right next to me. How can you hear one another. When you get loud, I must get louder so you must keep it down so that we can all hear one another.'

From working in pairs, group work developed and recently I moved all the desks around in my classroom in order to accommodate this new trend. Collective thinking seems to be very productive as long as the pupils are mature enough to make the most of this type of freedom. Many pupils see asking a friend as cheating. They have to be trained to turn to one another to confer. I encourage them by telling them that I do have the experience to distinguish between genuine discussion and cheating and when I mark I can tell whether there has been any cheating or not. If cheating does occur I have to come down hard by saying something like 'Now just a minute James, Charlie told you what to do . . . you tell me what he said . . . why does Charlie's idea work (James has copied). See James that's no good you've gained nothing. Charlie has done all the thinking. Your job is to go on asking Charlie until you understand. It's good for him too. Make him be exact. If he can't be, I'll come along and help both of you.'

This new way of teaching has released me and now I am more able to spend time with the 'struggling pupils' who need a lot of attention. Even so, I still tend to collect half a dozen or so pupils at a time for tutorials after school in order to go over certain difficulties.

I have learned to accept talk as an essential part of my teaching style, but I must admit I was not keen at first. I felt very threatened and I became most anxious for fear of losing my control over the classroom situation. It was only when I began to see how successful the pupils were making it that I really appreciated that the training had paid off. Quite often even when no answers are available some conclusive evidence as to what the answer probably should be is derived from a general consensus of opinion. I sometimes hear a comment like 'Well why do you think I'm $\frac{1}{10}$ out, Simon'. A general search now begins, to look for the $\frac{1}{10}$. Pupils check each other's work. They tend to discuss the different methods used to approach the problem. Some remember formulae, others search out pattern formations. As the pupils become used to do, talk and record methods they are convinced that all this talking really works and the atmosphere in the classroom is one of quiet, busy talk. If this does not remain at a low level I have no qualms about blowing up and threatening complete silence and a return to the traditional approach. But most of the time this way of working really makes for enjoyment all round.

One thing that pleases me most, and reassures me, is that before we adopted this approach the pupils were probably only responsible for about 10 to 15 per cent of their own work, whereas now they are coping with a good 60 per cent. This is where I want my pupils to be, learning through their own efforts, not simply mine.

INDEX